GUIDEBOOK FOR
MARINES

MARINE CORPS ASSOCIATION
EST 1913

GUIDEBOOK FOR
MARINES

23rd Edition

Published by the Marine Corps Association
Quantico, Virginia

PREFACE AND ACKNOWLEDGEMENTS

The Marine Corps Association is proud to publish this 23rd edition of the *Guidebook for Marines*. This edition includes the most current information available at printing on the subjects considered essential for Marines as they begin developing their professional skills and adopt the traditions of our Corps.

Charles G. Chiarotti
Lieutenant General, USMC (Ret)
President & CEO
Marine Corps Association

All readers and users are encouraged to report errors and discrepancies to:
The Editor, *Marine Corps Gazette*
Marine Corps Association
Box 1775
Quantico, VA 22134-1775

The *Guidebook for Marines* adheres to standard English usage, wherein the pronoun "he" refers to both sexes.

TABLE OF CONTENTS

CHAPTER 1

What is the Corps?

The United States Marine Corps is America's amphibious force-in-readiness. While that seems like a mouthful, it makes sense because of our country's position as a maritime nation with worldwide interests. The fundamental mission of the Corps can be simplified as readiness. This mission, combined with the Marine state of mind and culture, makes the Corps what it is today: a national force-in-readiness, prepared in fact and required by law to "perform such other duties as the President may direct," which means "ready for anything." Marines and Marine Corps missions have long been associated with the sea and with amphibious operations. The word "Marine" itself comes from the Latin "marinus," meaning "related to the sea." The "amphibious" comes from the Greek "amphibion"–literally, "living a double life." Marines today have a dual responsibility: to remain ready to serve on land, sea, and in the air and to maintain the expert skills required for amphibious operations.

Marine expeditionary forces of all sizes deploy by land, sea, or air. They provide the Nation's only major capability to forcibly enter any hostile area from the sea. They can proceed without interruption from a naval to land campaign with the ability to build up a strong fighting force. They are a combined force having all elements of combat power. Their versatility and responsiveness lend a significant dimension to the options available to our leaders in time of crisis.

Today's Marine Corps emphasizes three fundamentals: readiness, versatility, and the totally integrated capabilities of the Marine air-ground team. Operational readiness is the Marines' top priority. It is the cornerstone of the Marine Corps' existence as a fighting military organization.

Versatility refers to the Marines' method of tailoring air-ground teams in size, structure, and striking power to meet worldwide needs. It ensures, too, that Marine forces will remain flexible enough at all times "to perform such other duties as the President may direct," a mission deliberately expressed in general terms to permit the Marines to respond swiftly, when needed, as a general-purpose force.

The air-ground team originated in the U.S. Marine Corps. Marine aviation operates not just as a support for ground combat elements, but also as a fully integrated component of Marine expeditionary organizations.

So, today, as in the past, Marines must, and do, cast a constant eye seaward ... and beyond.

Mission

The present structure, missions, and functions of the Marine Corps are set forth in the National Security Act of 1947, amended several times in subsequent years. This act states that the Marine Corps' minimum peacetime structure shall consist of "not less than three combat divisions and three aircraft wings, and such other land combat, aviation and other services as may be organic therein." In addition, the Marine Corps maintains a 4th Marine Division (MarDiv) and Marine Aircraft Wing (MAW) in the standing Marine Forces Reserve (MFR).

To carry out its missions, the Marine Corps is periodically authorized personnel strength levels, which will permit it to maintain the forces stipulated by the National Security Act. During peacetime, these strength levels have remained essentially the same since 1953, providing an active duty strength of around 175,000 Marines. In addition, the MFR maintains a strength of approximately 100,000 made up of the Selected Marine Corps Reserve (SMCR), the Individual Ready Reserve (IRR), the Individual Mobilization Augmentee (IMA), and the Active Reserve (AR).

Beginning with their primary mission, the following specified missions have been assigned to the Marines under the National Security Act and its amendments.

The first mission is to provide Marine air and ground forces for service with the fleet as landing forces in the conduct of amphibious operations. This mission reflects the Marine Corps' statutory role as America's force-in-readiness and calls into play the full resources of the Navy and the Marine Corps operating together.

To execute an amphibious operation (assault, raid, demonstration, withdrawal) successfully requires special skills and equipment, intensive training, and the highest possible measure of coordination among the many different elements of the amphibious task force (ATF). It is costly, but in addition to its major objectives, it produces a range of other capabilities—to conduct rescue missions or to demonstrate force in a situation that could otherwise escalate into a major crisis.

The second mission is the oldest Marine Corps mission—duty afloat aboard armed vessels of the Navy.

The third mission is to develop in coordination with other services, the tactics, techniques, and equipment for landing forces in amphibious operations. It is a logical extension of the primary mission and establishes a distinct Marine Corps responsibility with respect to the other armed services.

The fourth mission is to be prepared for wartime expansion in accordance with Joint Mobilization Plans. It is common to all the armed services. Simply stated, mobilization plans require the activation of Marine Forces Reserve (MARFORRES).

The fifth mission is to perform such other duties as the President may direct. As noted earlier, this mission was deliberately expressed in general terms in the National Security Act. It permits the President to call upon Marines as a ready force in times of crisis. The Marine Corps is the only one of the armed services assigned such a mission by law.

Organization and Function

The overall organization of the Marine Corps falls into two broad categories: the operating forces and the supporting establishment. Together they comprise more than 90 percent of the total strength of the Marine Corps.

Operating Forces

Marine Security Forces. Marines provide approximately 3,400 Marines to the Marine Corps Security Forces (MCSF), protecting key naval installations and facilities worldwide. Although not assigned to combatant commands, they are part of the operating forces of the Marine Corps. These security forces include Fleet Antiterrorist Support Team (FAST) companies and Marine security force companies in the continental United States (CONUS) and abroad. Formerly made up of dozens of Marine

Barracks and Detachments, these declined in number over the years and then reformed in 1986 into MCSF companies, monitored by a single battalion headquarters.

Marine Security Guard Detachments. Under authority of the Foreign Service Act of 1946, the Marine Corps has a collateral mission of providing security guards for American embassies, legations, and consulates. For this duty, the Marine Corps Embassy Security Guard number approximately 1,000 Marines at 174 posts (also known as detachments) organized into 9 regional MSG commands and located in over 135 countries in 18 time zones, as well as its headquarters at Marine Corps Base, Quantico.

Marine Corps Forces. In 1992, Marine Corps "componency" was established, and Marine Corps component commanders, who are referred to as the Commander, Marine Corps Forces (COMMARFOR), were assigned or designated for each of the five geographic combatant commands. The former Fleet Marine Forces, Atlantic (FMFLANT) and Fleet Marine Forces, Pacific (FMFPAC) were redesignated Marine Corps Forces, Atlantic (MARFORLANT) and Marine Corps Forces, Pacific (MARFORPAC), respectively, and assumed the missions and responsibilities of service component commands. Headquarters, Fleet Marine Forces, Europe (FMFEUR), was redesignated Headquarters, Marine Corps Forces, Europe (MARFOREUR). Marine Corps component planning liaison cells were established in Central Command (CENTCOM) and Southern Command (SOUTHCOM). Upon the redesignation of the U.S. Atlantic Command as U.S. Joint Forces Command, the former MARFORLANT became Marine Corps Forces Command (MARFORCOM).

In addition to providing Marine Corps representation to each combatant command, these Marine Corps components have assumed most of the administrative and logistics requirements previously performed by Fleet Marine Forces. This change allowed the Marine Corps units of the air-ground task forces to concentrate on combat operations. The new joint force organization, supported by the activation of Marine Corps components, significantly changed the operational environment in which Marine Corps forces deployed and operated. Marine Corps forces also are provided to naval commands by the Marine Corps component commander, who also may perform the duties of a Fleet Marine Forces Commanding General with the status of a naval type commander. Assignments as a Commander, Marine Corps Forces, and Commanding General, Fleet Marine Forces, have separate, distinct command relationships and missions. For example, Commander, MARFORPAC— the Marine Corps component commander— provides Marine Corps forces to the Commander, U.S. Pacific Command. As the Commanding General, FMFPAC—a naval type commander—Commander, MARFORPAC, provides Marine air-ground task forces (MAGTFs) to the Commander, U.S. Pacific Fleet. The Marine Forces contain ground and aviation combat elements and logistics elements. The largest of these elements are the MarDiv, the MAW, and the Marine Logistics Group (MLG).

Marine Division. The mission of the MarDiv is to execute amphibious assault operations and such other operations as may be directed. The MarDiv must provide the ground combat power to an ATF and conduct subsequent land operations in any operational environment. The division commander fights by using combined arms tactics and tailors the force to the demands of each mission. The division is composed of a headquarters; infantry and artillery regiments; and tank, amphibious assault vehicle, light armored reconnaissance, reconnaissance, and combat engineer battalions, with approximately 18,000 personnel and more than 1,000 combat vehicles.

Marine Aircraft Wing. The MAW is task organized to provide a flexible and balanced aviation organization that is capable of providing the full range of aviation operations in a variety of areas without the requirement for prepositioned support, control, and logistical facilities. The MAW is the smallest unit with the inherent capability of performing all six functions of Marine aviation. The MAW is composed of a headquarters, a control group, a support group and fixed- and rotary-wing aircraft groups, with approximately 18,000 personnel and 350 aircraft. Aviation organizations smaller than a wing can provide the capabilities to accomplish any or all of the six aviation functions by using task organization.

Marine Logistics Group. The MLG is a composite grouping of functional organizations that provide combat service support (CSS) beyond the organic capability of supported units to all elements of the force. In this respect, it is structured to support, in garrison or deployed, a one division/one wing configured force. All elements of the MLG are structured to provide task-organized subordinate elements to support independently deployed battalions, regiments and equivalent organizations, or geographically separated units in garrison. The MLG headquarters provides general and direct support and sustained CSS in all levels of conflict. The MLG includes approximately 9,000 personnel and thousands of pieces of support equipment.

Supporting Establishment

The Marine Corps supporting establishment provides, trains, maintains, and supports the operating forces. The supporting establishment includes: Training and Education Command (TECOM); Training Command (TRNG CMD); Marine Corps Recruit Depot San Diego (MCRD SD); Marine Corps Recruit Depot Parris Island (MCRD PI); Education Command (EDCom); Marine Air Ground Task Force Training Center (MAGTFTC); Marine Corps Systems Command research, development, and evaluation organizations; supply installations; Reserve activities; certain Marine Corps bases, barracks, and air stations; Headquarters Battalion, Headquarters Marine Corps (HQMC); and miscellaneous small activities.

Marine Air-Ground Task Forces

The MAGTF is the principal organization used by Marine Corps operating forces for the conduct of all missions across the range of military operations, both combat and noncombat. MAGTFs are balanced, combined arms forces with assigned ground, aviation, and sustainment elements. They are flexible, task-organized forces that can respond rapidly to a contingency anywhere in the world and are able to conduct a variety of missions. (See Figure 1-1.)

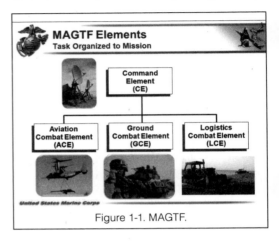

Figure 1-1. MAGTF.

Although organized and equipped to participate as part of naval expeditionary forces, MAGTFs also have the capability to conduct sustained operations ashore. A MAGTF provides a combatant commander or other operational commander with a versatile expeditionary force that is capable of responding to a broad range of crisis-and-conflict situations. MAGTFs are organized, trained, and equipped to perform missions ranging from humanitarian assistance to peacekeeping to full-scale combat and can operate in permissive, uncertain, and hostile environments. They may be shore or seabased in support of joint and multinational major operations and/or campaigns. MAGTFs deploy as amphibious, air-contingency or maritime prepositioning forces (MPFs), either as part of a naval expeditionary force or via strategic lift. They can present a minimal or a highly visible presence and are able to project combat power ashore in measured degrees or can provide secure staging areas ashore for follow-on forces. MAGTFs are prepared for immediate deployment overseas into austere operating environments, bringing all means necessary to accomplish the mission. When deployed aboard amphibious shipping, MAGTFs maintain a continuous presence at strategic locations around the globe and can be moved rapidly to and indefinitely stationed at the scene of potential trouble. The MAGTF provides the joint forces commander with the capability of reconstitution, which is the ability of an expeditionary force to regenerate, reorganize, replenish, and reorient itself for a new mission without having to return to its home base. MAGTF operations are built on a foundation of six special core competencies: expeditionary readiness, combined arms operations, expeditionary operations, seabased operations, forcible entry from the sea, and reserve integration.

The primary characteristics of the MAGTF (and of Marine Corps Forces) are summarized thus:

- Organized, trained, and equipped for combat essential to the prosecution of a naval campaign to seize objectives against the best and most modern equipped enemy.
- A balanced force of combined arms and services.
- Primarily trained, organized, and equipped for offensive employment.
- Adaptable to the active defense of advanced naval bases.
- Trained, equipped, and ready for prompt and effective employment in any climate or terrain.
- Trained and equipped for airborne operations as required, in accordance with policies and doctrines of the Joint Chiefs of Staff.
- Provided with sufficient organic CSS capability to establish and sustain combat power in the execution of normal missions and capable of supporting—
  - Supply.
  - Maintenance.
  - Transportation.
  - Deliberate engineering.
  - Services.
  - Health services.

- Provided with organic aviation units primarily organized, trained, and equipped to operate in conjunction with ground units in amphibious operations and capable of performing—
  - Offensive air support (OAS).
  - Antiair warfare (AAW).
  - Assault support.
  - Air reconnaissance.
  - Electronic warfare (EW).
  - Control of aircraft and missiles.

Although MAGTFs are task organized, each has the same basic structure, regardless of its size or mission. A MAGTF has four core elements: a command element (CE), a ground combat element (GCE), an aviation combat element (ACE), and a logistics combat element (LCE). The CE is the MAGTF headquarters. It is task organized to provide command and control capabilities (including intelligence and communications) necessary for effective planning, direction and execution of all operations. The GCE is task organized to conduct ground operations in support of the MAGTF mission. It is normally formed around an infantry organization reinforced with requisite artillery, reconnaissance, armor, and engineer forces and can vary in size and composition from a rifle platoon to one or more MarDivs.

The ACE is task organized to support the MAGTF mission by performing some or all of the six functions of Marine aviation. The ACE is normally built around an aviation organization that is augmented with appropriate air command and control, combat, combat support, and CSS units. The ACE can operate effectively from ships, expeditionary airfields or austere forward-operating sites and can readily and routinely transition between seabases and expeditionary airfields without loss of capability. The ACE can vary in size and composition from an aviation detachment with specific capabilities to one or more MAWs.

The LCE is task organized to provide the full range of CSS functions and capabilities needed to support the continued readiness and sustainability of the MAGTF as a whole. It is formed around a LCE headquarters and may vary in size and composition from a support detachment to one or more Marine Landing Groups (MLGs).

Marine Expeditionary Force

The Marine expeditionary force (MEF) is the principal Marine Corps warfighting organization. It is capable of missions across the range of military operations, through amphibious assault and sustained operations ashore in any environment. With appropriate augmentation, the MEF CE is capable of performing as a joint task force (JTF) headquarters. There are three standing MEFs: I MEF, based in southern California and Arizona; II MEF, based in North and South Carolina; and III MEF, based in Japan and Hawaii. Each standing MEF consists of a permanent CE and a MarDiv, MAW and MLG.

Marine Expeditionary Brigade

The Marine expeditionary brigade (MEB) is used for missions across the range of military operations, through amphibious assault and sustained operations ashore in any environment that does not require the combat power or sustainment of a MEF. With appropriate augmentation, the MEB CE is capable of performing as a JTF headquarters. The MEB is built around a reinforced regiment, a Marine aircraft group (MAG) and a combat logistics regiment (CLR). The MAG will contain all types of aircraft required by the mission. Presently, the MEB CEs remain cadred in the reserve or encapsulated in the MEF CE organizations, to be activated when required for a specific mission. As with the Marine expeditionary unit (MEU), below, they are even-numbered when organized in the Atlantic and odd-numbered in the Pacific theaters.

Marine Expeditionary Unit (Special Operations Capable)

The Marine expeditionary unit (special operations capable) (MEU(SOC)) is the standard forward-deployed Marine expeditionary organization. MARFORCOM and MARFORPAC deploy forward-deployed MEU(SOC)s to the Mediterranean Sea, the western Pacific and the Indian Ocean or Arabian Gulf region. The MEU(SOC) can be thought of both as a self-contained operating force capable of missions of limited scope and sustainment and as a leading element of an entire MEF. The MEU routinely receives special training before deploying that results in it being designated as "special operations capable." To receive the certification, the entire organization undertakes an intensive 26-week, standardized predeployment training program that includes a qualifying exercise and a final evaluation. The MEU must demonstrate competence across the entire spectrum of required capabilities, be able to plan and execute any assigned mission within six hours of notification and conduct multiple missions simultaneously. The MEU receives selected personnel and equipment as required to provide enhanced conventional and selected maritime special operations capabilities. There are seven standing MEU(SOC) CEs. Residing within I MEF are the 11th, 13th, and 15th MEU(SOC)s; residing within II MEF are the 22d, 24th, and 26th MEU(SOC)s; residing within III MEF is the 31st MEU(SOC). Although each MEU(SOC) is task organized, a typical MEU(SOC) includes:

- A permanent CE.
- An infantry battalion reinforced with artillery, reconnaissance, engineer, armor, assault amphibian units, and other detachments as required.
- A reinforced helicopter squadron with transport, utility and attack helicopters, a detachment of vertical/short takeoff and landing (V/STOL) fixed-wing attack aircraft, and other detachments as required.
- A task-organized LCE.

Special-Purpose Marine Air-Ground Task Force

A special-purpose MAGTF (SPMAGTF) is a MAGTF temporarily formed to conduct a specific mission. It normally is formed when a standing MAGTF is either inappropriate or unavailable. SPMAGTFs are organized, trained, and equipped to conduct a wide variety of missions ranging from crisis response, to regionally focused training exercises, to peacetime missions. Their SPMAGTF designation derives from the mission they are assigned, the location in which they will operate, or the name of the exercise in which they will participate (e.g., "SPMAGTF (X)," "SPMAGTF Somalia," "SPMAGTF UNITAS," "SPMAGTF Andrew," etc.). A SPMAGTF may be any size, but normally it is the size of a MEU (or smaller) with narrowly focused capabilities chosen to accomplish a particular mission. It may be task organized deliberately from the assets of a standing MEF or may be formed on a contingency basis from an already-deployed MAGTF to perform an independent, rapid-response mission of limited scope and duration. By definition, SPMAGTFs include all four of the basic elements of a MAGTF.

Disposition and Readiness

Headquarters, Marine Forces Command (MARFORCOM) is located in Norfolk, Virginia. Its major units comprise the II MEF, headquartered at Camp Lejeune, North Carolina. The MEF has three major subordinate commands (MSCs): 2d MarDiv; 2d MLG, both headquartered at Camp Lejeune; and 2d MAW, headquartered at Marine Corps Air Station (MCAS), Cherry Point, North Carolina.

Headquarters, Marine Forces Pacific (MARFORPAC) is located in Hawaii. Its major units are the I MEF, headquartered at Camp Pendleton, California, and the III MEF, headquartered in Okinawa, Japan. I MEF in California has three MSCs: 1st MarDiv and 1st MLG, located at Camp Pendleton, and 3d MAW, based at MCAS, Miramar. III MEF includes forward-deployed forces from I MEF and II MEF and has 3d MarDiv, 3d MLG, and 1st MAW as its MSCs, all located in Okinawa. Some units of III MEF are based permanently in Hawaii at Marine Corps Base, Kanehoe Bay, Hawaii.

In addition, units of the Reserve division-wing team—and 4th MarDiv and 4th MAW, headquartered in New Orleans under the Commander, Marine Corps Forces Reserve (MARFORRES)—train alongside regular Marine units and maintain the same high standards of readiness as the active forces. This side-by-side training supports overall readiness, the team concept and the "Total Force" policy. They are supported by the 4th MLG of MARFORRES, headquartered in New Orleans, Louisiana.

The Marine Corps demonstrates its global perspective in more than 40 major exercises conducted annually around the globe. Operating literally in "every clime and place," Marines take part in cold-weather training in Europe and Korea, as well as a variety of multinational exercises in other parts of the world.

The Marine Corps routinely conducts about 5 Integrated Training Exercises (ITXs) each year at the unique air-ground combat training center located at Twentynine Palms, California. In the open, unrestricted environment of the Mojave Desert, the readiness and combined arms capabilities of all elements of the Marine air-ground team and total force take part in exercises and receive evaluations. Each exercise includes live firing and is built around an infantry unit. Exercises are supported by fixed- and rotary-wing aircraft, artillery, light-armored reconnaissance vehicles, amphibious assault vehicles, engineers, and tanks. The exercises provide realistic training to prepare today's Marines for tomorrow's battlefields.

Summary

The Marine Corps exists in readiness for instant combat prepared for the battlefields of the future. Marines expect to be "first to fight." The close relationship between Marine Corps forces and the U.S. Navy helps ensure that ready Marine forces will be on or near the scene when a crisis erupts.

Marine Corps forces fulfill a broad range of general purpose missions. Equally important during peacetime, they serve as essential elements of U.S. deterrence. They project U.S. influence abroad by assisting diplomatic efforts, providing humanitarian relief and protecting U.S. nationals, embassy personnel, and

American interests abroad. In times of impending crisis, they provide a stabilizing influence or an on-the-scene initial response with a balanced combat capability within the MAGTF framework. They are capable of being rapidly deployed and rapidly reinforced, and they arrive combat-equipped and fully ready for action.

By any standards, Marine training has always been—and will remain—tough, realistic and extremely demanding. Marines 'Train as they fight and fight as they are trained' in order to survive in combat. Among the Corps' unchanging priorities is the team concept—Marines train and fight as a team. The fully integrated air-ground team stands at the core of the Marine battle ethic, bringing all of the weapons and firepower available to the combat Marine, in a well-coordinated combined arms array.

The overall mission of the Marine Corps has been defined by tradition and statute. Its organization and functions are keyed to its enduring task as a force-in-readiness. Since 1775, Marines have served "to advantage by sea when required." In pressing that "advantage by sea"—and land and air—Marines have founded proud traditions and established an enviable history.

CHAPTER 2

Marine Culture—
History, Tradition, and Courtesy

Marines through the ages have handed down to their Corps its most cherished traditions: traditions of duty, self-sacrifice, versatility, and dependability. Today, more traditions emerge or are reinforced by Marines in action. The thought of failure or letting down one's brother Marines remains unthinkable and has inspired new and already legendary feats of exertion and courage in the pantheon of Marine Corps history.

Marines learn their traditions with equal attention to their packs, rifles, or ammunition. Pride of person remains part of every Marine. The making of Marines is not alone a matter of smart appearance, drill, and discipline. Of equal importance, Marines know their culture and how to live up to it so that they can meet any emergency that may arise and report, "The Marines have landed, and the situation is well in hand."

Every Marine carries the colors of the Corps and the United States. These colors repeatedly have been uncased and cased with new battle streamers. That piece of fabric symbolizes many concepts. It represents more than a year of an individual life. It recalls the fellow Marines who lost their lives for the mission and who made the journey home ahead of the rest. It represents great courage in battle. It represents remarkable stamina over months and later years. It represents unshakable honor tested in the most complex environment imaginable. It represents immeasurable personal and Marine Corps family sacrifice.

Symbols of Tradition

The familiar emblem of globe and anchor, adopted in 1868, embodies worldwide service and sea traditions. The spread eagle, the symbol of the Nation itself, holds in its beak a streamer upon which is inscribed the famous motto of the United States Marines: "Semper Fidelis," which means in Latin "always faithful."

The term "Leatherneck," as applied to Marines, is widely used but few people associate it with the uniform. The fact that United States Marines wore a black leather stock, or collar, as part of their uniform from 1798 to 1872 may have given rise to the name. According to tradition, the stock originally was worn to protect the jugular vein from the slash of a saber or cutlass. However, official records fail to bear this out. The sword with a Mameluke hilt, came to Lieutenant Presley N. O'Bannon of the Marine Corps from a former Pasha of Tripoli, later becoming the symbol of authority of Marine

Corps officers since 1826. It symbolized the exploits of O'Bannon and his Marines on "the shores of Tripoli" in 1805, an episode climaxed by the raising of the American flag for the first time in the Old World. (See Figure 2-1.)

Figure 2-1. The Assault on Derna by Col Charles H. Waterhouse, USMCR. Following a 600-mile trek across the Egyptian and Libyan deserts, Marine Lt Presley O'Bannon leads his men in an attack against Dernain an effort to restore a friendly ruler to the throne of Tripoli. The Marines took the city, planting the flag there.

Marine Origins

The Marine Corps dates from November 10, 1775. On that day, the Continental Congress authorized formation of two battalions of Marines to form part of the naval service. Samuel Nicholas, named the first captain of Marines, remained senior officer in the Continental Marines through the Revolution and is properly considered our first Commandant.

The initial Marine recruiting rendezvous opened at Tun Tavern in Philadelphia, and by early 1776, the organization had progressed to the extent that the Continental Marines were ready for their first expedition. The objective was New Providence Island (Nassau) in the Bahamas, where a British fort and large supplies of munitions were known to be. With Captain Nicholas in command, 234 Marines sailed from Philadelphia in Continental warships. On March 3, 1776, Capt Nicholas led his men ashore, took the fort and captured the powder and arms for Washington's army. For the first time in U.S. history, the Marines had landed, and the situation was well in hand. (See Figure 2-2.)

Beginnings of the Corps

After an interval in which no organized military forces existed in the new United States, the Marine Corps, as it exists today, was reformed by the Act of July 11, 1798, at the beginning of the Naval War with France. The Marines took part in that war from 1798 to 1801 and in the war with the Barbary pirates from 1801 to 1805. They took an active part in the War of 1812, serving aboard practically all American warships that engaged the enemy;

with the Army in the Battle of Bladensburg, August 1814; and with Andrew Jackson at New Orleans.

In 1824, Marines formed part of a landing force, which operated against a nest of pirates in Cuba. In 1832, Marines again saw action against pirates as part of a combined landing force from the U.S. frigate *Potomac*. Their mission was to punish the Malay pirates at Quallah Battoo, Island of Sumatra, for the capture and plunder of the USS *Friendship*.

In 1824, Marines from the Boston Navy Yard suppressed a mutiny in the Massachusetts State Prison, which was beyond the control of the civil

Figure 2-2. Landing at New Providence, March 3, 1776, by Col Charles H. Waterhouse, USMCR. With the hope of gaining much needed powder for Washington's army, 234 Marines and 50 sailors under the command of Marine Capt Samuel Nicholas landed on the island of New Providence, Bahamas.

authorities. During 1836 and 1837, they helped the Army fight the Creek and Seminole Indians in Georgia and Florida, where they served under their Commandant, Colonel Archibald Henderson, who subsequently received a brevet promotion to brigadier general.

The Mexican War

During the war with Mexico and in the conquest of California, the Marines took an important part both on the Gulf and Pacific coasts, assisting in the capture of Monterey, Yerba Buena (San Francisco), Mazatlan, Vera Cruz, Tampico, and Tobasco. One battalion of Marines marched with General Winfield Scott to Mexico City, participating in the final attack on the Castle of Chapultepec and the march to the National Palace, the Halls of Montezuma. Thus came the words that for many years adorned the Corps' colors: "From Tripoli to the Halls of Montezuma." We commemorate these battle honors today in the first two lines of "The Marines' Hymn"— "From the Halls of Montezuma to the shores of Tripoli."

Marine Corps Mottos

Shortly after the Mexican War, the Marines carried the so-called "Tripoli-Montezuma" flag, which had the early motto, "By Land, by Sea." When the current Marine Corps emblem was adopted in 1868, the Navy Department authorized the current motto, "Semper Fidelis," on streamers above the eagle soon after the Civil War, and it was officially adopted as the motto in 1880.

The famous American bandsman, John Phillip Sousa, composed the march, "Semper Fidelis," in the year 1888, during the time when he was leader of the U.S. Marine Band.

The Uniform

Secretary of War James McHenry first authorized the famous blue uniform of the Marine Corps on August 24, 1797, even before the reforming of the Corps with the U.S. Navy. Blue or "Navy Blue," a conspicuous color of sea and employed generally by the naval forces of all countries, was selected by the U.S. Marines for their uniforms, while the pattern and trimmings of scarlet and gold served at the same time to make them appear distinctive. In view of the fact that the early organization, duties, and regulations of the American Marines were patterned somewhat after ways and customs of their forerunners, the British Royal Marines, it is possible that the traditional red of the British uniform had its effect in the adoption of scarlet for the uniform of the U.S. Marines.

The blue uniform with red trimmings was used from 1797 until July 4, 1834, when it was replaced by a grass green uniform with buff trimmings. This uniform lasted only six years until July 4, 1840, when the blue uniform trimmed with scarlet again was prescribed.

From Civil War to World War I

During the Civil War, Marines served afloat and ashore. A noteworthy incident before the beginning of the Civil War period (1859) was the participation of Marines in the capture of John Brown at Harpers Ferry. The Corps remained small, but Marines served ashore in the Mississippi Valley and in the defenses of Washington. All along the Confederate seaboard, from Hatteras Inlet to Hilton Head and Fort Pickens, shipboard Marines, sometimes in provisional battalions, executed successful landings, which put teeth into the Union blockade. (See Figure 2-3 on next page.)

Its strength remained at only 4,161 officers and men. As early as 1864 (and again in 1867), attempts were made to disband the Marine Corps and merge it with the Army. Both times, however, Congress stepped into the breach, and the Corps was saved.

Scattered Actions

The "peacetime" activities of the Marine Corps from the close of the Civil War until the War with Spain, established the Marine Corps tradition of versatility. Marines aided civil authorities in suppressing labor riots in

Figure 2-3. Fort Fisher by Col Charles H. Waterhouse, USMCR. Marines and sailors landed on the beach to attack Confederate held Fort Fisher.

Baltimore and Philadelphia and enforcing revenue laws in New York. At the same time, they participated in expeditions to the Caribbean area, Korea, China, and other foreign countries for the purpose of protecting American lives and property.

During the years 1867 and 1870, they formed part of the Formosa expedition. In 1871, a battalion of Marines, forming part of a naval brigade, led the advance against Korean forts along the Han River in reprisal for serious offenses against Americans. (See Figure 2-4.)

In 1882, a detachment of Marines landed at Alexandria, Egypt, to assist in restoring order.

Spanish War

During the War with Spain, at Guantanamo Bay, Cuba, Marines again were first to land in enemy territory. They also served aboard ship detachments on battleships and cruisers under Admirals Dewey and Sampson at the naval battles of Manila Bay and Santiago de Cuba. Following the spectacular naval victory in Manila Bay, the Marines from the cruiser *Baltimore* landed to seize the Spanish Naval Arsenal at Cavite, and from then on, Marines garrisoned this station.

Philippine Insurrection

Concurrent with the War with Spain came the continuation of the Philippine Insurrection, now against Americans instead of Spaniards. This three-year campaign saw the first modern Marine brigade organized, as well as three exploits for which the Corps will be remembered: the march across Samar, the storming of Sojoton Cliffs in Samar, and the pacification of the Subic Bay area on Luzon.

Boxer Rebellion

During the Boxer Rebellion in China, in the summer of 1900, Marines from ships on the Asiatic station took part in the defense of the Legation Quarter at Peking, and Marines formed part of the allied relief expedition that marched from Taku to Peking and fought in the Battle of Tientsin. (See Figure 2-5 on next page.)

A tradition of friendship between the Royal Welsh Fusiliers and the United States Marine Corps (USMC) began from this campaign. During the fighting at Tientsin, each of these two famous organizations supported the other on a number of occasions. Their mutual admiration continued, and each Saint David's Day (March 1) is marked annually by an exchange of

Figure 2-4. Storming Fort Chojin, Korea by John Clymer, Marines, Korea, 1871.

Figure 2-5. Defense of Peking—1900 by John Clymer. Marines defend the American Legation in Peking during the Boxer Rebellion of 1900.

messages that contain the ancient Welsh password, "And Saint David."

Marines elsewhere remained active. In 1903, Marines landed in Santo Domingo and returned in 1905 to Korea, while a detail of Marines served as guards for a diplomatic mission to Abyssinia by camel caravan across the desert to negotiate a treaty with Emperor Menelik II. From 1906 to 1908, the Marines participated in the army of occupation in the Cuban Pacification, a number of expeditions to Panama and Nicaragua from 1909 to 1912 and the 1914 naval expedition that seized Vera Cruz, Mexico.

Marines in World War I

In World War I, the Marine Corps expanded to 75,000 men, guarding ships and stations and forming eight regiments, some of which participated in the fiercest fighting Marines had ever known. The 4th Brigade of Marines (composed of the 5th and 6th Marine regiments and the 6th Machine Gun Battalion) served as one of the infantry brigades of the Army's 2nd Infantry Division, participating with distinction in the important battles of Belleau Wood, Soissons, St. Mihiel, Blanc Mont Ridge, and the Argonne.

After Belleau Wood, German Army intelligence reports evaluated the Marine brigade as "storm troops"—the highest rating on the enemy scale of fighting men. The French

government later renamed the area the "Woods of the American Marines."

The Marine Corps also sent the 5th Brigade (11th and 13th Marine Regiments and the 5th Machine Gun Battalion) to France, but Army policy relegated them to guard duty. The remaining regiments performed duties in the Caribbean. Marine aviation units under command of Major Alfred A. Cunningham (who had become the Marine Corps' first aviator in 1912) rendered conspicuous service as the Day Wing of the Northern Bombing Group in Northern France and Belgium. The Marine pilots flew 57 bombing missions, dropping 52,000 pounds of bombs and shooting down at least a dozen German planes.

Women Marines

Opha M. Johnson was the first woman Marine, enlisting on August 13, 1918, the day after the Secretary of the Navy granted the authority to enroll women in the Marine Corps Reserves (MCR) for clerical duty at HQMC and at other Marine offices in the United States.

A total of 305 women enlisted during World War I to "free a man to fight."

During World War II, the Women's Reserve began forming in 1943, reaching a total of 821 officers and 18,000 enlisted women led by Colonel Ruth C. Streeter. This was roughly the equivalent of one division of men free to fight. The end of the war brought demobilization for most women, but in 1948, they reformed as the Women Marines in the regular and reserve Marine Corps.

Between Two Wars

For more than a decade after World War I, Marines continually engaged in efforts to restore peace in the countries of the Caribbean area—always acting as the strong arm for carrying out the Nation's foreign policy.

In three Caribbean countries, they carried on extensive campaigns against insurgent elements, assisting the governments of those

Figure 2-6. Fort Riviere, Haiti-1915 by Col Donna J. Neary, USMCR. Marines under Major Smedley D. Butler captured Fort Riviere then destroyed the Haitian bandit hideout with dynamite.

countries to put down armed insurrection, and to organize efficient native constabularies (in which many Marines served) to maintain order after they withdrew.

In Haiti from 1915 to 1934, Marines fought two wars with the Cacos; in the Dominican Republic, it took them eight years to suppress banditry, and in Nicaragua, they fought the bandit elements from 1927 to 1932. (See Figure 2-6 and Figure 2-7.) The fighting in Nicaragua was the first evidence of the development of the famous Marine "air-ground team" concept that would later take shape as the MAGTF. Cargo resupply by aircraft also was used for the first time.

Duty in China

For almost a century, the Marines called China a duty station. As early as 1854, internal upheaval that endangered the lives of Americans required the presence of a landing force of Marines. From that time to the Boxer Rebellion of 1900, Marines and sailors landed on a number of occasions for the protection of our national interests. The decade from 1901 was a comparatively peaceful one, but in 1911 and 1912, Marines operated in China to protect Americans during the popular overthrow of the Manchu Dynasty.

Beginning in 1924, contingents of Marines and sailors landed from time to time to protect American citizens and American interests.

In 1927, upheavals of civil war in that country and the attending danger to Americans brought forth a force of about 5,000 Marines, dispatched and stationed at various trouble points, principally at Shanghai and Tientsin. Two aircraft squadrons, Fighting Three and Observation Five (VF-3M, VO-5M), formed the aviation component. During the next two years, Marine aviators flew more than 3,000 sorties, mostly reconnaissance.

By January 1929, the situation having improved, the force, which had grown into the 3rd Marine Brigade, returned to the United States after order had been restored, with the exception of the 4th Marines, which remained in Shanghai. The 4th Marine Regiment remained on duty in China until withdrawn just before the attack on Pearl Harbor in December 1941.

Fleet Marine Force

In 1933, the Fleet Marine Force (FMF) came into being, initially on paper, as an integral part of the United States Fleet. The troops regularly assigned to this organization were mostly stationed at San Diego, California, and Quantico, Virginia, and trained for their specialized duties as Marine expeditionary troops forming an integral part of the U.S. Fleet by participation in the annual maneuvers of the Fleet. (See Figure 2-8 on next page.)

At each of these stations the Marine Corps planned a reinforced brigade consisting of an

Figure 2-7. Marine infantry train with King armored car in Haiti, early 1920s.

Figure 2-8. Early publicity photo of the Fleet Marine Force, 1939.

infantry regiment, a battalion of light field artillery (pack howitzers), a battalion of antiaircraft artillery, an aviation group, a light tank company, and small contingents of engineer and chemical troops. The aviation planned at each of these posts comprised two fighting squadrons, two bombing squadrons, one observation squadron, and one general-utility squadron. However, the strength of the peacetime Marine Corps only permitted establishing the 1st Brigade at Quantico, with only the smaller 6th Marine Regiment stationed at San Diego. In its final year and a half of peace, the Marine Corps would grow not only in structure but in mission. Already in July of 1940, the Joint War Planning Committee Board planned the use of the 1st Marine Brigade to seize the Vichy-French island of Martinique as well as the Azores Islands in the Atlantic. The Corps thus was thrust into the same two-ocean war as the Navy, having thought mostly of Pacific campaigns for the FMF thus far in its existence. War planning now called for an FMF consisting of two complete divisions, several base defense battalions and two aircraft wings.

Marines in World War II

In 1941, Marine units stood on duty halfway around the world, with approximately 2,000 Marines serving in China and the Philippines under the command of the Commander in Chief of the Asiatic Fleet. In addition, several thousand Marines were serving at naval stations in the Hawaiian Islands, Guam, Wake, Midway, American Samoa, the Panama Canal Zone, and Cuba.

The 1st Provisional Marine Brigade, taken largely from the new 2nd MarDiv at San Diego, occupied Iceland, and provisional Marine companies guarded various islands in the Atlantic Ocean and the Caribbean.

The Japanese Attack

When the Japanese struck in the Pacific, the Marines from the stations in China had been successfully withdrawn to the Philippines with the exception of the Marine detachments at Beijing and Tientsin in North China. The Marine garrisons at Cavite and Olongapo in the Philippines participated in the defense of Bataan and Corregidor, until the American forces were finally overpowered and captured by the Japanese. The handful of Marines on Guam put up a heroic but futile defense. On Wake Island, the detachment of 1st Marine Defense Battalion, supported by fighter squadron VMF-211, repulsed the first Japanese landing attempt. This act stunned the Japanese with their first defeat of the war. A second landing was made by the Japanese on December 23. After a full night and morning of fighting, the Wake garrison surrendered to the Japanese. Marines lost 49 killed during the entire 15-day siege, while 3 U.S. Navy personnel and at least 70 civilians were killed. Japanese losses were recorded at between 700 to 900 killed, with at least 1,000 more wounded, in addition to the two destroyers Marines sank in the first invasion attempt and at least 28 landbased and carrier aircraft either shot down or destroyed. In Hawaii, an aircraft group consisting of one fighter and two dive-bomber squadrons was almost completely put out of action by the Japanese raid.

Marines to the Defense

Immediately after the Japanese attack on December 7, 1941, additional Marines with defense battalion equipment were sent out from the United States to reinforce the Hawaiian

Figure 2-9. Marine encampment, Guadalcanal.

Islands and the smaller islands (Midway, Johnston, and Palmyra) lying to the west.

At the same time, measures were taken to strengthen the chain of islands across the South Pacific that protected the line of communication to Australia. The 7th Defense Battalion of Marines had been stationed at Tutuila, American Samoa, since March 15, 1941, and had taken some steps toward fortifying the harbor at Pago Pago.

As further reinforcements for this important position, a brigade of Marines, the 2nd, taken mostly from the 2nd MarDiv at San Diego, was formed and together with Marine Aircraft Group 13 (MAG-13) preceded early in January of 1942 to American Samoa and set up defenses and air facilities on Tutuila.

An additional brigade of Marines, the 3rd, was organized from units of the 1st MarDiv at New River, North Carolina, and sent to Western Samoa, where they arrived on May 8, 1942. This brigade took up and organized positions on Upolu and Savaii Islands and, with naval units, established important air and naval facilities. The westward thrust of the Marines was resumed in October 1942 when a part of a Marine defense battalion occupied the island of Funafuti in the Ellice Islands.

Guadalcanal

In order to secure our line of communication to the southwest Pacific and prepare for the eventual Allied counteroffensive, the 1st MarDiv sailed to New Zealand in June of 1942. Even before they arrived in New Zealand, Major General Alexander A. Vandegrift read orders for his division (reinforced by the 2nd Marines of the 2nd MarDiv, the 1st Raider Battalion and the 3rd Defense Battalion) to carry out an amphibious assault in the Tulagi-Guadalcanal area.

On August 7, 1942, the 1st MarDiv landed on the north coast of the islands of Guadalcanal, Tulagi, and Florida. This amphibious assault marked the beginning of the United States offensive against the Japanese empire. By August 10, the Marines had destroyed the Japanese garrisons at Tulagi, Gavutu, and Tanambogo and had secured the airfield the Japanese had begun on Guadalcanal. (See Figure 2-9.)

For the next four months, the 1st MarDiv, later reinforced by Army troops and additional elements of the 2nd MarDiv, supported by the ships and aircraft of the Navy and planes of the Army and the Marine Corps, successfully repulsed numerous Japanese attacks made by land, sea, and air. This bitterly fought and grueling campaign was highlighted by the battles

Figure 2-10. The Marines stormed Tarawa inflicting more than 4,700 casualties in less than four days.

of the Tenaru River, the Matanikau River, and Bloody Ridge. Officers and enlisted men of the 1st MAW performed almost legendary feats in fighting off Japanese air attacks at Guadalcanal and carrying the fight to enemy ships and bases.

Up the Solomons

After winning Guadalcanal, seen as the first stepping-stone to Tokyo, our forces moved up the Solomons Island chain and seized bases in the New Georgia Islands. Army and Marine Corps units had landed on the Russell Islands in February of 1943, which gave us an air base for operations against enemy bases in the New Georgia group.

In June and July 1943, Marine Corps and Army troops landed on New Georgia and Rendova Islands, followed by landings on Vella Lavella, Arundel, and Kolombangara Islands.

The culmination came on November 1, 1943, when the 3rd MarDiv made a landing at Empress Augusta Bay, Bougainville. The Bougainville campaign marked the beginning of close-air support in the modern sense. For the first time pilots (forward air controllers) and enlisted men (radiomen) from the wing reported to the division for duty, where they helped company and battalion commanders obtain and direct air attacks on specific enemy emplacements holding up the advance of the Marine ground units.

During the next 45 days, the 3rd MarDiv fought off Japanese counterattacks and expanded the beachhead to eventually hold vital air bases. The Marines handed off the swampy, mosquito-infested island to the Army for the mopping up of resistance.

The Gilberts

After the seizure of Bougainville, the Allied offensive against Japan was intensified. Army forces accelerated their leapfrog tactics up the north coast of New Guinea, and our Central Pacific forces breached the Japanese outer line of defense when on November 20, 1943, the 2nd MarDiv landed on Tarawa, and elements of the Army 27th Division went ashore on Makin Island, both in the Gilberts Group.

Within four days, the Marines had wiped out all enemy resistance on Tarawa but had suffered very heavy casualties. The Japanese had boasted that a million Americans could not take the triangular coral atoll of Tarawa, where the island of Betio contained the Japanese base … not in a hundred years. It took the Marines 76 hours. (See Figure 2-10.)

Robert Sherrod wrote: "The Marines fought almost solely on espirit de corps, I was certain. It was inconceivable to most Marines that they should let another Marine down, or that they could be responsible for dimming the bright reputation of their Corps. The Marines simply assumed that they were the world's best fighting men. Of the 4,836 Japanese soldiers and Korean laborers on Betio, only 146 were taken prisoner."

In the meantime, American and Australian forces cleared New Guinea's north coast, and on December 15, 1943, crossed to Arawe, New Britain, supported by Marine tanks in a drive aimed at cutting the Japanese southern coastal line of communications to Rabaul.

On December 26, 1943, the 1st MarDiv went ashore on Cape Gloucester on the western end of New Britain, cutting the enemy northern line of coastal communications and forcing the enemy to fall back on their main base at Rabaul. In a series of bloody battles, Marines secured the Cape Gloucester airdrome and captured a number of strategic hills in the Borgan Bay area.

By March of the following year, the Japanese were fleeing eastward toward Rabaul. On April 28, 1944, the Commanding General of the 1st MarDiv turned over command of the Cape Gloucester area to the Army.

The 1st MarDiv's operations in the western New Britain placed U.S. forces, particularly aviation, in a half circle around Rabaul, their major base that once had threatened Allied communications with Australia. Now it became a strategic prisoner-of-war stockade as the Pacific War moved on toward Japan.

The Marshalls and Marianas

Farther to the north, our Central Pacific forces smashed through the Japanese defensive line by seizing a number of islands in the Marshalls group.

The 4th MarDiv, proceeding from their training base at Camp Pendleton, California, assaulted and captured Roi and Namur Islands at the northern end of Kwajalein Atoll, while the Army's 7th Infantry Division seized Kwajalein Island at the southern end. Organized enemy resistance ceased on Kwajalein Atoll on

February 7, 1944. Japanese resistance proved so weak that the landing force reserve, the 22nd Marine Regiment, launched against Eniwetok Atoll, seizing this important fleet anchorage on February 18 to facilitate the next stop, the Marianas, the main line of resistance in the Japanese island defense system.

The new III and V Amphibious Corps consisting of Marine Corps and Army infantry divisions now turned to confronting large units of the Japanese Army, defending large Pacific islands presenting all possible variations of terrain.

The Marianas formed the inner island defense barrier of Japanese strategy for the Pacific War, and a decisive battle fought on land, at sea, and in the air settled the fate of the Empire. On June 15, 1944, the 2nd and 4th MarDivs (V Amphibious Corps) landed on Saipan, followed in by the 27th Infantry Division. On July 9, after 25 days of heavy fighting, all organized enemy resistance had ceased, and the island was officially secured.

Eleven days later, July 21, 1944, the III Amphibious Corps, composed of the 3rd MarDiv, the 1st Provisional Marine Brigade and the 77th Infantry Division, began landing on Guam. Organized resistance ceased on Guam August 10, 1944. (See Figure 2-11 on next page.)

Three days after the landing on Guam, the 2nd and 4th MarDivs went ashore on Tinian and completed its seizure on August 1. On November 23, 1944, Marianas-based B-29s made their first raid on Tokyo and brought the war directly to the Japanese homeland.

Defeating Japan

The succession of Central Pacific battles—Tarawa (1943), the Marshalls, Saipan, Guam, Tinian, Peleliu (all 1944), Iwo Jima and Okinawa (both 1945)—was by hard necessity a series of frontal assaults from the sea against positions fortified with every refinement that Japanese ingenuity and pains could produce. To reduce such strongholds, the amphibious assault came of age.

On the morning of February 19, 1945, hundreds of landing boats roared through the pounding surf to spill thousands of V Corps' 4th and 5th Division Marines onto Iwo's southeastern beaches. The 3rd MarDiv was held in

Figure 2-11. Marines and equipment mass ashore on Guam, 1944.

reserve, landing when room became available on the small island. (See Figure 2-12.) On the morning of February 23, members of the 2nd Battalion, 28th Marines crested Mount Suribachi crater. A 40-man patrol of Company E crawled to the lip of the crater and raised the first flag, photographed by *Leatherneck* magazine photographer Technical Sergeant Louis Lowery. Meanwhile, a larger flag was procured; this flag raising became the outstanding symbol of America's war effort. Six men were depicted in the Pulitzer Prize-winning photo.

In the final great land battle of the Pacific area, the invasion of Okinawa, the Marine Corps was represented by the 1st and 6th MarDivs of the III Amphibious Corps, under the U.S. Tenth Army, landing on the western beaches of Okinawa on April 1, 1945. After mopping up the lightly held northern half of the island, the Marines joined the Army divisions in breaking the main resistance in the south, playing major roles in the final victory, joined in the end by the 8th Marines, 2nd MarDiv. (See Figure 2-13.)

Figure 2-12. The 5th Marine Division attacks across the center of Iwo Jima, 1945.

Figure 2-13. Okinawa was one of the most difficult campaigns of World War II. Fought at Japan's doorstep, it was also the last campaign of the war.

Marine aviation flew more than 14,000 close-air-support sorties in the Okinawa campaign, more than half of them in support of Army troops. Marine nightfighters also recorded a highly increased effectiveness as they held off increasingly desperate Japanese air attacks. Meanwhile, other Marine aviators were fulfilling the U.S. Marine tradition of being ready for any emergency. Japanese kamikaze planes threatened to overcome the air superiority of U.S. aircraft carriers. During the first six months of 1945, the Marine fighter squadrons moved from landbases in the southwest Pacific to aircraft carriers to increase defensive capabilities of the fleet.

The successful conquest of Okinawa enabled our ships, planes, and submarines to tighten the blockade around Japan's home islands and sever her vital sea links to the Asiatic mainland and the resource areas to the south. On September 2, 1945, in a brief but solemn ceremony aboard the battleship *Missouri*, representatives of Japan signed the surrender documents. Thereafter, Allied occupation of Japan and the overseas territory under Japanese control went steadily ahead, with Marines playing an important role.

Demobilization and Peacetime Posture

By the end of the war, the FMF, with aviation and ground units, were poised for the invasion of Japan—an invasion rendered unnecessary by U.S. sea and air power and the use of the atomic bomb. The Corps had grown from 19,354 in 1939 to nearly 500,000 in 1945. The victories in World War II cost the Corps 86,940 casualties. In the eyes of the American public, the Marine Corps was second to none and seemed destined for a long and useful career. Admiral Nimitz's ringing epitome of Marine fighting on Iwo Jima very well might be applied to the entire Marine Corps during World War II: "Uncommon valor was a common virtue."

After brief occupation duty in Japan, the 2nd MarDiv and 2nd MAW moved to North Carolina, and the 1st Division and 1st MAW to southern California after duty in postwar China.

Continued Development of Amphibious Techniques

Intensive effort was made in the Marine Corps after World War II to develop and perfect the techniques and equipment associated with amphibious warfare. New concepts emerged in transport submarine operations; air transport, and especially helicopter transport of troops; cold-weather operations; and improvement of amphibious vehicles and weapons. Marines continued their heavy schedules of training troops of all services for amphibious operations. (See Figure 2-14.) In support of this growing program, the Marine Corps Schools at Quantico were reorganized in 1950 into two major subdivisions, the Marine Corps Education Center and the Landing Force Development Center.

Figure 2-14. Marines land at Camp Pendleton as part of Amphibious Exercise Demon III, May 1950.

"Pathbreakers"

African-American Marines

African American Marines were initially segregated from normal recruit training sites and were sent to Montford Point (renamed Camp Johnson), which is adjacent to Camp Lejeune, North Carolina, to conduct training. Approximately 20,000 African American Marines were trained at Monford Point and went on to serve with honor and distinction.

Navajo Code Talkers

Code Talkers were Navajo men who transmitted secret communications on the battlefields of WWII. At a time when America's best cryptographers were falling short, these modest Native Americans were able to fashion one of the most ingenious and successful codes in military history. They drew upon their proud warrior tradition to brave the dense jungles of Guadalcanal and the exposed beachheads of Iwo Jima. Serving with distinction in every major engagement of the Pacific theater from 1942 to 1945, their unbreakable code played a pivotal role in saving countless lives and hastening the war's end.

Figure 2-15. Rocket teams of the Antitank Company, 5th Marines, move past their first tank targets during the First Battle of the Naktong Bulge.

Marines in Korea

On June 25, 1950, the Communist North Korean Army invaded the Republic of South Korea. The President alerted U.S. forces in the Far East to render all possible assistance, and the Security Council of the United Nations called on all members to do the same. When Army-occupation troops from Japan proved unable to stem the North Korean invasion, reinforcements, including U.S. Marines, began to embark for the peninsula.

Within two weeks of the alert, the 1st Provisional Marine Brigade, consisting of the 5th Marines (Reinforced) and Marine Aircraft Group 33, formed and embarked in shipping from California bases, with the first loaded ships sailing on July 12. (See Figure 2-15.)

First offensive action against the enemy was made by MAG-33's fighter-bombers on August 3, and the brigade first engaged the enemy ashore on August 7. The 1st Provisional Marine Brigade was attached to the Eighth U.S. Army in the Pusan Perimeter at the time when the North Korean advance had come within 35 miles of Pusan. The battle became one of holding actions against aggressive enemy attacks, and the Marine brigade fought as did a few Army units as "firemen"—hard-hitting mobile reserves that shifted from one threatened area to another for counterattacks. Three times the Brigade helped roll back the enemy in such operations. The famous Marine Corps "air-ground team" immediately began to prove the soundness of the post war developments in close-air support.

The Inchon-Seoul Landing

September 15, 1950, was D-Day for the 1st MarDiv, landing at Inchon, a daring amphibious assault that led to the capture of Seoul and the seizure of Kimpo airfield as a base of operations for the 1st MAW units and the outflanking of the entire North Korean Army. Within 24 hours, Marines had secured this west coast Korean seaport and swept on, covered by F4U Corsairs of MAG-33, which alternately attacked, screened with smoke, observed and kept the sky free of enemy aircraft. (See Figure 2-16.)

The enemy recovered enough to resist Marine Corps and Army units along the approaches to Seoul, and three days of street fighting were necessary to secure this city of a million and a half prewar population. The end of the war seemed likely as Marines pushed north of Seoul to seize Uijongbu and the main road to the North Korean capital of Pyongyang. On October 7, the 1st MarDiv was relieved by advancing Eighth Army elements and sent by sea around the peninsula.

Chosin Reservoir

After an administrative landing at Wonsan on October 25, the 1st MarDiv carried out patrolling and blocking missions under the Army's X Corps around Hamhung on the east coast, while advancing inland toward the Chosin Reservoir.

On November 3, the 7th Marines encountered the first of many Chinese Communist Forces (CCF). On November 26, the advancing Eighth Army in western Korea and X Corps in the northeast came under attack by massed Chinese forces in overwhelming numbers. On the night of the 27th, the Chinese attacked the 5th and 7th Marines, which had advanced together to Yudam-ni, west of the Chosin Reservoir. Other Chinese divisions cut the main supply route. From November 28 to December 2, the 1st MarDiv held its own against several such divisions and began a fighting withdrawal, bringing out shattered Army units with it.

Over 70 miles of tortuous road through mountain passes and canyons dominated by CCF, Marines fought and advanced back to the

Figure 2-16. Flight deck handlers of USS Badoeng Strait load 5" rockets on the F4U Corsairs of Marine Fighter Squadron 323, at sea during September 1950.

coast, reuniting all of the regiments of the 1st MarDiv that had deployed along the way. The Chinese troops hovering along reverse slopes and flanks became targets for the supporting aircraft of the 1st MAW.

The 1st MarDiv reached Hamhung on December 11, having brought out its wounded, most of its dead, and vehicles and equipment, including those of several Army units. The main body was evacuated on the 15th to South Korea by the Navy, which pulled out the remaining units of X Corps and 91,000 civilian refugees to complete its "amphibious landing in reverse."

Stopping the Chinese Advance

Upon arrival at Pusan, the 1st MarDiv again passed into Eighth Army reserve. Marines then participated in Operation Killer and Operation Ripper, limited offensives in east central Korea designed to keep the enemy off balance. Meanwhile, operating under 5th Air Force control, 1st MAW planes performed interdiction missions, seeking enemy military targets far into North Korea. The Chinese struck back with a large-scale counterattack. The 1st MarDiv at the Hwachon Reservoir, also known as "The Punchbowl," beat off repeated enemy attacks, inflicting heavy enemy casualties, stopping the advance of the Chinese and North Koreans, and stabilizing the lines. A second enemy offensive was stopped the following month. This was followed by attacks in which the Marines pursued and severely punished the enemy.

Truce Talks

Marines ended their first year in Korea in the "Punchbowl" area just north of the 38th parallel, former dividing line of North Korea and South Korea. Early in July 1951, United Nations, Chinese, and North Korean representatives met for the first peace talks, which created a lull in the activities at the front. During 1952, Marines continued experimenting with troop and supply lifts, using helicopters to bypass Korean hills. Beginning on Saint Patrick's Day, the 1st MarDiv was shifted to the extreme west side of the Korean Peninsula. There, Marines fought their last engagements in a series of outpost fights on a static battlefield. The truce came on July 27, 1953, but the 1st MarDiv did not return to the United States until 1955, after almost five years of outstanding service in Korea. The 1st MAW remained in Japan to support the newly reformed 3rd MarDiv.

Marine Corps Readiness

The U.S. rearmament for the Cold War in the face of the fighting in the Korean War included legislation endowing the Marine Corps with a minimum peacetime strength of three combat divisions and three aircraft wings, with supporting troops. The Commandant of the Marine Corps (CMC) also was authorized full status with the other service chiefs in the Joint Chiefs of Staff in matters directly concerning the Corps. The 3rd MarDiv reactivated on January 7, 1952. It deployed to Japan the following year. The 3rd MAW reactivated on February 1, 1952.

In the decades following the Korean War, the Marine Corps resumed the role of the Nation's force-in-readiness. To fulfill this mission, two regiments of the 3rd MarDiv deployed to bases on the island of Okinawa, Japan, in mid-1955, and one regiment deployed to Hawaii as the nucleus of the permanent 1st Marine Brigade.

Camp Pendleton is "home" for the 1st MarDiv and the I MEF. The huge base was named during World War II in honor of Joseph H. Pendleton, who served the Corps for 40 years. He was a veteran of the Spanish-American War and the "Banana Wars" of Nicaragua and the Dominican Republic. He died in February 1942 after retiring as a major general of Marines.

Meanwhile, the 2nd MarDiv, at Camp Lejeune, North Carolina, continued to provide landing forces for the U.S. Sixth Fleet on duty in the Mediterranean and First Fleet in the Atlantic.

Camp Lejeune was named in honor of John Archer Lejeune, the 13th CMC who served as a Marine officer for nearly 40 years. During World War I, he became the first Marine officer to command an Army division. He was appointed CMC in June 1920 and is credited with establishing the Marine Corps Schools at Quantico, Virginia, and directing the Marine Corps toward its role as an amphibious force-in-readiness. He retired in 1929 and died in November 1942. Camp Lejeune is the "home" of the 2nd MarDiv and II MEF.

In the years following the hostilities in Korea, the Corps' activities proved as varied as they were scattered. In August 1953, Marines of the Sixth Fleet assisted in relief activities following an earthquake in Greece. Elements of the 2nd MarDiv cruised off the coast of riot-torn Guatemala during July 1954, prepared to land security forces if necessary. In the summer of 1958, the government of Lebanon requested U.S. troops to bolster its army against a growing rebel threat. On July 15, the first of four Marine Corps battalions landed at Beirut. Additional American forces reinforced the Marines who, after the crisis had subsided, withdrew on October 4.

While peacetime operations continued, the Marine Corps also developed concepts, tactics, and equipment to continually update its readiness. In 1948, Marine planners began work on the development of an integrated amphibious and heliborne force designed for a rapid assault from the sea. (See Figure 2-17 on next page.) Eventually, this concept gave birth to the Navy's amphibious assault ship (LPH), a combat vessel capable of carrying a Marine battalion landing

Figure 2-17. Beginning with the HO3S-1 helicopters of 1950, the Marine Corps advanced the development of the helicopter and its employment in combat.

team (BLT) and a medium helicopter squadron (HMM). The early LPHs were converted aircraft carriers, but in 1961, the Navy commissioned the first ship specifically designed to support such a force, USS *Iwo Jima*. To provide close air support for an expeditionary force, the Marine Corps developed the short airfield for tactical support (SATS). Rapidly installed on prepared ground, this landbased carrier deck consisted of 4,000 feet of aluminum matting, catapult, arresting cable, and portable control units to base Marine attack aircraft ashore with the landing force.

The 1960s

Two main areas of conflict loomed next for the Marine Corps–Southeast Asia and the Caribbean.

Following Communist insurgent invasion of Laos in late 1960, BLTs on board Seventh Fleet ships in the South China Sea remained on alert for possible deployment, and the following year, Marine helicopters provided logistical support for the Laotian government. In May 1962, a Marine expeditionary unit, a BLT

with helicopter and fixed-wing squadrons, reinforced Thailand because of similar insurgent threats.

Meanwhile, HMM-362 deployed from 1st MAW to Vietnam, where the helicopter squadron flew combat missions in support of the South Vietnamese armed forces. Under the code name Shu-Fly, the air crews operated in the Mekong Delta and later deployed to Da Nang in the northern military district, called I Corps. This initial Marine commitment to South Vietnam reached approximately 600 men, including advisors to Vietnamese ground units.

In October 1962, came the major Cold War crisis with the Soviet Union in the Caribbean when U.S. intelligence reported the installation of Soviet offensive missiles at several bases in Communist Cuba.

President John F. Kennedy issued an ultimatum to the Russian and Cuban governments, demanding the removal of these weapons and simultaneously ordered U.S. forces into the region. In response to this alert, the Marine garrison at the U.S. Naval Base, Guantanamo Bay, Cuba, received reinforcements and combat elements of the 2nd MarDiv, and the 2nd MAW deployed to forward positions for an immediate reaction. An expeditionary brigade from the 1st MarDiv arrived shortly off the coast of Cuba. These and other demonstrations of American resolve led to delicate negotiations that eventually resulted in the removal of Russian missiles from Cuban soil.

Conflict in South Vietnam and the Dominican Republic

In early 1965, Marines conducted two important landings, one of which would commit the Corps to one of the longest wars in its history. The U.S. Navy skirmished briefly with North Vietnamese torpedo boats in the Tonkin Gulf incident of August 1964. President Lyndon B. Johnson ordered retaliatory air strikes against selected North Vietnamese bases.

During February, the Viet Cong VC, (North Vietnamese directed insurgents in South Vietnam) attacked two U.S. installations in South Vietnam, killing several Americans, while U.S. planes bombed North Vietnam. To guard against Communist retaliatory air strikes, the Marine Corps deployed the 1st Light Antiaircraft Missile Battalion from Okinawa to Da Nang Air Base for air defense.

On March 8, 1965, the 9th MEB, began landing at Da Nang, bringing additional security to the base, and by March 12, some 5,000 Marines stood ashore, sent from the III MEF headquartered on Okinawa.

Two days later, an additional battalion from the 1st Marine Brigade in Hawaii arrived at Phu Bai, seven miles south of Hue. The Marines took up defensive positions at both enclaves, but conducted no major offensive operations against insurgents. They did, however, bolster the South Vietnamese forces who were losing ground to the VC.

Halfway around the world, the 6th MEU moved into another trouble spot.

On April 24, 1965, the Navy's Task Group 44.9, with BLT 3/6 and HMM-264 embarked, received orders to move close to the coast of the Dominican Republic, then being rocked by internal disorder. The U.S. ambassador had reported that a coup was in progress against the existing government and the Marines were to stand by for possible evacuation of Americans and other foreign nationals.

With the rebels in control of the capital city of Santo Domingo, 500 Marines landed on April 28, 1965, to protect the refugees, since the local police could no longer handle the situation. As conditions continued to deteriorate, additional elements of the 6th MEU were committed to protect civilians and the U.S. Embassy. By the 29th, some 1,500 Marines were ashore. The next day, U.S. Army airborne units arrived, and on May 1, the Corps activated the 4th MEB for operations there. Marine and Army troops engaged rebel bands in sporadic firefights, and there were numerous sniping incidents.

On May 6, the Organization of American States voted to send an Inter-American Peace Force to help restore peace and constitutional government in the Dominican Republic. The first contingent of Brazilian troops arrived on May 25, and the Marines began their withdrawal. On June 6, the last elements of the 4th MEB departed Santo Domingo, having controlled some 8,000 Marines either ashore or afloat off the coast of the Dominican Republic. Final Marine casualties were 9 killed and 30 wounded.

Establishment of III MAF

As the 4th MEB departed Santo Domingo, the Marine Corps accelerated its commitment to the Republic of Vietnam. On May 3, 1965, 9th MEB stood down and the III MEF established itself ashore, along with the 3rd MarDiv (Forward). At that time, ground elements consisted primarily of the 3rd Marine Regiment, and all aviation units were under the control of MAG-16.

On May 11, the 1st MAW (Advance) arrived at Da Nang to provide the senior headquarters for all Marine aviation in the country. The designation of III MEF was changed to III Marine Amphibious Force (MAF) on May 7, a cosmetic change in name only. The same day, the 3rd MAB landed at Chu Lai, 55 miles south of Da Nang and established the third Marine enclave in I Corps. Two days after this landing, Marine engineers and U.S. Navy Seabees began construction of a SATS field at Chu Lai.

Laboring under extremely adverse conditions, the working parties completed an operational strip by June 1, when the first A-4 Skyhawks of MAG-12 arrived. As of June 5, the Marine Corps leadership in III MAF exercised U.S. military command over all I Corps responsible to the Commander, U.S. Military Assistance Command, Vietnam headquartered in Saigon. The Marine Corps still maintained a defensive posture in Vietnam with orders to conduct only those limited offensive operations necessary to ensure the security of its base perimeters.

Full-Scale Combat Operations in Vietnam

On July 1, 1965, Viet Cong assault squads launched their first attack on the Da Nang air base, and it became apparent that the Marines would have to expand their areas of responsibility and conduct deep patrolling to prevent further attacks. This decision coincided with the August arrival of the 7th Marines (1st MarDiv) at Chu Lai.

Within four days of landing, Regimental Landing Team (RLT) 7 took part in the first major American battle of the war—Operation Starlite. By the end of 1965, there were 38,000 Marines in I Corps, with more on the way. In January 1966, the President authorized the deployment of the 1st MarDiv to Vietnam. The division established its headquarters at Chu Lai on March 29, 1966, and held responsibility for the two southern provinces of I Corps. From its headquarters at Da Nang, the 3rd MarDiv took over the central and northern provinces.

Marines knew the war in Vietnam was not entirely a military struggle. In a counterinsurgency environment, the people were the key to success, and III MAF initiated several programs to win the support of the populace.

In late 1965, Marines initiated Golden Fleece operations whereby units protected the villagers' rice crop from the guerrillas during harvest time. This effort proved so successful in denying the VC logistical support that commanders expanded the program throughout I Corps.

County Fair was a combined U.S./ARVN (United States/Army of the Republic of Vietnam) cordon-and-search process aimed at the local guerrillas. Moving into position before dawn, the Marines threw a cordon around a target hamlet to prevent the VC from escaping or receiving reinforcements. At last light, South Vietnamese troops entered the hamlet, where they took a census, fed the people, provided medical attention and entertainment, and searched the area. Those VC who were not killed or captured were disposed of by the Marines when they fled the hamlet.

With the Combined Action Program, begun by the 3rd Battalion, 4th Marines, at Phu Bai, Marines reverted to their traditional antiguerrilla technique for the villagers by preparing the militia-like Popular Forces (PF) for local defense. The basic operating unit integrated a 14-man Marine squad, with a Navy Corpsman, with a 35-man PF platoon, forming a Combined Action Platoon (CAP). The Marines lived in the village, assisting in the military training of the PFs and initiating self-help projects for the peasants. These local defense groups soon were able to deny the VC access to rice and recruits from the hamlets and provided the villagers with a life free of insurgent terror and intimidation. By late 1966, the various pacification and civic action programs, shielded by Allied military operations, had extended government influence over 1,690 square miles and 1,000,000 people in I Corps.

War in the North

As a result of allies military and pacification successes along the coastal plain, the North Vietnamese opened a new front along the northern border of I Corps. In July 1966, the 324th NVA (North Vietnamese Army) Division moved south across the demilitarized zone (DMZ) in its first major incursion. Besides seizing Quang Tri Province, the enemy hoped to draw the Marines away from the populated areas, thin out their forces and take pressure off the VC insurgents in the south.

In Operation Hastings, Marine commanders pitted 8,000 Marines and 3,000 South Vietnamese troops against the enemy division. Heavy fighting continued until August 3, when the 324th retreated to the north, leaving over 700 dead behind.

To counter the threat from the north, the 3rd MarDiv displaced to Phu Bai in October. 1st MarDiv, then shifted to Da Nang as U.S. Army troops moved into the Chu Lai area, thus freeing Marines for duty farther north. In the spring of 1967, the 325th NVA Division made a thrust into the south, this time against the combat

The Tet Offensive and Withdrawal

On January 31, 1968, the North Vietnamese unleashed their biggest offensive of the war. Taking advantage of the Tet (Vietnamese Lunar New Year) holiday season and the poor weather associated with the northeast monsoons, the VC infiltrated some 68,000 troops and insurgents into the major population centers of South Vietnam. The allies responded quickly, drove the invaders from the cities and in three weeks killed 32,000 enemy troops. Prolonged fighting continued in Saigon and Hue, where die-hard remnants held out for several weeks. In Hue, a near division-size NVA force occupied the city and its Citadel, which encompassed the old imperial grounds. Marine, Army, and South Vietnamese troops, including the 1st and 5th Marines, cleared the southern half of the city in brutal street fighting and then turned to the walled Citadel. This was the Marines' first combat in a built-up area since fighting in Seoul during the Korean War. On February 24, the enemy flag, which had flown over the Citadel for 24 days, was ripped down and the last enemy pockets of resistance collapsed the next day. The battle cost the NVA 5,000 men.

While the fighting raged in Hue, the men of the 26th Marines (from the reactivated 5th MarDiv) were engaged in a different type of struggle at Khe Sanh. Beginning in late 1967, two NVA divisions, the 325th and the 304th, had invested that garrison and on January 21, 1968, unleashed their first attack. Marines reinforced the three organic battalions of the 26th Marines with the 1st Battalion, 9th Marines, and the 37th ARVN Ranger Battalion, setting the stage for one of the most dramatic battles of the war. For two and a half months, the Khe Sanh defenders fought off enemy ground attacks and weathered daily artillery, rocket, and mortar attacks. During the siege, U.S. aircraft dropped more than 100,000 tons of bombs on the hills surrounding Khe Sanh, while Marine and U.S. Army batteries fired in excess of 150,000 artillery rounds. Literally blown from their positions, the NVA withdrew in the face

The long war in Vietnam saw the Marines operating less from landing tracked vehicles such as these and using helicopters to operate against Communist aggressors along Vietnam's DMZ.

outpost at Khe Sanh. Two battalions of the 3rd Marines responded and, behind pinpoint bombing of Marine attack aircraft as well as massive artillery fire, drove two enemy regiments from the hills overlooking the base. In two weeks of bitter, uphill fighting, the Marines killed 940 NVA at a cost of 125 dead. In July 1967, the action shifted farther to the east, where the 9th Marines blocked another invasion attempt and the enemy retreated after losing almost 1,300 men. The direct assaults across the DMZ had resulted in heavy enemy losses. As a result, the NVA shifted to heavy artillery, rocket, and mortar attacks along the northern border. The focal point for much of this fire was Con Thien artillery fire base. The Marines there endured heavy shelling throughout the late summer and the fall of 1967.

of a combined Marine, Army, and South Vietnamese task force, advancing toward Khe Sanh from the east. All told, the NVA lost about 3,000 men during the two operations, although some estimates of enemy dead ran as high as 12,000.

On March 31, 1968, President Johnson made a television address to the Nation, during which he announced that he was limiting the U.S. air strikes against North Vietnam. This action eventually led to peace talks in Paris, which began on May 13, 1968. Even with talks underway, the fighting continued in South Vietnam. Additional reinforcements also arrived in I Corps: the 1st Air Cavalry Division, elements of the 101st Airborne Division, and the 27th Marines all came under III MAF control, totaling 163,000 American troops, more than any Marine Corps command in history.

During early 1969, President Richard M. Nixon announced that 25,000 U.S. troops would depart South Vietnam, beginning in July 1969. By mid-November, the 3rd MarDiv had redeployed to Okinawa. This withdrawal movement continued into mid-1970 when the 1st MarDiv departed Vietnam, leaving only a reinforced regiment in place. The Army's XXIV Corps replaced III MAF in March 1970 and assumed operational control of the remaining American troops in I Corps. Slightly more than a year later, all Marines had returned to their permanent bases except for small numbers remaining to complete the final administrative and logistical tasks.

Returning to Readiness

Mayaguez Incident

On May 12, 1975, just two weeks after the evacuation of Saigon at the end of the Vietnam War, the unarmed American container ship *Mayaguez* was seized by a Cambodian gunboat and taken to the Cambodian offshore island of Koh Tang. Since no amphibious units were near the area, Marine units from Okinawa were airlifted to Utapao air base in nearby Thailand for an assault on the ship and island using U.S.

Air Force helicopters. Recapture of the ship proceeded on May 15 when Marines boarded and seized the ship, which they found had been recently abandoned.

At the same time, a 210-man raiding force of Marines from Company G, 2nd Battalion, 9th Marines assaulted the island of Koh Tang, where it was believed the American crew was being held. Landing from Air Force CH-53 and HH-53 helicopters, the assault encountered heavy ground fire. The Marines fought on the island until their evacuation on the night of May 16. Shortly after the assault landing, the crewmembers of *Mayaguez* were picked up by a U.S. Navy ship and were able to sail away while the fighting on Koh Tang Island was still going on. Casualties in this operation were heavy, with 11 Marines killed, 3 Marines missing, and 50 other servicemen wounded. Three of the 15 helicopters used in the operation were shot down, and 10 others received battle damage.

Marines in Lebanon, Grenada and Panama—1982–89

Marines returned to Lebanon on August 25, 1982, with the landing of roughly 800 men of the 32nd Marine Amphibious Unit (MAU) to join a multinational peacekeeping force. The other troops participating were 400 French and 800 Italians, and the mission of the force was evacuation of Palestine Liberation Organization (PLO) guerrillas who were under siege in Beirut by Israeli forces. The evacuation was completed on September 10, but shortly afterward the MAU returned, and for the next 16 months, a MAU was maintained in Beirut on rotation. Marines experienced a variety of both combat and noncombat situations. A suicide truck packed with explosives attacked the BLT 1/8 headquarters building at the Beirut International Airport killing 241 Americans and wounding 70 others on October 23, 1983. After civil strife worsened, American civilians and other foreign nationals were evacuated by helicopter on February 10–11, 1984, leaving a residual force behind to protect the U.S. Embassy. The 22nd MAU completed the last such deployment on February 26, 1984.

Following the assassination of the Prime Minister and overthrow of the government of Grenada, U.S. intervention was requested by neighboring Caribbean nations. On October 25, the Marines of the 22nd MAU made helicopter and beach landings to seize Pearls Airport and rescue several hundred American students attending the local medical college. Simultaneous landings by U.S. Army airborne troops were aimed at seizure of a second larger airfield in the south of the island. 22nd MAU accomplished its mission, while capturing large quantities of weapons and ammunition, as well as large numbers of Cubans and Grenadian insurgents.

Instability in Panama threatened the safety of Americans there as well as international use of the Panama Canal. Further complicating the issue were American criminal charges of narcotics smuggling against the Panamanian dictator. On December 20, 1989, five days after a Panamanian gunman killed a Marine officer, the U.S. Army inserted a combat force to preserve the Panama Canal Treaty and apprehend the dictator. Marines from Company K, 3rd Battalion, 6th Marines, and Company D, 2nd Light Armored Infantry Battalion, also deployed to provide security for defense installations, participated in the Army attack on the Panamanian Defense Force (PDF). Marines were tasked with protecting the Pacific entrance to the canal, establishing roadblocks, and apprehending PDF members. By the end of the first day, Marines had seized several PDF compounds, apprehended 1,200 Panamanians, and confiscated more than 550 weapons.

Operations to Liberate Kuwait: Desert Shield and Desert Storm

On August 2, 1990, Iraq invaded neighboring Kuwait. The American government anticipated a possible Iraqi attack on Saudi Arabia, which led President George H. W. Bush to order U.S. forces to the region. This began one of the most rapid overseas buildups of an American force in history. Much of the 1st MarDiv stood in the Saudi desert by the end of the month. Other elements of the I and II MEFs followed through February 1991. In addition, the President authorized the first large-scale activation of Reserve units since the early 1950s.

With forces in place to defend Saudi Arabia, Kuwait became the focus of the United States and an American-led coalition of nations. On January 16, the allies launched air strikes that began a five-week strategic and tactical air campaign. Allied air forces quickly achieved and maintained air supremacy throughout the theater. Marine Corps F/A-18 Hornets, A-6E Intruders, AV-8B Harriers, and EA-6B Prowlers participated in the campaign. (See Figure 2-18.) In the fourth week, even Marine C-130s took an offensive role, dropping several fuel-air-explosive bombs on tactical targets.

Figure 2-18. In modern times, Marine aviation continues to contribute decisive combat power and operational flexibility. Shown here is an AV-8B Harrier.

Marine ground forces—two divisions and service support of a large I MEF were positioned on the border south of Kuwait during the air campaign. The 1st MarDiv held positions near the Persian Gulf, while the 2nd MarDiv was farther inland. The 4th and 5th MEBs and the 13th MEU remained on board amphibious shipping in the gulf. After assisting in the repulse of the January 29 Iraqi attack into the Saudi town of Khafji, the Marines attacked with their two divisions on the morning of February

24. They quickly breached the mined defensives and engaged the Iraqis in ground combat.

The two MarDivs and combined Arab forces on either flank carried out a supporting attack, fixing the Iraqis in place while U.S. Army and allied forces were to move into Iraq west of Kuwait to isolate and surround the Iraqi invasion force. Each attack caused the Iraqis to crumble; however, President Bush ordered a ceasefire on February 28 with the 2nd MarDiv pursuing Iraqi units near the city's western suburb, and the 1st MarDiv consolidating its gains near the international airport to the south of the city. A formal truce took place shortly afterward. Twenty-three Marines died in action during the four-day ground war.

More Stabilization Operations

In the aftermath of the Gulf War, the 24th MEU deployed to northern Iraq to assist refugee Kurds, a minority group in Iraq and Turkey. The Marines served in a 10-nation force that provided humanitarian relief. It was one of several such military operations other than war (MOOTW) that, in addition to the Iraqi campaign, characterized the use of American forces in the 1990s.

In August 1990, as Marines were preparing to deploy to Southwest Asia, the 22nd MEU landed in the African nation of Liberia, where political instability was threatening the security of foreign nationals. They established a security zone at the U.S. embassy in Monrovia, and evacuated 1,705 foreign nationals. The 22nd MEU was relieved by the 26th MEU, which acted as a peacekeeping force and helped transport relief workers until reembarking on amphibious shipping in January 1991. Also in January, the 4th MEB landed in Somalia to evacuate more than 400 foreign nationals from that nation's capital, Mogadishu.

While returning from the Iraqi campaign, the 5th MEB provided humanitarian relief after

a major typhoon decimated much of Bangladesh in south Asia during May 15–19, 1991. The next month, the 15th MEU joined reinforcements from Okinawa in the Philippines to help provide relief following the volcanic eruption of Mount Pinatubo.

In May 1992, the 3rd Battalion, 1st Marines and the 3rd Light Armored Infantry Battalion provided support to civilian law-enforcement agencies during riots in Los Angeles. The Marines, as well as national guardsmen, provided security but did not directly participate in police activities, in accordance with American law.

In June 1992, the 9th Engineer Support Battalion and the 3rd Recon Battalion helped provide drought relief to the Micronesian island of Chuuk. Two months later, the 1st MEB supported typhoon victims in Guam. The action was followed shortly by domestic hurricane disasters in Dade County, Florida, and Kauai, Hawaii. The 1st MEB supported victims in Kauai from August to October 1992, while about 1,000 Marines from various commands supported hurricane victims in Florida.

The Marine Corps played a key role in one of the largest humanitarian operations in Somalia. On December 9, 1992, the 15th MEU landed in Mogadishu to take control of the massive famine relief effort, followed by reinforcements from I MEF. After a successful performance, they turned over control of the operation to the United Nations five months later.

Though immediate relief needs were met in Somalia, the political situation there slowly deteriorated during the rest of 1993 and 1994. Marines played a minor role in the U.N. operation during those months, but in March 1995, they were called back to center stage by President Bill Clinton. The 13th MEU, with elements of 3rd Battalion, 1st Marines and 3rd Battalion, 7th Marines, protected the extraction of multinational peacekeepers and recovery of U.S. equipment and weaponry. Marines engaged Somalis in light fighting during the 73-hour operation. The most significant aspect of the encounter was the Marine use of nonlethal weapons, including sticky foam and stun grenades. It was the Corps' first employment ever of such weapons.

Throughout 1994, Marines participated in joint Caribbean Sea operations to prevent Haitian and Cuban boat people from reaching the United States illegally. Marines also maintained separate refugee camps for Haitians and Cubans at the U.S. Naval Base at Guantanamo Bay, Cuba. After a military coup in Haiti, President Clinton demanded that the Haitian military leaders return governmental control to that nation's democratically elected officials. American forces, including Marines, deployed as peacekeepers during the transfer of power.

On April 20, 1996, a reinforced rifle company from the 22nd MEU was airlifted into Monrovia, Liberia, to assist with the evacuation of American and designated foreign citizens once again because of decreasing stability in that country. Operations in Africa continued sporadically through July 1997, when 22nd MEU evacuated more than 2,500 civilians from Freetown, Sierra Leone.

Conflict in the Balkans

With United Nations peacekeepers unable to stabilize a war between the newly independent states of the former Yugoslavia, NATO established a no-fly zone in 1993 with the intention of preventing Serb aircraft from attacking or supporting attacks in Bosnia. Marine F/A-18 Hornets and EA-6B Prowlers participated in patrols to enforce that no-fly zone. Marine pilots also participated in air strikes during 1994 and 1995, including a recovery operation by 24th MEU rescuing a downed U.S. Air Force pilot.

In June 1996, VMU-1, a Marine unmanned aerial vehicle squadron, deployed to Bosnia to provide reconnaissance support for the American elements of the NATO peacekeeping force. In June 1999, 26th MEU went ashore as the first American forces into Kosovo, again on NATO peacekeeping duty. The Marines remained in Kosovo for six weeks, before handing the mission off to Army forces, and redeploying to amphibious shipping. Such Balkan activities subsided at the end of the century, but Marines continue to deploy and train in the region.

Conflict in Southwest Asia

The 2001 attack on two U.S. cities by terrorists led to the successive deployment of U.S. forces to Afghanistan, the initial terrorist base, and then the widening of the prosecution known as the "Global War on Terror" into Yemen and Somalia and the epic invasion of Iraq in 2003. These measures produced crushing military defeats of the enemy in each case. However, they also led to long-term campaigns in Iraq and Afghanistan to occupy, pacify, and conduct security and stabilization operations in order to establish native governments that would lead their nations into the peaceful international community.

The Marine air-ground team, projected ashore from Navy amphibious shipping, has responded to repeated employment in crisis and war.

The Marine Corps contribution for the campaign in Afghanistan, beginning in October of 2001, initially consisted of a two MEUs, under Brigadier General James N. Mattis, launching combat forces and supporting aviation hundreds of miles inland to envelop the southeast portion of the country around the cultural center of Khandahar. These actions, combined with the U.S. assisted antigovernment forces of Afghans in the north, caused the scattering of the Taliban leaders and the terrorist bands they had sheltered. A U.S. approved provisional government took office in December, and the pacification program for that country continues.

Such an unusual campaign, resembling the Caribbean antibandit operations of the early 20th century, remained small scale compared to the Marine Corps contribution to the invasion and occupation of Iraq. Operation Iraqi Freedom (OIF), beginning in March 2003, saw Marines comprising half of the initial U.S. assault forces and a third of the overall forces in the initial campaign. The I MEF employed the 1st MarDiv and a regimental task force of 2nd MarDiv with a reinforced 3rd MAW and 1st Force Service Support Group to sweep into Southeastern Iraq, detaching the British Army and Royal Marine contingents and a Marine MEU to take Basra and the Faw Peninsula. Continuing onward, Marines shattered the Iraqi army in a fast-moving battle and pursuit between the Euphrates and Tigris Rivers past Kut and into Baghdad from the south. As the Iraqi government and military collapsed, the Marine Corps and Army forces secured Baghdad, while more Marines swept northward to prevent any consolidation by Iraqi remnant forces.

Marine Corps forces then undertook the occupation of south-central Iraq between Baghdad and Basra for another six months while the United Nations sorted out an international coalition to relieve U.S. forces. In the end, a continuing U.S. presence became necessary, and I MEF returned to Iraq in February 2004 after a brief absence. A continuous occupation of western Iraq by Marine Corps Forces (I and II MEF in rotation) ensued.

More than 20,000 Marines and sailors of I MEF took up their new positions for the 2004 campaign. The combat operations of the campaign beginning in 2004 have seen major urban battles in the cities of Fallujah and Ramadi counterinsurgency operations, both rural and urban, all over western Iraq, and a continuing effort to rebuild, protect, and nourish the native society and economy of a former enemy nation.

Those mission successes and achievements did not come without cost. During the campaign of 2004 to 2005, some 500 Marines of Multinational Force-West lost their lives while serving in Iraq with thousands more wounded—many grievously—in combat. Since March 20, 2004, elements of I and II MEF (augmented by the rest of the active and Reserve establishment) provided continuous presence in Iraq. Throughout these rotations, Marines have demonstrated the same great courage in battle as did those cited at the beginning of this chapter. Marines have shown remarkable stamina over months and later years, maintaining unshakable honor tested in the most complex environment imaginable. It represents immeasurable personal sacrifice and that of Marine Corps families.

These most recent actions illustrate the continuity in the Marine Corps story. In every clime and place Marines have stood vigil ashore and afloat. Readiness and amphibious expertise remain our hallmark. As long as our Nation possesses and exercises command of the seas, Marines will form its cutting edge.

Traditions

To continue from the beginning of the chapter, traditions obviously have come to us from the generations of Marines who preceded us. As we observe them, we do honor to our predecessors and ourselves. Among the more significant are:

Semper Fidelis ("Always Faithful"). The motto of the Corps, adopted about 1883. Before that, there had been three mottos, all traditional rather

Just as Marines responded to their first call to arms in 1775, other Marine riflemen took up arms and equipment for a new fight in 2002.

than official: Fortitudine ("With Fortitude"), "By Sea and by Land," and "From the Halls of the Montezumas to the Shores of Tripoli."

"The Marines' Hymn." The hymn of the Marine Corps, as contrasted with "Semper Fidelis," the Corps march. Every Marine knows the words of "The Marines' Hymn," the oldest of the official songs of the U.S. Armed Services and will sing them at the drop of a field hat.

First on foot, and right of the line. Marines form at the place of honor—at the head of column or on right of line—in any naval formation. This privilege was bestowed on the Corps by the Secretary of the Navy on August 9, 1876.

"First to fight." The slogan has appeared on Marine recruiting posters since World War I.

Marine Talk and Terminology. Because of our naval origins, we speak in a combination of soldier and sailor. Thus floors, walls, ceilings become "decks," "bulkheads," and "overheads." The water fountain is a "scuttlebutt," and the rest room, the "head." Never feel self-conscious

about using Marine terms—especially the prescribed and traditional "Aye, aye, Sir (or Ma'am)."

"Tell it to the Marines!" Marines go everywhere and see everything, and if they say it is so, it is to be believed. This yarn is an old one, found in print as early as 1726.

Military Courtesy: The Finer Touch of Marine Culture

Courtesy is the accepted form of politeness among civilized people. Courtesy smoothes the personal relationship among individuals in all walks of life. A good rule of thumb might be the golden rule: "Do unto others as you would have them do unto you." The Marine remains an absolute model of military courtesy to all other services, as is the case with fighting spirit.

The Salute

The most important of all military courtesies is the salute. This is an honored tradition of the military profession throughout the world. The saluting custom goes back to earliest recorded history.

It is believed to have originated in the days when all men bore arms. In those days, warriors raised their weapons in such a manner as to show friendly intentions. They sometimes would shift their weapons from the right hand to the left and raise their right hand to show that they did not mean to attack.

Just as you show marks of respect to your seniors in civilian life, military courtesy demands that you show respect to your seniors in the military profession. Your military seniors are the officers and noncommissioned officers (NCOs) senior to you. Regulations require that all officers be saluted by their juniors and that they return such salutes. In saluting an officer, a junior Marine is formally recognizing the officer as a military superior and is reaffirming the oath to obey the order of all officers appointed over the Marine. By returning the salute, the senior officer greets the junior as a fellow Marine and expresses the appreciation of the junior's support. Enlisted personnel do not ordinarily exchange salutes.

The Hand Salute

Today, the salute has several forms. The hand salute is the most common. When a salute is executed, the right hand is raised smartly until the tip of the forefinger touches the lower part of the headgear. Thumb and fingers are extended and joined. The palm is turned slightly inward until the person saluting can just see its surface from the corner of the right eye. The upper arm is parallel to the ground with the elbow slightly in front of the body. The forearm is inclined at a 45-degree angle, hand and wrist in a straight line. Completion of the salute is executed by dropping the arm to its normal position in one sharp, clean motion. (See Figure 2-19.)

Figure 2-19. The hand salute.

Some General Rules

- When meeting an officer who is either riding or walking, salute when six paces away in order to give time for a return of your salute before you are abreast of the officer.
- Hold the salute until it is returned.
- Accompany the salute with "Good morning, Sir/Ma'am," or some other appropriate greeting.
- Render the salute but once if the senior remains in the immediate vicinity. If conversation takes place, however, salute again when the senior leaves or when you depart.
- When passing an officer who is going in the same direction, as you come abreast of the officer, on the left side if possible, salute and say, "By your leave, Sir/Ma'am." The officer will return the salute and say, "Carry on" or "Granted." You then finish your salute and pass ahead of the officer.
- Members of the naval service are required to render a salute to officers, regular and Reserve, of the Navy, Army, Air Force, Marine Corps, Coast Guard, and to foreign military and naval officers whose governments are formally recognized by the government of the United States.
- Upon the approach of an officer superior

in rank, individuals of a group not in formation are called to attention by the first person noticing the officer, and all come smartly to attention and salute.

Do Not Salute:

- If you are engaged in work or play unless spoken to directly.
- If you are a prisoner. Prisoners are denied the privilege.
- While guarding prisoners.
- Under battlefield conditions.
- When not wearing a cover.
- With any item in your right hand.
- With a pipe or cigarette or other items in your mouth.
- When in formation, EXCEPT at the command "Present Arms."
- When moving at "double time"— ALWAYS slow to a normal walk before saluting.
- When carrying articles in both hands, or otherwise so occupied as to make saluting impractical. (It would be appropriate, however, to render a proper greeting, e.g., "Good evening, Sir/Ma'am.")
- In public places where obviously inappropriate (theaters, restaurants, etc.).
- When a member of the guard engaged in performance of duty which prevents

saluting. (See Chapter 7 for saluting procedures for sentries.)

Saluting Officers Wearing Civilian Clothing. A junior in uniform who recognizes a senior in civilian clothing is required to render the proper greeting and salute.

Saluting Civilians. Civilians entitled by reason of their position to gun salutes or other honors, such as the President of the United States or the Secretary of the Navy, rate a hand salute.

Saluting While Standing in a Group. When a group of junior personnel approaches a senior, the senior in the group initiates a salute by calling out, "Attention," and all in the group face and salute the approaching officer.

Saluting a Group of Officers. When several officers in company are saluted, all return the salute. For example: as a lieutenant, you approach a colonel accompanied by a captain. You salute the officers. The colonel returns your salute, and at that point, the captain also salutes. If you, as an enlisted Marine are accompanying a captain and a lieutenant approaches, you would not salute until the lieutenant renders the proper salute to the captain you are with. When the captain returns the salute, you then render the proper salute.

Saluting indoors. Persons in the naval service never salute "uncovered," that is, not wearing a cover or headgear. If indoors, you are required to remove headgear and would not salute except under the following condition:

- When under arms, that is, carrying or having attached to you by sling or holster, a weapon. A person wearing a "duty belt" is considered "under arms" if the belt is worn in the performance of their duties. (Wearing a belt for the sole purpose of carrying canteens is not considered "under arms.")

Saluting Officers in a Vehicle. Salute all officers riding in motor vehicles. Those in the vehicle render and return salutes. The driver of the vehicle is obligated to salute only if the vehicle is stopped. To do so while moving might endanger the safety of the occupants and, therefore, may be omitted.

Personal Honors Being Rendered. When personal honors are being rendered to individuals of high rank and you are NOT IN FORMATION, salute at the first note of music, and hold the salute until the completion of the ruffles, flourishes, and march.

Military Funerals. During funerals, officers and enlisted personnel remain covered while in the open. During religious services when you are attending officially, a salute would be appropriate whenever honors are rendered: when the body is removed from the hearse to the chapel, from the chapel to the caisson, from the caisson to the grave, and when volleys are fired and "Taps" is sounded.

As a participant in a nonmilitary funeral or burial service, an individual may follow the civilian custom and uncover (rather than salute) when such honors are called for, as during the procession to the grave and the lowering of the body.

Other Forms of Military Courtesy

- When ordered to report to an officer, either outdoors or indoors if under arms, approach the officer at attention and halt about two paces away, render the appropriate salute and say, "Sir/Ma'am, Private Jones reporting as ordered," using proper names and grades. Hold the salute until it is acknowledged. When the business is completed, take one step backward, salute, and after your salute has been returned, execute about face and depart at attention.
- When reporting to an officer indoors when not under arms, follow the same procedure except remove the headgear before approaching the officer and do not salute.
- When accompanying a senior, walk on their left.
- When entering an automobile or small boat, the junior goes first, and the others follow in inverse order of rank. In leaving an automobile or a small boat, the senior goes first, and the others follow in order of rank.
- The greeting of the day is proper at the conclusion of business, when rendering the departing salute.

Honors to Colors and Anthem

Honors to the "National Anthem" or "To the Colors" are rendered as follows:

• Whenever the "National Anthem" or "To the Colors" is played to accompany raising or lowering the colors, and you are not in formation or not in a vehicle: come to attention and face the colors when "Attention" is sounded. Render the prescribed salute at the first note of the "National Anthem" or "To the Colors." Hold the salute until the last note of the "National Anthem" or "To the Colors." Remain standing at attention until "Carry On" is sounded.

• If no flag is near, face the music and salute.

• If in formation, salute only on the order "Present Arms."

• Vehicles in motion are brought to a halt. Troop formations riding in vehicles do not disembark. They and the driver remain seated at attention and do not salute. Drivers and passengers riding in either military or private vehicles remain seated at attention and do not salute.

• If outdoors and uncovered, stand at attention and face the direction of the flag or music. When the "National Anthem" is played indoors, officers and enlisted persons will stand at attention and face the music or the flag if one is present.

• When passing or being passed by an uncased color that is being paraded, presented, or is on formal display, salute at six paces distance and hold the salute until six paces beyond it or until it has passed you by six paces.

• If uncovered, stand or march at attention when passing or being passed by an uncased color.

• The marks of respect shown above are also rendered to the "National Anthem" of any friendly country when played upon official occasions.

Boarding Naval Vessels

When boarding a naval ship, upon reaching the top of the gangway face aft and salute the national ensign. After completing this salute, salute the officer of the deck who will be positioned on the quarterdeck at the head of the gangway, and request permission to come aboard. When leaving the ship, render the same salutes in reverse order, requesting permission from the officer of the deck to leave the ship as you salute him.

Miscellaneous

When "under arms," uncover only when seated in attendance at a court or board (but sentries guarding prisoners do not uncover), when entering places of divine worship or when indoors not on duty, e.g., eating, etc.

The term "outdoors" is construed to include such buildings as drill halls, gymnasiums, and other roofed enclosures used for drill or exercise of troops, theater marquees, covered walks, and other shelters open on the sides to the weather. "Indoors" includes offices, hallways, kitchens, guard rooms, washrooms, squadrooms, etc.

The Rifle Salute

Figure 2-20. Rifle Salute (right shoulder arms).   Figure 2-21. Rifle Salute (order arms).

When armed with the rifle, and not in formation, salutes are rendered in accordance with the rules outlined previously, except, instead of the hand salute, the rifle salute is rendered. (EXCEPTION: when carrying the rifle at sling arms, the hand salute is used.)

Suppose you are returning to your barracks from the armory and have your rifle at "port arms" and are moving at "double time." You are approaching an officer. Your actions would be: first, come to "quick time," and then either (1) come to "Order Arms" and render the rifle salute, or (2) go to "Right Shoulder Arms" and render the rifle salute. (See Figures 2-20 and 2-21 on previous page.) In addition, there is a third position in which you may render a proper rifle salute: Rifle Salute at Trail Arms.

CHAPTER 3

Law of War

The laws of armed conflict are the concern of every Marine from the Commandant of the Marine Corps to the newest private. Because of the terminology, "laws of armed conflict," you may think that only the highest officials of government concern themselves with the rules of war. While the government has drafted the basic legal documents governing man's treatment of his fellow man in wartime, the laws of armed conflict remain the direct concern of everyone who is ever engaged in war activities.

The laws of armed conflict can be defined simply: How should you, an individual Marine, conduct yourself in wartime operations to accomplish your mission while still respecting the rights of civilians, your enemies, and allies? This chapter of your guidebook provides some basic information on what to do and, just as importantly, what not to do in wartime situations. For all Marines, the official Law of War Program in a Department of Defense Directive 2311 01E of May 9, 2006, states that "members of the Department of Defense comply with the law of war during all armed conflicts, however such conflicts are characterized, and in all other military operations." Therefore, as a matter of policy, we will comply with the law of war across the spectrum of operations, from humanitarian assistance all the way up to international armed conflict. These rules apply to all U.S. citizens (not just the military forces), including the responsibility to report violations. The law of war obligations of the United States are observed and enforced by all Defense Department personnel and Defense Department contractors assigned to or accompanying deployed armed forces.

All reportable incidents committed by or against U.S. personnel, enemy persons, or any other individual are reported promptly, investigated thoroughly, and, where appropriate, remedied by corrective action. All reportable incidents are reported through command channels for ultimate transmission to appropriate U.S. agencies, allied governments, or other appropriate authorities. Once it has been determined that U.S. persons are not involved in a reportable incident, an additional U.S. investigation shall be continued only at the direction of the appropriate combatant commander. The on-scene commanders shall ensure that measures are taken to preserve evidence of reportable incidents pending transfer to United States, allied, or other appropriate authorities.

Why We Need Laws in War

Unfortunately, war is as old as man himself. People cause wars. Weapons don't. Man creates the weapons, which are merely the instruments that a nation uses to carry out its war objectives.

Genghis Khan, the ancient Asian warlord, reputedly killed or maimed a greater percentage of people than any other leader in history. He did it with bows and arrows and other similarly primitive weapons. During Genghis Khan's era, there were no rules of war. Although man continues today to be the force behind the weapons, there exists now a certain orderliness to which people of most countries who find themselves on a battlefield subscribe.

The positive side of mankind has managed to improve the conditions under which war is conducted since the era of Genghis Khan. As newer weapons of warfare have made it easier for man to kill his fellow man, nations have sensed a need to eliminate unnecessary death, destruction, and suffering. This need has been reflected in the moral values of civilized man and also of his military policies.

Binding customs and formal laws of war, presented in the Geneva Conventions and Hague Regulations, have evolved. They legally bind most nations to the practices set down at Geneva and the Hague. The United States has agreed to these rules. Any violation to them is the same as violation of the laws of the United States itself. The United States has led the world in adopting rules for its military forces that recognize that enemies are also human beings and that captured or detained people are entitled to retain their fundamental rights as humans regardless of their past conduct or beliefs. It is every Marine's duty, therefore, to know and obey the laws of armed conflict.

History shows that discipline and moral courage led our military forces to victory in battle after battle. These same characteristics apply to obedience to the laws of armed conflict. Although you will be in uniform and be an instrument of our Nation (the United States) in an armed conflict, this does not give you license to do anything you wish to do. There are limits on what you can do when waging war, and the laws of armed conflict establish those limits. This chapter explains what you can and cannot do.

General Precepts of the Laws of Armed Conflict

When you enter into an armed conflict in another country, you should be aware of many of the characteristics of the country. Knowledge of these characteristics will better prepare you to follow the tenets of the laws of armed conflict.

Geography

A general understanding of a nation's geography will permit you to know where the country's population is concentrated. That knowledge should prepare you to deal with civilians and the enemy as you encounter them. In addition, you should know the general area of the country in which you are operating and the nations which border it, so that you may understand any trends that may impact the implementation of the laws of armed conflict. You should know the capital and other major cities, the characteristics of the land (mountains, deserts, plains, etc.), and the climate. Knowledge of all these features will help you to better confront rules of war situations that might arise during your time in the country. You should receive information about the general characteristics of a nation's geography as part of instructional briefings given in connection with operational deployments.

People

Knowledge of the country's people can be invaluable to you in how you conduct yourself under the rules of war. Since nearly all offenses under the laws of armed conflict involve people, the more you know about the civilian populace of a country and of your enemy, the better off you will be. Know their ethnic backgrounds, their language, the educational level of the people, the very important cultural characteristics (particularly if they are different than the culture of the United States), the religions of the country, and the social customs of the people.

Knowledge of the people is probably the most important thing for you to know about the country. Without it, you cannot begin to understand the way the people think and act. Accordingly, the chances of doing something in violation of the rules of war increase. If the enemy and the people are one and the same, then the questions posed above will serve for both. If not, you will need to ask the same questions about your enemy. You must know the military and nonmilitary characteristics of your enemy. Again, listen carefully to briefings that tell you important facts about the country's people.

History

Pay particular attention to the history of a country as it relates to why you are there. Historical circumstances involving politics, religion, or cultural values may have led you to being in the country. You need to have knowledge of and be sensitive to the historical circumstances dictating USMC involvement in the country. Pay attention when you receive briefings on these matters. Read what you can find on the subject (newspapers, periodicals, etc.). Knowing the country's history as it relates to your involvement can serve you well in a situation where you might have to decide what to do in a wartime situation under the laws of armed conflict.

Economy

Is the country poor or wealthy? Does it have wealth concentrated in a few people and enormous pockets of poverty among the general populace? You need answers to these questions because such conditions may contribute to how you deal with the country's people and the enemy. Current economic conditions are also important: these include the conditions of growth, inflation, deflation, unemployment, poverty, and so forth. Knowledge of the economic condition of a country can lead you to understand better how a country's people and the enemy might behave toward you and might assist in preventing a violation of the rules of war.

Foreign Relations

Knowing the country's alliances, allies, traditional enemies (if any), and the country's role in international organizations (such as the United Nations) can provide you with an understanding of what to expect. Will the country comply with the laws of armed conflict that you fight under, or can you expect behavior contrary to your training?

Government

Knowing something about the nature of the national government in a country may better prepare you to understand the nature and conduct of your enemy as well as the civilian populace. Is the country's government bound by the Geneva Conventions and Hague Regulations? More importantly, will the government prosecute you for a crime against civilians or against the enemy for a violation of the rules of war? Even if the government does not comply with the rules of war in any way, it is your obligation as a Marine to conduct yourself under the laws of armed conflict which you are taught.

U.S. Relations with the Country

The United States' relationship with the country that you are entering may be good, bad, or somewhere between these two extremes. The country's government may want the U.S. Marines to be there, but some of its people may not. You may encounter situations or actions from the enemy, from the government or from the general population that will try your patience. They may communicate the message, "Yankee, go home!" If so, you must maintain your self-control and not violate the principles you have learned under the laws of armed conflict. You should be familiar with our relations with the country you are entering because it can serve you well in precluding the creation of a situation where you might violate the rules of war.

Basically, what you have just read can be summed up in eight words: *know the country in which you are serving.* That's as important as knowing terrain features and enemy tactics.

Along with knowledge of the country in which you are operating, make sure you understand your mission fully. It is while you are conducting your mission that you will encounter situations when you will have the opportunity to succeed or fail in your practice of the laws of armed conflict.

When you complete this chapter, you should have sufficient knowledge of what to do and what not to do under most combat situations, which will protect you from violating the laws of armed conflict. If you encounter a situation where you are not sure what action to take to accomplish your mission, get clearance from the next higher authority before continuing. For example, if some military action by you might endanger the lives of some local civilians and you are not sure how to proceed, be certain to get approval of your next action from the next higher authority.

Your Conduct Under the Laws of Armed Conflict

The laws of armed conflict tell you what you can and cannot do in combat situations. With the training you will receive, you will have the necessary discipline to do the right thing. But if you do not learn how you should conduct yourself in combat, you can be punished for mistakes.

All persons in uniform, carrying a weapon, or participating in any way in military operations or activities are known as combatants. Under the laws of armed conflict, only combatants are considered proper targets and may be fired upon. All others are either noncombatants or civilians. Noncombatants are a special group of personnel, including full-time medical personnel and chaplains. Civilians not taking a direct part in hostilities are entitled to be respected and protected at all times. Distinguishing between combatants, noncombatants, and civilians in guerrilla-war situations sometimes may be difficult and requires great care. Humane treatment of noncombatants and civilians may also assist you in obtaining valuable intelligence to allow you to better pursue your mission. If you are in doubt in differentiating between combatants, noncombatants, and civilians, consult your superior before pursuing any course of action.

Enemy Combatants

Never attack enemy soldiers who surrender or who are captured, sick or wounded. When you have an enemy prisoner of war (EPWs) you should treat them with STRESS: search, tag, report capture to higher headquarters (HQ), evacuate EPW to the nearest collection point, segregate, and safeguard. You must never kill, torture, or mistreat a prisoner because such actions are a violation of the law and because prisoners may provide you vital information about the enemy. Treating a prisoner badly will discourage other enemy soldiers from surrendering and harden the enemy's will to resist. But if we treat our prisoners well, this will encourage the enemy to treat his prisoners (our buddies) well. Humane treatment of EPWs is right, honorable, and required under the laws of armed conflict. Improper treatment of prisoners by us is punishable by court-martial.

Let enemy soldiers surrender. The enemy may use different signals to convey to you that he is surrendering, but all of the signals should be noticeable. It is illegal to fire on an enemy who has thrown down his weapon and offered to surrender.

You also should provide medical care to the wounded whether friend or foe. You are required under the laws of armed conflict to provide the same kind of medical care to the sick and wounded as you would provide for your own.

When you capture someone, you may not be certain if the person is an enemy. That determination is made by specifically trained personnel at a higher HQ. You may question your captives about military information of immediate value to your mission, but you may never use threats, torture, or other forms of coercion to obtain information.

You may not take personal property from a prisoner, except those items that are clearly of a military or intelligence value (weapons, maps, or military documents). You do this only after the prisoner has been secured, silenced, and segregated. You take nothing that is not of military value. Only an officer may confiscate money from a prisoner.

Captives may perform some types of work, but the work must not relate to assisting your war effort. The acceptable work performed must be limited to allowing captives to dig foxholes or build bunkers only for their own protection. Under the laws of armed conflict, you may never use captives as a shield for your attack or defense against the enemy; to search for, clear, or place mines or booby traps; or to carry your ammunition or heavy gear.

Under the rules of armed conflict, you are not permitted to attack villages, towns, or cities. But you are allowed to engage the enemy that is in a village, town, or city and destroy any equipment or supplies that the enemy has there when your mission requires it. In all cases, you must not create more destruction than is necessary to accomplish your mission. When you use firepower in a populated area, you must attack only the military targets.

You may not attack protected property. While some protected property may mean little to you, the property in question may be of cultural importance to the people of the country. Examples of protected property include buildings dedicated to religion, art, science or charitable purposes; historical monuments; hospitals and places where the sick and wounded are collected and cared for; and schools and orphanages for children. If the enemy uses these places for refuge or for offensive purposes, your commander may order an attack. It is common sense to destroy no more than the minimum amount of protected property consistent with the accomplishment of your mission. To do more may undermine your mission.

Special Situations

Earlier in this chapter, we discussed why you should know as much as possible about the country in which you are operating. Once there, you need to treat civilians humanely and private property as if it were your own.

Do not violate civilians' rights in war zones. If you know something about the people's culture and practices, you will have little trouble recognizing civilians' rights. Make sure civilians are protected from acts of violence, threats, and insults both from the enemy and from any of your fellow Marines.

On occasion, it may be necessary to move or resettle civilians because such action is urgently required for military activities. Under no circumstance do you burn civilian property without approval of higher authority. Similarly, you do not steal from civilians. Failure to obey these rules is a violation of the laws of armed conflict and punishable by court-martial.

Under no circumstances should you fire upon any medical personnel or equipment used for the medical welfare of the people or the enemy. Most medical personnel and facilities are marked with a red cross on a white background. However, a few countries use a different symbol. This is one reason why it is important to be familiar with the customs of the country in which you are operating. Similarly, never pose as a Red Cross person when you are not one. Your life may depend on the proper use of the Red Cross symbol.

Parachutists, such as air crewmen who bailed out, are considered helpless until they reach the ground. Under the rules of war, you are not allowed to fire at them until they reach the ground. If they then resist with weapons or do not surrender, you may fire on them. Paratroopers, on the other hand, are combat soldiers in an assault and always considered combatants and may be fired at while they are still in the air.

Under the law of armed conflict, you may not use poison or poisoned weapons. However, you may use other weapons to destroy the enemy's food and water in order to prevent their use.

You may not alter your weapons in order to cause unnecessary suffering to the enemy. You cannot use altered rounds to inflict greater destruction on the enemy. These alterations are forbidden under the laws of armed conflict.

What Happens When Rules Are Violated

This chapter established some basic rules showing what you can and cannot do in a wartime situation as it relates to the laws of armed conflict. This section instructs you on what to do if one of the rules is violated.

You must do your best to prevent violations of the laws of armed conflict because those are criminal acts. If you see a criminal act about to be committed, you should try to prevent it by arguing against it, threatening to report the criminal act, repeating the orders of your superiors, stating your personal disagreement, or asking a senior individual present to intervene. You will be able to do this if you are totally familiar with the country in which you are operating and are knowledgeable about the rules of war. In the event the criminal act immediately endangers your life or the lives of others, you may use the exact amount of force needed to prevent the crime, but only as a last resort. You should immediately report the criminal act through your chain of command. If the criminal act is committed or about to be committed by your immediate superior, report the act to his immediate superior. You are required to do this by the laws of armed conflict. Conversely, you are not required to commit a crime under the laws of armed conflict. If you are ordered to commit a crime under the rules of war, you must refuse to follow the order and report your refusal to the next higher authority. You can be prosecuted for carrying out an unlawful act under the laws of war, so you must know what is legal and act in accordance with the rules of armed conflict. All reportable incidents are reported through command channels for ultimate transmission to appropriate U.S. agencies, allied governments, or other appropriate authorities. A reportable incident signifies a possible, suspected, or alleged violation of the law of war for which there is credible information or conduct during military operations other than war that would constitute a violation of the law of war if it occurred during an armed conflict.

Code of Conduct

The code of conduct for members of the Armed Forces of the United States was first promulgated by President Dwight D. Eisenhower August 17, 1955. The code, including its basic philosophy, was reaffirmed on July 8, 1964, in DOD Directive No. 1300.7. In March 1988,

President Ronald Reagan issued executive order 12633, amending the code with language that is gender-neutral. The code, although first expressed in written form in 1955, is based on time-honored concepts and traditions that date back to the days of the American Revolution.

The Korean War revealed a need to provide a standard of behavior for American military personnel engaged in combat and in enemy captivity. The code of conduct required two things from U.S. military personnel. First, to fight until resistance is useless and second, continue resisting enemy captors when captured.

The code of conduct was promulgated on August 17, 1955, in response to the behavior of U.S. personnel during the Korean War. In March 1988, the code of conduct was amended to make the language gender-neutral. The legality and enforcement of the code of conduct comes from the Uniform Code of Military Justice (UCMJ).

Code of Conduct ("The Code")

Article I

I am an American, fighting in the Armed Forces which guard my country and our way of life. I am prepared to give my life in their defense.

Article II

I will never surrender of my own free will. If in command I will never surrender the members of my command while they still have the means to resist.

Article III

If I am captured, I will continue to resist by all means available. I will make every effort to escape and aid others to escape. I will accept neither parole nor special favors from the enemy.

Article IV

If I become a Prisoner of War, I will keep

faith with my fellow prisoners. I will give no information nor take part in any action which might be harmful to my comrades. If I am senior, I will take command. If not, I will obey the lawful orders of those appointed over me and will back them up in every way.

Article V

When questioned, should I become a Prisoner of War, I am required to give name, rank, service number and date of birth. I will evade answering further questions to the utmost of my ability. I will make no oral or written statements disloyal to my country and its allies or harmful to their cause.

Article VI

I will never forget that I am an American, responsible for my actions, and dedicated to the principles which made my country free. I will trust in my God and in the United States of America.

Rights of a POW

The rights of Prisoners of War (POWs) are primarily derived from the 1949 Geneva Conventions. The purpose of the POW rights are: protecting both combatants and noncombatants from unnecessary suffering, safeguarding certain fundamental human rights of person who fall into the hands of the enemy, and facilitating the restoration of peace.

POW's have twelve distinct rights:

1. A POW has the right to receive sanitary, protective housing and clothing.

2. A POW has the right to receive a sufficient amount of food to sustain good health.

3. A POW has the right to receive adequate medical care.

4. A POW has the right to receive necessary facilities for proper hygiene.

5. A POW has the right to practice religious faith.

6. A POW has the right to keep personal property except weapons, military equipment, and military documents.

7. A POW has the right to send and receive mail.

8. A POW has the right to receive packages containing non-contraband items such as food and clothing, or educational, religious, and recreational materials.

9. A POW has the right to select a fellow POW to represent himself.

10. A POW has the right to receive humane treatment.

11. A POW has the right to have a copy of the Geneva Convention and its annexes, including any special agreements, posted where it can be read. The Geneva Convention and its annexes, etc., must be written in the proper language and available upon request.

12. A POW has the right to have a copy of all camp regulations, notices, orders, and publications about POW conduct posted where it can be read. Regulations, notices, etc. Must be in the proper language for POWs to understand and available upon request.

Conclusion

Marines recognize that full compliance with the laws of armed conflict does not come easily, especially in the confusion and passion of battle. For instance, you might be extremely angry and upset because your unit has taken several casualties from enemy booby traps or hit-and-run tactics, but you must never engage in reprisals or acts of revenge that violate the laws of armed conflict.

CHAPTER 4

Core Values and Leadership

Every private in the Marine Corps serves as a potential squad leader. Every squad leader can become a sergeant major. These concepts have provided the Corps with the world's finest body of small unit leaders since 1775. The backbone of the Marine Corps is its NCOs. Every one of them started as a private.

Marine Corps sergeants and corporals provide the most direct and personal leadership found anywhere. They do it in peacetime as well as in war. And like their forerunners of the "old Corps," none of them was a "born leader." They became leaders through hard work, skill, and a strict sense of duty.

All Marines embrace our basic Core Values of Honor, Courage, and Commitment, and our leaders must model them in all that they do. These values and their attributes are defined in detail on the next page. This chapter deals with character development of Marines and the principles and traits used to develop leadership. When you have developed them, you will have achieved as well that all-important sense of duty. The hard work is up to you. You will see that a leader with an ethical mindset knows right from wrong and has a firm moral compass that guides every action. You will begin to understand that this mindset cannot be developed in Marines at the moment of action; NCOs who demonstrate the steady resolve of a principled warrior must ingrain it beforehand. Marines must possess an ethical instinct to make instinctive decisions and an ethical mindset to frame the problem. It takes the moral and physical courage of a Marine to do the right thing.

If you are now a private, this chapter informs you what is expected of leaders in the Marine Corps. Study it, and be ready to take on the responsibilities of higher rank when they come your way. This era of the "Strategic Corporal" means that tactical decisions made on your part of the battlefield can affect the Marine Corps and the United States. Make no mistake; your actions do have an impact.

Warrior Ethos

Marines are warriors, and warriors are professionals and part of a profession of arms. It's not just what we do; our ethos is who we are and what we believe. Although war is a violent, chaotic, and destructive environment, the Marine warrior is guided in all actions by principles and values that are embraced within the Corps and the Nation. For this reason, Marines have earned the trust and respect from those they serve and defend.

As Marines, we are distinguished by our commitment to our core values and our warrior ethos. Ethos means the distinguishing character, sentiment, moral nature, or guiding beliefs of a

Definitions of **HONOR, COURAGE & COMMITMENT**

Honor: *To live your life with integrity, responsibility, honesty and respect.*

Integrity: To do what is right legally and morally.

Responsibility: To be accountable for all actions and inactions.

Honesty: To be trustworthy: to never lie, cheat or steal, nor tolerate those who do.

Respect: To value human life and dignity, our customs and courtesies, and our proud heritage.

Courage: *The mental, moral and physical strength to do what is right in the face of fear, uncertainty or intimidation.*

Mental Strength: A disciplined mind committed to personal and professional excellence.

Moral Strength: A warrior spirit guided by our values, leadership traits and principles.

Physical Strength: A body conditioned to succeed in combat and withstand hardships in any clime and place.

Commitment: *Unwavering, selfless dedication to mission accomplishment and personal and professional responsibilities.*

Unwavering: Firm resolution and unbendable perseverance.

Selfless: Place duty and others before self..

Dedication: Bound to an ideal: God, Country, Corps.

person, group, or institution. When we say we have a warrior ethos, it means we are focused on being warriors: "Marines fight and win–that's what we do, that's who we are. To be a Marine is to do what is right in the face of overwhelming adversity." It's upholding our core values and demonstrating honor through integrity; doing what is right, morally, and legally; taking responsibility for actions; and holding ourselves and others accountable.

Core Values

The Marine Corps formally established Honor, Courage, and Commitment as our core values in 1996. Our Core Values do not diminish our ability to fight and win; in fact, ethical conduct on the battlefield is a combat multiplier. As leaders, NCOs are responsible for making sure that their Marines understand the impact of ethical conduct on the mission of their unit and the Marine Corps. It is important to know that the battlefields may change, but our values will not. Modern war by its very nature, often blurs the lines between friend and foe, but our values remain constant. Our enemies may not be bound by the same rules we are and may kill without conscience—but that does not change who we are as Marines or what we believe in.

The success of the Marine Corps on the battlefields of today and the future will come as a result of the discipline and ethical conduct of the individual Marine. An ethical mindset in action in the operational environment is an absolute requirement. Knowing right from wrong and having a firm moral compass that guides your actions as a Marine cannot be developed in combat. It will be ingrained beforehand by leaders sustaining the foundation laid during recruit training, through realistic training, and by the commitment to excellence of every Marine.

Leadership Traits

You don't inherit the ability to lead Marines. Neither is it issued. You acquire that ability by taking an honest look at yourself. See how you stack up against 14 well-known character traits of a Marine NCO. These are:

1. Integrity.
2. Knowledge.
3. Courage.
4. Decisiveness.
5. Dependability.
6. Initiative.
7. Tact.
8. Justice.
9. Enthusiasm.
10. Bearing.
11. Endurance.
12. Unselfishness.
13. Loyalty.
14. Judgment.

Set out to acquire those traits that you might lack. You improve those you already have, and you make the most of those in which you are strong. Work at them. Balance them off, and you're well on the road to leading Marines in war or peace. Marines expect the best in leadership, and they rate it. Give them the best and you'll find that you accomplish your mission and have the willing obedience, confidence, loyalty, and respect of your charges. In fact, you will have lived up to the official definition of a military leader.

Now, take a closer look at each of the character traits a leader must have.

1. Integrity. The stakes of combat are too high to gamble leadership on a dishonest person. Would you accept a report from a patrol leader who had been known to lie? Of course you wouldn't. All your statements, official or unofficial, are considered by your Marines to be plain, unadorned fact. When you give your word, keep it. Do what is right legally and morally. Many others will depend upon you.

2. Knowledge. Know your job, weapons, equipment, and techniques to be used. Master this *Guidebook* and your other training material. Be able to pass on that knowledge to your Marines. You can't bluff them. They are expert at spotting a fake. If you don't know the answer to a question, admit it. Then find out. Most important, know your Marines. Learn what caliber of performance to expect from each of them. Put confidence in those who you can. Give close supervision to those who need it.

3. Courage. This comes in three kinds: mental, moral, and physical. If you are in a tight place and feel fear, recognize it. Then get control over it and make it work for you. Fear stimulates the body processes. You can actually fight harder, and for a long time, when you are scared. So don't let a little fear make you panic inside. Your physical strength comes from personal conditioning and your ability to withstand hardships in any clime or place. Keep busy when under fire. Fix your mind on your mission and your Marines. Courage grows with action. When things are really tough, take some action, even if it only amounts to a gesture or a distraction for you or your Marines.

As for moral courage, know what's right and stand up for it. Marines are not plaster saints by any means. But they serve God, Country, and Corps and maintain their warrior spirit. A combat leader also must be a moral leader.

When you're wrong, say so and openly. Don't try to evade your mistake. Everybody makes a mistake now and then. The trick is not to make the same one twice. When a job is left undone, true leaders don't harp, "Sir, I told those people … " They fix the breakdown, instead of blaming. Be prepared to take responsibility.

4. Decisiveness. Get the facts, all of them. Make your mind up when you've weighed them. Then issue your order in clear, confident terms. Don't confuse your Marines by debating with yourself out loud. Say what you mean, and mean what you say. Make up your mind in time to prevent the problem from becoming bigger, but don't act with half-thought ideas. If the decision is beyond the scope of your authority, take the problem up the chain of command to the person authorized to make that decision. But if the decision is yours, make it. Don't pass the buck.

5. Dependability. If only one word could be used to describe Marine NCOs over the years, that one word would have to be "dependable." They accomplish the job, regardless of obstacles. At first, they may not agree with the ideas and plans of their seniors. Being dependable,

if they have a better plan, they tactfully say so. But once the decision comes, they carry out the tasks to the best of their ability, whether or not it was their own plan that went into effect. Follow orders to the letter, in spirit, and in fact. The mission comes first, then the welfare of their Marines, then their own requirements.

Dependable NCOs are solid citizens. They're always on time, never make excuses and stay hot on the job until it's done. They're on board when needed and out of the way but ready when not needed. Duty demands that they often make personal sacrifices. They sense what has to be done, where duty lies.

6. Initiative. Think ahead. Stay mentally alert and physically awake. Look around. If you see a job that needs to be done, don't wait to be told. If the barracks shows the clutter of newspapers and food wrappers on a Sunday morning, organize a detail and get the place squared away. Your situation and the lot of your Marines can always be improved. Do what you can. Use the means at hand. Think ahead, and you'll stay ahead.

7. Tact. The right thing at the right time, that's what we mean by tact. It embraces courtesy, but it goes much further. It's the Golden Rule; consideration for others, be they senior or subordinate. Courtesy is more than saluting and saying "Sir" or "Ma'am." It doesn't mean you meekly "ask" your Marines to do a job, either. You can give orders in a courteous manner which, because it is courteous, leaves no doubt that you expect to be obeyed. The tactful leader is fair, firm, and friendly. You always respect another's property and person. Learn to respect human life, dignity, customs, and courtesies as well. If an individual needs counseling then do it—but in private. Don't make a spectacle of them and yourself by doing it in public. On the other hand, when they do a good job, let their friends hear about it. They will be a bigger person in their eyes, and you will too.

There are times, particularly in combat, when a severe "dressing down" of one person or a group of people may be required. Even so, this is tactful, when it is the right thing at the right time.

In dealing with seniors, the Golden Rule again applies. Approach them in the manner you would want to be approached were you in their position with their responsibilities.

When you join a new outfit, just keep quiet and watch for a while. Don't assert that your old outfit was a better one just because it happened to do things differently. Make a few mental notes when you find something that is wrong. When you have established yourself, make those changes that you have the authority to make.

8. Justice. Marines rate a straight-shooting leader. Be one. Don't play favorites. Spread the liberty and the working parties around equally. Keep anger and emotion out of your decisions. Get rid of any narrow views that you may have about a particular race, creed, or section of the country. Judge individuals by what kind of Marines they are; nothing else.

Give your Marines a chance to prove themselves. Help those who fall short of your standards, but keep your standards high.

9. Enthusiasm. The more you care about something, the greater your interest and enthusiasm. Show it. Enthusiasm is more contagious than the measles. Set a goal for your unit, and then put all you have in the achievement of that goal. This is particularly applicable in training. Marines are at their best when in the field. After all, they joined the Corps to learn how to fight. They'll learn, all right, but only when their instructor is enthused about what is being taught. Show knowledge and enthusiasm about a subject, and your troops will want that same knowledge. Show your dislikes and gripe about what's going on, and you'll still be leading—but in the wrong direction. The choice is yours.

Don't get stale. "Take your pack off" can sometimes be good advice. Do it once in a while. Rethink your issues and then come back strong with something new. When you find yourself forced to run tactical problems over the same old terrain, run them from the other direction.

10. Bearing. Think of drill instructors: lean, leather-lunged, and firm. With superb posture and impeccable uniform, they didn't walk, they marched! And they taught you to do the same. You learned from them that a uniform is more than a mere "suit of clothes." You wear a suit—but you believe in a uniform. Therefore, you maintained it—all the time. Every stripe, every ribbon, every piece of metal that you see on a Marine was earned. You earned your uniform and everything on it. Wear it with pride.

That's part of what is meant by bearing. The rest of it is how you conduct yourself, in or out of formation, ashore or on board, verbally and emotionally. Manage your voice and gestures. A calm voice and a steady hand are confidence builders in combat. Don't ever show your anxiety over a dangerous situation, even if you feel it.

Speak plainly and simply. You're more interested in being understood than in showing off your vocabulary. If you ever rant and rave, losing control of your tongue and your emotions, you'll also lose control of your Marines. Swearing at subordinates is unfair. They can't swear back. It's also stupid, since you admit lack of ability to express displeasure in any other way. There may be one exception to this rule. The time might come, in battle, when tough talk, a few oaths and the right amount of anger is all that will pull your outfit together. But save your display of temper until it is absolutely needed. Otherwise, it won't pay off because you'll already have shot your bolt.

Sarcasm seldom gets results. Wisecrack to Marines—they've been around—they'll wisecrack back. Make a joke out of giving orders, and they'll think you don't mean what you say. This doesn't mean to avoid joking at all times. A good joke, at the right time, is like good medicine, especially if the chips are down. As a matter of fact, it is often the Marine Corps way of expressing sympathy and understanding without getting sticky about it. Many wounded Marines have been sent to the rear with a concerned smile, a grasp, and a remark about, "What some people won't do to get outta' work!"

Dignity, without being unapproachable—that's what bearing is. Work at it.

11. Endurance. A five-foot Marine sergeant once led his squad through 10 days of field training in Japan. He topped it off with a two-day hike, climbing Mt. Fuji on the 36 miles back to camp. When asked how a man of his size developed such endurance, he said, "It was easy. I had 12 guys pushing me all the way." What he meant, of course, was that 12 other Marines were depending on his endurance to pull them through. He couldn't think about quitting. Leaders must have endurance beyond that of their troops. Squad leaders must check every fighting position and then go build their own. On the march, they often will carry part of another's load in addition to their own. An unfit body or an undisciplined mind could never make it.

Keep yourself fit, physically and mentally. Learn to stand punishment by undertaking hard physical tasks. Force yourself to study and think when tired. Get plenty of rest before a field problem. Don't stay on liberty until the last place is closed. The town will still be there when you get back. A favorite saying of Marines is that you don't have to be trained to be miserable. That's true. But you do have to train to resist misery.

12. Unselfishness. Marine NCOs don't pull the best rations from the case and leave the rest to their Marines. They get the best they can for all unit members all the time.

Leaders get their own comforts, pleasures, and recreation after troops have been provided with theirs. Look at any chow line in the field. You'll see squad leaders at the end of their squads. You'll find staff noncommissioned officers (SNCOs) at the end of the company. This is more than tradition. It is leadership in action. It is unselfishness.

Share your Marines' hardships. Then the privileges that go with your rank will have been earned. Don't hesitate to accept them when the time is right, but until it is, let them be. When your unit is wet, cold, and hungry—you'd better be too. That's the price you pay for leadership. Give credit where credit is due. Don't grab the glory for yourself. Recognize the hard work and good ideas of your subordinates and be grateful you have such Marines. Your leader will look after you in the same way. They know the score, too.

13. Loyalty. This is a two-way street. It goes all the way up and all the way down the chain of command. Marines live by it. They even quote Latin for it—*Semper Fidelis*. As a leader of Marines, every word, every action must reflect your loyalty—up and down. Back your Marines when they're right. Correct them when they're wrong. You're being loyal either way. Pass on orders as if they were your own ideas, even when they are distasteful. To rely on the rank of the person who told you to do the job is to weaken your own position. Keep your personal problems and the private lives of your seniors to yourself. But help your Marines in their difficulties, when it is proper to do so. Never criticize your unit, your seniors, or your fellow NCOs in the presence of subordinates. Make sure they don't do it either. If deserving persons get into trouble, go to bat for them. They'll work harder when it's all over.

14. Judgment. This comes with experience. It is simply weighing all the facts in any situation, application of the other 13 traits you have just read about, then making the best move. But until you acquire experience you may not know the best move. What, then, do you use for experienced judgment in the meantime? Well, there are more than 200 years' worth of experienced judgment on tap in the Marine Corps. Some of it is available to you at the next link in the chain of command. Be a good observer of these leaders. Ask, and you'll receive. Seek, and you'll find.

Leadership Principles

Now that you've had a look at the character building leadership traits required of Marine leaders, let's see how these are fitted into what we call the Leadership Principles. The Marine Corps has set forth eleven principles and is not concerned as much about the words and phrases as we are about their application. They're all common sense items, anyway, and when you get right down to it, a discussion of leadership is only common sense with a vocabulary.

1. Set the example. As a leader, you are in an ideal spot to do this. Marines are already looking to you for a pattern and a standard to follow. No amount of instruction and no form of discipline can have the effect of your personal example. Make it a good one.

2. Develop a sense of responsibility among your subordinates. Tell your Marines what you want done and by when. Then leave it at that. If you have junior leaders, leave the detail up to them. In this way, kill two birds with one stone. You will have more time to devote to other jobs, and you are training another leader. A leader with confidence will have confidence in subordinates. Supervise and check on the results. But leave the details to the person on the spot. After all, there's more than one way to skin a cat. And it's the whole fur you're after, not the individual hairs.

3. Seek responsibility and take responsibility for your actions. The leader, alone, is responsible for all that the unit does or fails to do. That sounds like a big order, but take a look at the authority that is given you to handle that responsibility. You are expected to use that authority. Use it with judgment, tact, and initiative. Have the courage to be loyal to your unit, your Marines, and yourself. As long as you are being held responsible, be responsible for success, not failure. Be dependable.

4. Make sound and timely decisions. Knowledge and judgment are required to produce a sound decision. Include some initiative and the decision will be a timely one. Use your initiative and make your decisions in time to meet the problems that are coming. If you find you've made a bum decision, have the courage to change it before the damage is done. But don't change the word any more than you absolutely have to. Nothing confuses an outfit more than a constant flow of changes.

5. Employ your unit in accordance with its abilities. Don't send two Marines on a working party that calls for five. Your Marines may be good, but don't ask the impossible. Know the limitations of your outfit, and bite off what you can chew. In combat, a "boy sent to do a man's job" can lead to disaster. In peacetime, it leads to a feeling of futility. Conversely, those who have a reasonable goal and then achieve it are a proud lot. They've done something and done it well. Next time, they'll be able to tackle a little more. Don't set your sights clear over the butts; keep them on the target.

6. Be technically and tactically proficient. Know your job. This requires no elaborations. It does require hard work on your part. Stay abreast of changes. Techniques, Tactics, and Procedures (TTPs) are constantly being changed and updated. Stay up-to-date on the latest weapons and equipment. Stay current with international and national news and recent developments in the Marine Corps and other services.

7. Know yourself and seek self-improvement. Evaluate yourself from time to time. Do you measure up? If you don't, admit it to yourself. On the other hand, don't sell yourself short. If you think you're the best leader in your platoon, admit that also to yourself. Then set out to be the best leader in the company. Learn how to speak effectively, how to instruct, and how to be an expert with all the equipment that your unit might be expected to use.

8. Know your Marines and look after their welfare. Loyal NCOs will never permit themselves to rest until their unit is bedded down. They always get the best they can for their Marines by honest means. With judgment, you'll know which of your troops is capable of doing the best job in a particular assignment. Leaders share the problems of their Marines, but they don't pry when an individual wants privacy.

9. Keep your Marines informed. Make sure your Marines get the word. Be known as the person with the "straight scoop." Don't let one of your unit be part of the so-called "10 percent." Certain information is classified. Let your Marines have only that portion that they need to know but make certain they have it. Squelch rumors. They can create disappointment when they're good but untrue. They can sap morale when they exaggerate enemy capabilities. Have the integrity, the dependability to keep your unit correctly posted on what's going on in the world, the country, the Corps, and your unit. Never forget that the more your Marines know about the mission that has been assigned the better they will be able to accomplish it.

10. Ensure that the task is understood, supervised, and accomplished. Make up your mind what to do, who is to do it, where it is to be done, when it is to be done, and tell your Marines why, when they need to be told why. Continue supervising the job until it has been done better than the person who wanted it done in the first place ever thought it could be.

11. Train your Marines as a Team. Train your unit as a unit. Keep that unit integrity every chance you get. If a working party comes up for three, take your whole fire team. The job will be easier with an extra hand, and your unit will be working as a team. Get your Marines on liberty together now and then. They work as a team; get 'em to play as one. Put your Marines in the jobs they do best, then rotate them from time to time. They'll learn to appreciate the other person's task as well. When one member of your team is missing, others can do that share, but don't ever permit several Marines to do another person's job when they're around. Everybody pulls their load in the Marine Corps.

When you and your unit have done something well, talk it up. This builds esprit de corps. You can't see it, but you can feel it. An outfit with a lot of esprit holds itself in very high regard while sort of tolerating others. There's nothing wrong with that. All Marines have a right to figure their unit is the best in the entire Corps. After all, they're in it!

What You Can Expect as a Leader

We've spent some time on what the Corps expects of you as a junior leader. Remember, Marines are warriors, and warriors are professionals, and as professionals, the NCOs have the toughest tasks of all. NCOs are charged with upholding our core values and demonstrating honor through integrity; doing what is right, morally, and legally; taking responsibility for actions; and holding yourself and others accountable. In garrison, you are tasked with the maintenance of good order and discipline.

In combat, you make hard decisions—often in a split second. However, it's not all one way. There are certain things that you have a right to expect in return. First of all, since you are the link in the chain of command that lies squarely between your senior and your subordinates, you can expect the same leadership from above that you've just read about.

Then there's the additional pay you'll be getting along with every promotion—and promotion comes to real leaders, regularly. Also with promotion comes additional authority. It's granted to you on a piece of paper known as a Certificate of Appointment, commonly called a warrant. When you get one, take the time to actually read it and digest what it says.

You'll see more there than simply a piece of paper—much more. First, there's an expression of "special trust and confidence" in your "fidelity and abilities." That is recognition of the highest order. It says you are a professional. It's appreciation for your hard work thus far. But look further. You don't rest on your laurels in the Marine Corps. There's a charge to "carefully and diligently discharge the duties of the grade to which appointed by doing and performing all manner of things thereunto pertaining." That means additional responsibility, which, when you think about it, is also a reward.

Next, you'll find that additional authority we mentioned a while back. It's in the words, "and I do strictly charge and require all personnel of lesser grade to render obedience to appropriate orders." Commanding officers who sign that Certificate are delegating a part of their authority to you. They get their authority from the President of the United States and have chosen you to help them in the execution of their responsibility. Notice, however, that they haven't delegated their responsibility to you or to anybody.

When it comes to leadership, there is no truer statement. Only the NCO is in a position to give the close, constant, personal type of leadership that we've been discussing. When you, as a Marine NCO, have provided your unit with that type of leadership, then you already will have reaped the greatest return. By definition, you'll (1) have accomplished your mission and (2) command the willing obedience, confidence, loyalty, and respect of the U.S. Marines under you. There is no more satisfactory reward, anywhere.

Marine Leader Development Program

Sponsored by Education Command's Lejeune Leadership Institute, the Marine Leader Development (MLD) program directs and encourages leaders to engage their Marines across the six functional areas of fidelity, fighter, fitness, family, finances, and future as a comprehensive approach to foster development of all aspects of Marines' personal and professional lives. The "teach, coach, counsel, mentor" model provides the framework for leader-led developmental discussions to occur and sets the conditions for engagements on career goals/plans. The MLD directs a combination of required and event-driven engagements between leaders and Marines across the six Fs, with supporting resources and tools found at https://usmcu.edu/lli/marine-leader-development.

The Components of the Decision Cycle (OODA) Process

Boyd's decision cycle is the constantly revolving cycles that the mind goes through when dealing with tasks that range from the mundane to the most complicated. This cycle follows the pattern of Observe, Orient, Decide, Act (OODA). (See Figure 4-1 on next page.) Boyd theorized that each party to a conflict first observes the situation. On the basis of observation, one orients; that is, makes an estimate of the situation. On the basis of the orientation, one makes a decision. Finally, one implements the decision—acts. Because their action has created a new situation, the process begins anew. Boyd argued that the party who consistently completes the cycle faster gains

an advantage that increases with each cycle. The enemy's reactions become increasingly slower by comparison and, therefore, less effective until, finally, the enemy is overcome by events.

Observation, the first step in the OODA loop is a search for information relative to the tactical situation. Information could include the environment, enemy tactics, techniques, and procedures. It is an active effort to seek out all the available information by whatever means possible.

During orientation, the Marine uses information to form an awareness of the circumstances. As more information is received, the Marine updates the perceptions as needed. Orientation helps to turn information into understanding. It is understanding that leads to making good decisions.

Decide on a course of action. This is a conscious activity following orientation. The decision is based upon your perceived observations, training, experience, rules of engagement (ROEs), orders, and directives. Through repetitive training, some decisions can become automatic or reflexive.

An act is the implementation of the decision. It is crucial to understand the action taken will influence the environment, potentially changing it. This change in the environment will require that Marine to recycle through the OODA loop process. Instead of remaining fixated on the object, the Marine reassesses the situation.

The Dangers of Social Media

Remember that you are a Marine 24/7—in person and online. Participation on these sites makes you "the Marine Corps"—your conduct is a direct reflection of the Marine Corps. The best advice is to approach online communication in the same way we communicate in person—by using sound judgment and common sense; adhering to the Marine Corps' core values of honor, courage, and commitment;

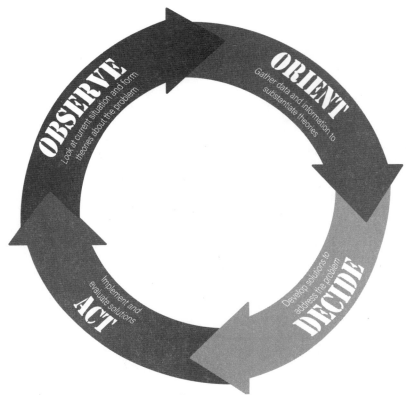

Figure 4-1.

following established policy; and abiding by the UCMJ.

Violations of federal law and DOD regulations or policies may result in disciplinary action under the UCMJ.

Dangers associated with social media include but are not limited to:

- Divulging Personal Identifiable Information (PII) that could be used by the enemy/ threats (e.g. family info, address, telephone number, email address, etc.).
- Inadvertently exposing unit information (e.g. deployment schedule, troop movements/locations, size, capabilities, etc.).

- Susceptibility to hacking, phishing, malware, spyware, viruses, etc.
- Friends unknowingly make you vulnerable (privacy issue).
- Identity thieves.
- Fake profiles.
- Third party sharing/selling of your information.

CHAPTER 5

Discipline and Military Justice

Military Discipline

Military discipline is the state of order and obedience among military personnel resulting from training. When we speak of discipline in the Marine Corps, we do not refer to regulations, punishments, or a state of subservience. What we mean is the exact execution of orders resulting from an intelligent, willing obedience rather than one based solely upon habit or fear. Habit plays its part, however, and for this reason, the Marine benefits from such things as gun drill, close-order drill, or bayonet drill. Punishment of individuals for breaches of discipline sometimes is necessary, but only to reform or eliminate those who are unfit to serve on the team. Such remedial action becomes the function of military justice, the second part of this chapter.

Discipline supports orderly action, which alone can triumph over the seemingly impossible conditions of battle. The individual must be able to recognize and face fear because fear is the enemy of discipline. Fear unchecked will lead to panic, and a unit that panics is no longer a disciplined unit but a mob. There is no sane person who is without fear, but with good discipline and high morale, all can face danger.

Some Marines do not appreciate the necessity for discipline until they have undergone the experience of battle. However, when a Marine learns to be a disciplined Marine, the individual has learned a sense of obligation to one's self and to one's comrades, commander, and Corps. Disciplined Marines act to support a team that

is organized, trained, and equipped for the purpose of engaging and defeating enemies of their country. Military discipline produces effectiveness in combat—ensuring that a unit performs correctly in battle, that it reaches its objectives, that it performs its assigned mission, and that it helps other units and forces to accomplish their missions.

A military commander is vested with a high degree of authority. This authority extends to matters that in civilian life would be considered of personal concern to the individual alone. These include such things as eating, the care and manner of clothing, health habits, and morale factors, all of which directly or indirectly affect the lives of the individuals under his command. It is important that a Marine promptly obey the orders of the commander even in matters that might, at first thought, appear to be of an individual or personal nature. The commander genuinely is interested in the welfare of the individuals within his unit, and developing the habit of prompt obedience to all orders will improve the discipline of each individual and the unit.

Once on the battlefield, no time remains to learn discipline. Therefore, we train for it in the Marine Corps. A Marine trains together with other Marines so that as a team they can accomplish increasingly difficult tasks in an effective manner. As an added advantage, we Marines take pride in such accomplishments, forming the basis of our "esprit de Corps" or "spirit of togetherness." You must not forget that you wear the insignia of your Corps and your country, and everybody will see you as the Corps whose insignia you wear. If you appear smart, alert, and efficient, they will not only say, "That is a good Marine," but also, "That is a good outfit."

The word "discipline" is frequently combined with other words to refer to specific phases of living and fighting. For example, we speak of "fire discipline," which means obedience to fire orders and the observance of all instructions pertaining to the use of weapons during firing or in combat. When a platoon first goes into action, its fire discipline may be poor. Even after an outfit has been through several actions, there may be one or two "trigger-happy" Marines in it. A trigger-happy Marine is one who wastes ammunition in battle and shoots at every sound heard at night. An entire platoon may pay with their lives for one person's lack of fire discipline. "Water discipline" means the proper use of water during marches, field exercises, or battle. "March discipline" means prompt obedience to march orders and alert, orderly conduct when on the march. The foundations of an individual's performance as a Marine are discipline, a sense of duty, courage, self-assurance, and cooperative thinking. These qualities support the Marine as he endures hardships and strives to accomplish the mission. Of these, discipline plays the indispensable role in maintaining the combat power of a unit. Undisciplined behavior must be countered immediately and appropriately. In well-disciplined units, a sense of comradeship emerges and soldierly values, such as confidence and unselfishness, predominate. A unit that has grown together into a "band of brothers" will be able to withstand severe stress.

Military Justice

Military Jurisdiction

As stated in the *Manual for Courts-Martial*, the sources of military jurisdiction include the Constitution of the United States and international law. International law includes the law of war. The specific provisions of the Constitution relating to military jurisdiction are found in the powers granted to the Congress, in the authority vested in the President and in the provisions of the 5th Amendment.

Uniform Code of Military Justice

In keeping with the powers granted to the Congress and by the authority vested in the President of the United States and the provisions of the 5th Amendment, all of the armed services were brought under a unified system of justice. That system was enacted by the Congress and signed into law by the President on May 31, 1951, and from that day on has been known as the UCMJ.

The Code is of great importance to all members of the armed forces because it not only explains the legal responsibilities of the members of the armed forces but also clearly states legal requirements for the protection and guarantees of the rights of all members of the armed forces. It is imperative, therefore, that extensive instruction, training, and guidance be given. Accordingly, Article 137, UCMJ, requires that important articles of the Code be carefully explained to every enlisted person at the time of entrance on active duty, or within six days thereafter, and explained again after the enlisted person has completed six months of active duty and upon reenlistment.

It also should be noted that a complete text of the UCMJ, and of the regulations prescribed by the President, thereunder must be made available to all persons on active duty upon their request for their personal examination. For this reason, you will find copies of the UCMJ posted in conspicuous places throughout the various commands of the Marine Corps and Navy.

The Code has been amended on a few occasions, and all of the amendments have been designed to ensure even greater protection of the individual rights of each servicemember than were stated in the original Code provisions. The intent and purpose of the UCMJ is to provide uniform application of such substantive and procedural due process as relates to these rights and to assure safeguards in a system of justice for all members of the armed forces.

Agencies

These agencies through which military jurisdiction is exercised include military commissions; provost courts; courts-martial for the trial of offenders against military law; and in the case of general court-martial, trial of persons who by the laws of war are subject to trial by military tribunals; commanding officers and officers in charge for nonjudicial punishment (NJP) under Article 15, UCMJ; and courts of inquiry for the investigation of any matter referred to such court by competent authority.

Of these agencies, those with which the members of the armed forces are most familiar are those relating to commanding officers' NJP, and courts-martial, which in order of ascendancy in power and jurisdiction are the summary court-martial (which is the lowest court), the special court-martial (which is an intermediate court of limited jurisdiction), and the general court-martial (which is the highest trial court in the military). A review of the function of these more familiar agencies for the exercise of military jurisdiction follows.

Commanding Officers' NJP. Nowhere in any legal system are persons given more protection of their rights and more procedural due process than in the military under the UCMJ. The procedural due process generally begins when it is alleged that someone has committed an offense. Preliminary inquiry is then ordered into the alleged offense, and if there is some indication that the individual may have been involved as alleged, the Marine is brought before the commanding officer (CO) for a hearing pursuant to the UCMJ. This hearing commonly is called "office hours."

Among other things, the CO informs the alleged offender of the offense of which accused and explains rights under Article 31, UCMJ. This is advice concerning self-incrimination. The CO also explains to the accused the rights concerning consultation with lawyer counsel as required by cases handed down by the Supreme Court of the United States and the United States Court of Appeals for the armed forces. If the alleged offense is a serious offense, the CO will refer the charges either to trial by court-martial if the officer is a convening authority of an appropriate court, or if one lacks such powers, forward the charges to an appropriate convening authority recommending trial by court-martial. The type of case will determine what additional pretrial procedures are followed at this point.

If, on the other hand, the alleged offense is a minor offense, the CO may administer NJP under Article 15, UCMJ, pursuant to the procedural requirements and punitive limitations outlined in Part V, *Manual for Courts-Martial.*

The rank of the CO dictates what punishments may be imposed. For example, if the officer is a Captain or below, as the commanding officer, seven days of correctional custody may be imposed, the reduction of one grade, provided the officer has the authority to promote to that grade; 14 days extra duty; 14 days restriction and forfeiture of seven days of pay. If the CO is a major or higher, 30 days of correctional custody may be imposed; reduction of one grade, provided the officer has the authority to promote to that grade; 45 days extra duty; 60 days restriction or combination of both; and forfeiture of one-half of one month's pay, per month, for two months. Note that these punishments are limitations as to the maximum punishment that can be administered. In no way is the CO bound to administer the maximum in any given circumstance.

In addition to the individual punishments outlined above, certain combinations of punishments are permitted under the UCMJ. These combinations are limited by the precise language of the law. A military person has the right to refuse NJP, and demand trial by court-martial except on board ship.

It should be noted that not only may the individual refuse NJP, but he may also refuse a summary court-martial in the event that one is ordered upon refusal to accept NJP under Article 15. The only exception to the rule that the accused may refuse punishment under Article 15 is in the case of a member attached to or embarked in a vessel. Personnel attached to, or embarked in a vessel may receive NJP under Article 15, despite the fact that they do not desire the imposition of such punishment.

Any person punished under Article 15, who considers the punishment unjust or disproportionate to the offense may, through the proper channels, appeal to the next superior authority, and the appeal must be promptly forwarded and decided. In the meantime, while the appeal is pending, the individual may be required to undergo the punishment imposed.

However, if the appeal is granted later by the next superior authority, all rights, property and privileges of which the person has been deprived, by virtue of the imposition of NJP, will be restored. The appeal from NJP must be taken within a reasonable time, and this period has been determined to be a five-day period.

NJPs are recorded in the service record book of each Marine. They reflect in the conduct markings or fitness reports of each Marine and are considered at promotion time. In addition, Article 15 punishment during any Good Conduct Medal marking period changes the commencement date for the Good Conduct Medal period. Obviously, it is to the advantage of all Marines not to involve themselves in disciplinary matters wherein they are referred to their commanding officers for NJP or to a court-martial for trial. The essence of Marine Corps professionalism is discipline.

The word "discipline" in this sense does not mean punishment but rather adherence to the rules, regulations, laws, traditions, and customs of the Marine Corps. Discipline makes the individual Marine the finest military person in the world. Punishment for breaches of discipline reflects only partially on discipline itself, and we must not confuse one with the other.

Kinds of Courts-Martial

There are three kinds of courts-martial in each of the armed forces. They are:

General Court-Martial. The general court-martial consists of a military judge and not less than five active duty armed servicesmembers, or only a military judge, if, before the court is assembled, the accused, knowing the identity of the military judge and after consultation with defense counsel, requests in writing or orally a court composed only of a military judge, and the military judge approves this request.

Special Court-Martial. This court-martial consists of a military judge and not less than three active duty armed servicesmembers, or only a military judge, if the accused so requests under the same conditions prescribed in the general court-martial section above.

Summary Court-Martial. The summary court-martial consists of one commissioned officer with the rank of captain or higher, whenever practicable.

General Court-Martial

As mentioned above, the general court-martial must consist of a military judge and not less than five members, or if the accused requests trial by judge alone and the judge grants it, then the case can be heard by the judge without the presence of the members.

A general court-martial is convened for the most serious offenses, such as, but not limited to, desertion, homicides, seriously aggravated assaults, most sex offenses, and the like. When the general court-martial convenes with the members present, then the function of the members is to hear and weigh the evidence in order to determine the guilt or innocence of the accused and to impose a sentence if found guilty.

If the accused agrees to be tried by the judge alone, then the judge is the trier of the guilt or innocence of the accused and also imposes the sentence.

In all cases where members are present, the judge only sits as the ruling officer on the law and does not take part in the deliberations on either the findings or the sentence. The military judge must be approved by the Judge Advocate General of the Navy as meeting rigorous professional requirements as a lawyer and as a judge. The judge decides the legal technicalities and ensures that the trial is conducted fairly. The military judge is very closely akin to a federal district judge who presides over a United States District Court.

An example of the functions performed by the judge is the ruling on objections by counsel, giving detailed instruction to the court members on all matters of law and on the correlation between matters of law and fact that must be considered by the members in their deliberations on both the guilt or innocence of the accused and also upon the imposition of sentence.

In all general courts-martial, counsel for both the accused and the government must be duly qualified lawyers. This ensures the full protection of all of the rights of the accused. This is in keeping with the emphasis contained in the law, i.e., the full protection of the individual standing before the bar of justice.

The only limit to sentences that may be imposed by a general court-martial is the maximum punishment provided for each offense, either in the articles of the UCMJ or in the Table of Maximum Punishments, which is determined by the President of the United States as a matter of executive decree.

There are, for example, some offenses for which the maximum punishment is death and others for which the maximum punishment is life imprisonment. The remainder of punishments varies down to those that have maximum punishments of only a few months confinement. These maximum punishments are directly proportionate to the gravity of the offense of which the individual is accused.

Special Court-Martial

The next higher court is the special court-martial. As stated above, the special court-martial consists of a military judge and not less than three members together or only a military judge sitting alone if the accused requests that the judge alone hear the case and the judge approves the request.

The members and the judge, or the judge when sitting alone, assure that the trial is conducted fairly, and the members when they are present, or the judge when sitting alone, determine the guilt or innocence of the accused, and in the case of guilt, impose the sentence.

In the special court-martial, the accused is acquitted unless two-thirds or more of the members sitting in judgment find the accused guilty or, in the case of the judge sitting alone, unless the judge finds the accused guilty. Any sentence imposed must have the vote of at least two-thirds of the members sitting, or in the case of the judge sitting alone, the judge imposes the sentence.

If the accused so requests, and is an enlisted person, one-third of the membership of the court may be enlisted personnel, unless it is wished that the military judge sit alone. The military judge is always a commissioned officer under the law. The enlisted members of the court cannot be detailed from the accused's company or from the crew of the accused's ship if they are members of a ship's detachment.

Normally, enlisted members assigned to courts are mature SNCOs. For the special court-martial, a trial counsel and a defense counsel and such assistants are detailed as appropriate. Certain persons are disqualified from acting as trial and defense counsel, depending upon how much they were involved prior to the trial itself. Examples are the investigating officer, a military judge, a court member who acted in the same or related cases. The trial counsel in a special court-martial does not have to be a lawyer. However, a defense counsel who is a lawyer shall represent the accused person.

The accused also may ask to be represented by lawyer counsel of his own choice and may decide whether the appointed counsel and counsel of his choosing should work together or whether or not the counsel of his choosing is to conduct the defense alone.

Under no circumstances will military personnel accept a fee for defending an accused before a court-martial, and no expenses are incurred by an accused for representation by an appointed lawyer before a court-martial, except in those cases where the accused chooses to hire a civilian lawyer. All other counsel furnished by the military are furnished without cost, and the entire trial is free from any expense to the accused. If a civilian lawyer is hired, the accused must pay whatever fees and expenses the civilian counsel may charge.

The military judge in a special court-martial will be a commissioned officer of the armed forces, who is a member of the bar of a federal court, or a member of the bar of the highest court of a state, and who is certified as qualified for duty as a military judge by the Judge Advocate General of the Navy. No person is eligible to act as a military judge in a case if the individual is in fact the accuser or is a witness for the prosecution or has acted as an investigating officer or a counsel in the same case.

The military judge of a court-martial may not consult with the members of the court, except in the presence of the accused, trial counsel, and defense counsel, and the judge may not vote with the members of the court on either the guilt or innocence of the accused or on the sentence, unless the judge is sitting in trial of the case alone, and there are no members present.

Only in cases in which the accused asks to be tried by the judge alone and waives the presence of other members does the judge then act as the trier of the facts, determiner of the law, and in the event of a guilty finding does the judge impose sentence.

Special courts-martial are empowered by the UCMJ to "adjudge any punishment not forbidden by the Code except death, dishonorable discharge, dismissal, confinement in excess of twelve months, hard labor without confinement in excess of three months, forfeiture of pay exceeding two-thirds pay per month, or forfeiture of pay for a period exceeding twelve months." Thus, it can be seen that the special court-martial, although it tries more serious offenses, is limited by law as to the jurisdictional amount of punishment that it can impose. The maximum is a bad conduct discharge, confinement at hard labor for 12 months, forfeiture of two-thirds pay per month for 12 months, and reduction to private, along with reprimands, as may also be deemed appropriate.

In addition, it is important to note that a bad conduct discharge may not be adjudged unless a complete record of the proceedings and testimony at the trial has been made.

Note carefully that a special court-martial sentence, when the court is properly constituted, can include a bad conduct discharge. This is a very serious type of discharge that can genuinely handicap the future of anyone who receives it. The bad conduct discharge is only slightly less grave than a dishonorable discharge and is a serious blot on one's record and future.

Summary Court-Martial

Only enlisted personnel can be tried by summary court-martial. Before being tried, an accused must be charged with an offense under the UCMJ by someone who is subject to the UCMJ, and who has either personal knowledge of the offense, or has investigated the offense. This person, who prefers (swears) the charge against the accused, is known as the accuser.

Normally, the person accused is ordered to trial by court-martial by a CO who is in the chain of command. If the officer who would normally order the trial is the accuser, i.e. the person who either prefers the charges against the accused or has ordered someone to do so in a case in which there is a personal interest, then that officer cannot order the trial but must refer the entire matter to the next superior in the chain of command.

The reason for ordering ("referring") charges to trial by court-martial is that many offenses are too serious in nature to be disposed of by the CO at office hours. However, some offenses are not grave enough to warrant trial by a special or general court-martial, and thus, these offenses are referred to trial by summary court-martial.

The law provides, however, that no person may be brought to trial before a summary court-martial if objected thereto, and as stated above, the accused may object to the summary court-martial even though there was also objection to Article 15 NJP. If objection to trial by summary court-martial is made by an accused, trial may be ordered by a special or general court-martial. One officer conducts a summary court-martial. This officer must, according to law, impartially bring out the evidence on both sides, i.e. protecting the rights of the accused, as well as prosecuting the case for the government. The officer then must decide whether the accused is guilty or not guilty, and one always starts with the presumption of innocence.

In the case of a verdict of guilty, the summary court-martial officer also imposes the sentence. The UCMJ provides that the summary court officer may, under such limitation as the President may prescribe, adjudge any punishment not forbidden by the Code "except death, dismissal, dishonorable or bad conduct discharge, confinement for more than one month, hard labor without confinement for more than 45 days, restriction to specified limits for more than two-months, or forfeiture of more than two-thirds of one month's pay."

Court Procedures

No person who is subject to the UCMJ may be tried by a general court-martial until a formal investigation pursuant to Article 32 has been made of all charges and specifications that have been preferred against the individual and upon which the accused is to be tried. The investigation corresponds to the grand jury and other indictment proceedings as found in civil jurisdictions.

The investigation, however, is far more protective of the rights of the individual than any grand jury proceeding, since it does allow the individual to be present during all of the proceedings, to be represented by lawyer counsel, to confront and cross-examine witnesses against the accused to present witnesses on behalf of the accused, and to present any other evidence and make such argument as the accused may deem appropriate to bring out full consideration in the hearing.

The accused in the pretrial investigation enjoys the same rights that one does at office hours or before a court-martial, which, among other things, are the right to remain silent, the right to make no statement either written or oral, the right to be represented by counsel before and during any period of interrogation, and the right to submit whatever evidence may be desired. The investigation results in either a recommendation for trial by general or lesser courts-martial on some or all of the charges, or it may, in fact, result in a recommendation that the accused not be tried and that the charges be either dismissed or reduced to lesser offenses and be handled on a level appropriate to the reduced offenses.

Rights of the Accused

The accused has certain basic rights before a court-martial and before any judicial or non-judicial proceedings in which the accused is subject to charges or in which conduct is subject to inquiry. The most significant of these rights are those guaranteed by Article 31 of the UCMJ and the 5th Amendment to the Constitution, which basically is a right against self-incrimination.

In addition, an accused is entitled to confer with lawyer counsel prior to any interrogation and to have lawyer counsel present during any interrogation that is consented to by the accused. Military counsel will be provided to an accused without expense by the appropriate military authority. Civilian counsel may be retained at the accused's own expense.

In addition to the rights against self-incrimination, and the right to confer with lawyer counsel and have counsel present during the proceedings, one of the more important safeguards is that the accused is presumed innocent until proven guilty beyond a reasonable doubt. The burden of proof is always on the prosecution. If the evidence presented in court by the prosecution should leave a reasonable doubt in the minds of the required majority of the court, or in the mind of the judge if the judge is sitting alone as requested by the accused, then the accused is acquitted, even though the defense may not have presented one shred of evidence.

The accused does not have to take the witness stand, and no inference may be drawn from the fact that the accused chooses to remain silent and does not present any evidence either personally or through other witnesses or documentary type evidence. Witnesses who can present evidence favorable to the accused can be compelled to appear and testify before a court-martial, both by subpoena, for which their fees and travel expenses are paid by the government or by military orders issued to the witnesses if they are in the military.

An accused who has been tried and acquitted by a legally constituted court-martial having jurisdiction in the case cannot be tried again by a court-martial for the same offense. This is known as the Doctrine of Former Jeopardy or Double Jeopardy. If the accused is convicted by court-martial but granted a rehearing because of some error in the record and is once again convicted at the rehearing, the accused is guaranteed the right to not receive a harsher sentence than the sentence imposed at the original trial. In other words, the new court-martial that is holding a rehearing in the case cannot impose a greater sentence than that which was imposed at the original trial, even though the Table of Maximum Punishments provides for a greater sentence.

Every conviction and sentence is subject to review. In every case, there is more than one agency that must study the record of trial to see that no error was committed that might have been prejudicial to the substantial rights of the accused. In the case of a court-martial involving a punitive discharge, there will be not less than two, and often there will be three or four, subsequent reviews of the case before any such sentence is approved. In addition, the accused has a right to present new evidence at any time within two years of a conviction, asking for a new trial and reconsideration of the former findings and sentence, when it is discovered that there is some new evidence available that might change the outcome of the case or that there has been some fraud committed on the court.

The accused also has the right to appeal to the Judge Advocate General of the Navy in any case which has not required review by the Court of Criminal Appeals, in cases of newly discovered evidence, fraud on the court, lack of jurisdiction, or error prejudicial to the substantial rights of the accused. This review can be requested at any time, and there is no time limitation.

Finally, although the UCMJ does not provide for a system of bail, either pending trial or subsequent thereto, pretrial confinement of an accused is limited to those cases in which the cognizant commander determines such to be necessary to ensure the presence of an accused at trial, or it is foreseeable that the accused will engage in serious criminal misconduct.

After trial, it is possible for the convening authority to permit the accused to remain unconfined pending the reviews of the case. In this event, the sentence does not commence to run until all reviews are final and the accused ultimately is confined if the sentence to confinement is approved.

Thus, it can be seen from a review of this entire area that emphasis is absolutely placed on the protection of the rights of each of us as citizens of the United States and members of the military. Safeguards provided under the Code are the finest to be found in any judicial system in the world, and these rights are protected zealously so as to assure the complete fairness of the system for all of us.

The best course of conduct is, without question, to know and understand the law and to live within its framework. This not only will assure each Marine of a fine record and the opportunity for promotion, but at the end of service, the Marine will be released, retired, or discharged under the finest of conditions by means of an honorable discharge representing excellence of character and performance of duty.

CHAPTER 6

General Administration

The term "administration," as used in the Armed Services, means the management of all phases of military operations not directly involved in tactics and strategy. The administration of your unit means the interior management of the unit. It includes feeding, clothing, equipping, sheltering, paying, transporting, and maintaining the health and welfare of the unit as a whole and of its individual members. A large portion of the Marine Corps is engaged in administration, but the four people who are directly responsible for administration as it concerns you as an individual are you, your platoon commander, your company or detachment commander, and your first sergeant.

When you have an administrative (e.g., pay, correction of records, etc.) or personal (i.e., financial, family related issues, etc.) challenges that require assistance, each member of your chain of command, from bottom to top, will help to ensure resolution of your problem.

All Marines have a right to directly seek assistance from, or communicate grievances to, their CO. The correct exercise of this right is through the formal process of Request Mast. Efforts to subvert the good order of a unit, distract the CO from his duties, or carry out personal attacks are inappropriate uses of the process of Request Mast.

It is the duty of every Marine to assist in the smooth administration of the unit. The way that you can do this is to keep yourself informed. Effective administration requires obedience to regulations and orders. To obey a regulation or order, you must know it and understand it. If you do not understand it, ask for an explanation. Most of the orders and regulations that you will have to comply with will either be announced at unit formations or posted on your unit's bulletin board. Keep your ears open at formations. When you join an organization, familiarize yourself with all of the material on the official website. Thereafter, ensure continuous awareness for new material. Ignorance of what is on the bulletin board is no excuse for failing to comply with regulations or orders. Read your unit's official website.

Every Marine Corps unit is authorized to provide the NAVMC form 11296, which is the first step to Request Mast. This form is filled out and submitted via the chain of command to the CO with whom the Request Mast is desired. Your personal interview with the CO should take place as soon as possible, a working day being ideal.

The Marine Corps focuses on employing Marines in the manner that does the most to maintain a force in readiness for our Nation's defense. Unit administration is conducted with the objective of doing everything for your welfare that does not interfere with the primary objective of maintaining combat readiness. By looking out for its men and women, the Marine Corps has maintained its enviable *esprit de corps*. You are given considerable choice in your duty station, the type of work you do, the type of specialist training you receive, and the time you go on leave as long as it does not conflict with the effectiveness of your unit or of the Marine Corps as a whole. Also, the Marine Corps will assist you when you are faced with serious financial or other emergencies, either directly or by securing the help of specialized agencies. The remainder of this chapter will explain briefly some of the features of personnel administration with which you should be familiar. For more complete information, consult your chain of command.

Military Specialty Structure

Marines are trained in the basic techniques of infantry ground combat and are taught how to take care of themselves in the field. In addition, each Marine learns a special job and, when they master it and progress in experience and grade, goes on to learn a more difficult and responsible job along the same line of work. Your qualifications for your specialty appear in your service record and in all personnel records all the way to HQMC. The qualifications are classed as your Military Occupational Specialty (MOS). An MOS is described by both a title and a code number—for example, machine gunner 0331. Your primary MOS is the basis for your assignment and promotion. Every Marine has a primary MOS. Some Marines have one or more additional MOSs. The machine gunner might, for example, have the additional MOS of 0317, scout-sniper.

Marine Corps units are organized in accordance with Tables of Organization (T/Os) approved by the CMC. The T/O for a unit shows a number of billets equal to the authorized number of officers and enlisted personnel in the unit. Each billet is shown by grade, duty in the unit, and MOS code number of the individual who is supposed to fill it. However, "billet" and "MOS" do not mean the same thing. The title of a billet may differ from the title of the MOS that is required to fill that billet.

Classification is that part of personnel administration that entails interviewing individuals, testing them, preparing and maintaining their qualification records and classifying their military qualifications. The objective of our classification system is the assignment of a suitable MOS to every Marine. The *Marine Corps Manual* notes that the primary MOS "will normally identify billets for which the Marine is best qualified, with due consideration given to such factors as:

a. The needs of the Marine Corps as a whole, determined by the CMC.

b. The duty assignment policy for enlisted personnel.

c. The technical skills required.

d. The Marine's education, experience, aptitudes, and capabilities.

e. The duty preference of the Marine.

The military specialty structure is divided into occupational fields. The first two digits of an MOS identify the occupational field and are used often in conversation in place of the name of that field. Thus, if one Marine mentions the occupational field of 03, the Marine refers to the infantry. If one Marine mentions 04, the Marine refers to the logistics field.

Normally, a Marine is not assigned to an occupational field until recruit training is finished. The Marine is then assigned the basic MOS of an occupational field. The basic MOS for an occupational field is a four-digit number. The first two digits identify the occupational field; the second two are a double zero.

Upon completion of basic specialist training, on-the-job training, or a formal school, Marines are assigned a primary MOS to identify the particular skill learned. Thus, a Marine joins Marine Corps forces or reports to a new duty station fully trained to occupy a specific T/O billet.

The Billet Identification Code (BIC) replaced the former T/O Line Number and is used for many administrative purposes. BIC is a unique, 11-byte, alphanumeric field and consists of the 6-byte Unit Identification Code (UIC) to which the billet belongs, followed immediately by the 5-byte numeric billet identification. For example, the CO of an aviation squadron might have a BIC such as M0223100001.

The Marine Corps' military specialty structure also serves in career planning for the individual. The assignment of the right person to the right job is made in accordance with a plan. The plan is designed to advance your professional value as a Marine in the type of duty that is suited to your experience, ability, and interest. The plan will benefit you and the Marine Corps.

Promotion

As a general rule, Marines are never promoted more than one grade at a time. Promotion to private first class is achieved in accordance with policies established by the CMC. In general, such promotion is based upon completion of a given period of time in grade, satisfactory personal conduct, certain standards of proficiency in duty performance, and other factors of this nature. Promotion to lance corporal and to each of the noncommissioned officer grades comes to Marines who meet the specified requirements of service in grade, conduct, performance of duty, and the specialist knowledge required to hold the MOS in the next higher grade. The Marines selected throughout the Corps are those who are best qualified. The number determined within each occupational field or MOS depends upon the vacancies at the time. Upon determination, their COs are authorized to promote qualified Marines. However, a CO is not required to promote a Marine unless satisfied that the Marine has the necessary leadership, physical capability, and moral character for the next higher grade.

For SNCOs (staff sergeants through sergeants major/master gunnery sergeants), the CMC sends the promotion warrent of those who have been selected by a promotion board. These boards are centralized and convene annually, examining qualifications of each Marine using the Performance Evaluation System. Demonstrated performance, leadership, military proficiency, physical fitness, conduct, motivation, and maturity are a few of the qualities examined before a Marine is recommended by the promotion board.

It is a Marine Corps policy to maintain a Personnel Evaluation System (PES) in order to establish a record of marking for grading an individual Marine's proficiency and conduct. In the case of sergeants and above, a fitness report form is used, which provides an in-depth evaluation. Marines with a rank of private through corporal receive periodic proficiency and conduct marks by their CO. These marks then are entered in the Marine's Official Military Personnel File (OMPF) in the Marine Corps Total Force System (MCTFS), which automatically computes a composite score and compares it to the "cutting score" announced for the appropriate promotion period. If the Marine's score meets or exceeds the cutting score, MCTFS will automatically issue an advisory remark to the Marine's organization.

The guidelines shown in Figure 6-1 (on next page) will be used in assigning conduct marks; however, full discretion is left to commanders to deviate from them for good and sufficient reasons.

The guidelines shown in Figure 6-2 (on page 67) will be used in assigning duty proficiency marks, however, full discretion is left to the commanders to deviate from them for good and sufficient reasons.

Eligibility for promotion is determined from a composite score, which includes such elements as service in grade, total active duty service, past performance of duty, physical fitness, off-duty education, etc. All elements are included in the score according to a mathematical formula established by the CMC. Figure 6-3 (on page 68) is an example of a composite score worksheet and an explanation of how the composite scores are computed.

The ratings for lines 1–3 are derived from rating tables in Marine Corps Order P1400.32D.

The General Military Proficiency (GMP) score (line 5) is obtained by dividing line 4 by the number of lines above line 3 that have a rating other than "not considered." This number is then multiplied by 100 and entered on line 6.

Lines 7 and 8 are the average of all duty proficiency and conduct marks assigned prior to the cut-off date designated in the appropriate HQMC directive but on or after the date of last promotion, reduction, or enlistment (whichever is latest).

MARK	CORRESPONDING ADJECTIVE RATING	STANDARDS OF CONDUCT
0.0 to 1.9	Unacceptable	Habitual Offender. Conviction by general, special, or more than one summary court-martial. Give a mark of "0" upon declaration of desertion. Ordered to confinement pursuant to sentence of court-martial. Two or more punitive reductions in grade.
2.0 to 2.9	Unsatisfactory	No special court-martial. Not more than one summary court-martial. Not more than two NJPs. Punitive reduction in grade.
3.0 to 3.9	Below Average	No Court-martial. Not more than one NJP. No favorable impression of the qualities listed in paragraph 4007.6a. Failure to make satisfactory progress while assigned to the weight control or military appearance program. Conduct such as not to impair appreciably one's usefulness or the efficiency of the command, but conduct not sufficient to merit an honorable discharge.
4.0 to 4.4	Average	No offenses. No unfavorable impressions as to attitude, interest, cooperation, obedience, after-affects of intemperance, courtesy and consideration, and observance of regulations.
4.5 to 4.8	Excellent	No offenses. Positive favorable impressions of the qualities listed in paragraph 4007.6a. Demonstrates reliability, good influence, sobriety, obedience, and industry.
4.9 to 5.0	Outstanding	No offenses. Exhibits to an outstanding degree the qualities listed in paragraph 4007.6a. Observes spirit as well as letter of orders and regulations. Demonstrates positive effect on others by example and persuasion.

Figure 6-1. Standards of Conduct.

Line 9 is the total time in grade from date of rank to the designated cut-off date.

Line 10 is the total time in service the Marine will have accrued on the designated cut-off date.

Line 11 is the number of approved self-education courses completed since promotion to the current grade. A maximum of 100 points may be awarded between MCI and college courses combined.

Line 12 is reenlistment bonus points.

Line 13 is command recruiting points

Line 14 is composite score, which is the sum of lines 6–13.

Line 15 is the composite score needed for promotion.

MARK	CORRESPONDING ADJECTIVE RATING	STANDARDS OF PROFICIENCY
0.0 to 1.9	Unacceptable	Does unacceptable work in most duties, generally undependable, needs considerable assistance, and close supervision on even the simplest assignment.
2.0 to 2.9	Unsatisfactory	Does acceptable work in some of the duties but cannot be depended upon. Needs assistance and close supervision on all but simplest assignment.
3.0 to 3.9	Below Average	Handles routine matters acceptably but needs close supervision when performing duties not of routine nature.
4.0 to 4.4	Average	Can be depended upon to discharge regular duties thoroughly and completely but usually needs assistance in dealing with obedience, after-affects of intemperance, courtesy and consideration, and observance of regulations.
4.5 to 4.8	Excellent	Does excellent work in all regular duties but needs assistance in dealing with extremely difficult or unusual assignments.
4.9 to 5.0	Outstanding	Does superior work in all duties. Even extremely difficult or unusual assignments can be given with full confidence that they will be handled in a thoroughly competent manner.

Figure 6-2. Standards of Proficiency.

Bonus points are obtained from the following:

Course	Bonus Points
• MCI course or other military service correspondence course (to include sub courses)	15
• College-Level Examination Program (CLEP) test (Each Portion)	10
• College course (Semester or Quarter)	10
• Vocational School course (Semester)	10

The scores for lines 5–11 are obtained by multiplying each element by the number indicated in the example on page 68.

The Command Recruiting Bonus (line 13) is earned while on permissive TAD. If you assist a recruiter, for every person you convince to join the Marine Corps, you earn 20 points. A maximum of 100 points can be earned.

Line 14 the Marine's composite score, is the sum of the values under the "Score" column for lines 5–13.

At HQMC a cutting score is established so that the number of those Marines whose composite score is above the cutting score equals the number of vacancies in the rank and occupational field being considered.

Leave and Liberty

Leave is authorized vacation or absence from duty, as distinguished from liberty. Liberty is the authorized absence of a Marine from a place of duty for short periods and not chargeable to the leave account. In a civilian job, your annual vacation would be the counterpart of leave. Weekends, periods between the end of one work day and the beginning of work the next, and occasional days or afternoons off not counting against your annual vacation would correspond to liberty.

Manual Composite Score Worksheet

2501. COMPUTATION (USMC/USMCR). The following format is used in the computation of composite scores for LCpl and Cpls. It is also used to manually compute the composite score prior to the submission of a remedial promotion request for any LCpl or Cpl (USMC or USMCR).

1. Rifle _____ _____ = _____
           Score   (Date of test YYMMDD)   Rating

2. PFT _____ _____ = _____
           Score   (Date of test YYMMDD)   Rating

3. CFT _____ _____ = _____
           Score   (Date of test YYMMDD)   Rating

4. Subtotal (lines 1 through 3)   = _____
           Total

5. GMP score (line 4 divided by 3)   = _____
           Total

6. GMP score (line 5) x 100   = _____
           Total

7. Average Proficiency Marks x 100   = _____
           Total

8. Average Conduct Marks x 100   = _____
           Total

9. Time In Grade (DOR/Months) _____ x 5   = _____
           Total

10. Time In Service (AFADBD/Months) _____ x 2   = _____
            Total

11. Education Points (100 Max)

        a. _____ MCI x 15

        b. _____ College x 10

        c. _____ MarineNet x 15   = _____
        Total

12. Reenlistment Bonus Points   = _____
            Total

13. Command Recruiting Points (100 Max) 000 x 20   = _____
            Total

14. Composite Score (sum of lines 6 through 13)   = _____
            Total

15. Composite Score Needed for Promotion
            1st Month of Qtr _____

            2nd Month of Qtr _____

            3rd Month of Qtr _____

Figure 6-3. Manual Composite Score Worksheet.

All Marines use the website Marine OnLine (MOL) to submit their leave requests, special liberty/out of bounds chits and permissive TAD requests.

Marines may be granted annual leave at any time the absence would not be inconsistent with operational readiness requirements or the accomplishment of the mission of the command. You may not always be able to take your annual leave at the particular period or periods you would like. COs are restricted as to the number of Marines they may allow to be on leave at one time. They must grant leave so that there is the least interference with duty and training schedules. You should not execute all of your annual leave during one continuous period. You may take portions of it at different times during the year.

Leave is earned at the rate of 2.5 days a month. In 12 months, you earn 30 days leave. No leave is earned during periods of unauthorized absence or during periods of confinement, serving sentence of a court-martial. You can check your monthly Leave and Earnings Statement (LES) or MOL for your leave balance.

A Marine may not be authorized more than 60 days annual leave during any fiscal year and may not be authorized annual leave for a continuous period of more than 60 days unless specifically authorized by the CMC.

Advance leave is leave granted to a Marine, with pay and allowances, prior to its accrual based on the reasonable expectation that the amount advanced will be earned before a Marine's separation, or in the case of a Marine who has executed a first extension of enlistment, before the effective date of that extension. Excess leave is leave granted in excess of accrued and advance leave and is the term used to describe a negative leave balance on the effective date of separation. The members taking advance leave resulting in a negative leave balance on date of discharge or release should be aware that if that leave becomes excess the member will be subject to checkage of pay and allowances.

A negative balance on the date of discharge for the purpose of immediate reenlistment is excess leave only to the extent that it exceeds the leave accrual potential of the unserved period of enlistment terminated by the discharge.

Emergency leave may be authorized under the following circumstances as verified by such means as the leave granting authority considers sufficient.

- Upon the death of a member of a Marine's immediate family, i.e., father, mother, father-in-law, mother-in-law, legal guardian, spouse, son, daughter, brother, sister, including step or half relationships.
- When the return of a Marine will contribute to the welfare of a dying member of his immediate family as defined above.
- When due to any serious illness or injury of a member of a Marine's immediate family as defined above, important responsibilities are placed upon a Marine that cannot be accomplished from the duty station.
- When failure to return home would create a serious and unusual hardship on a Marine or the family.
- Emergency leave is deducted from your balance.

A structure exists for maintaining written forms for leave, but the correct way to submit and manage leave requests is through MOL. You may not go on leave without authorization on a written form or on your online MOL leave request. Following are the instructions for submitting leave requests in writing: (Rev. 2-05. See Figure 6-4 on next page.) You may wish to plan additional leave while traveling to a new duty station. Unless orders from higher authority to your CO directing your transfer to another station prevent them, your CO is authorized to grant you leave en route to your new station. This delay will count as annual leave. The authorized number of days required to travel between your old and new stations is additional and does not count as leave. Your travel orders will outline the member the date you are to report to your new station. If you are granted delay and report to your new station before the date specified, the unused portion of your delay is not counted as leave. You gain nothing, however, you are allowed to spend less time between

LEAVE AUTHORIZATION (OFFICER AND ENLISTED) (1500)
NAVMC 3 (REV. 03-11) (EF) (Previous editions will not be used)
FOUO - Privacy sensitive when filled in.

> BEFORE SIGNING LEAVE REQUEST,
> READ INSTRUCTIONS ON PAGE 2 AND
> PRIVACY ACT STATEMENT ON PAGE 3

1. TO:

LEAVE REQUEST

2. FROM (Name, Grade, SSN, MOS)	3. ORGANIZATION AND DUTY TELEPHONE NUMBER

4. NUMBER OF DAYS REQUESTED AND INCLUSIVE DATES	5. DATE & TIME LEAVE EFFECTIVE	6. DATE & TIME LEAVE EXPIRES

7. TYPE OF LEAVE REQUESTED	8. NO. OF DAYS TAKEN THIS FISCAL YEAR	9. LEAVE BALANCE	10. ECC

11. ADDRESS WHILE ON LEAVE (Include telephone number and area code. If any change notify your commanding officer)	12. SIGNATURE OF PERSON REQUESTING LEAVE AND DATE: I will wear my seatbelt while driving or riding in a PMV while in an authorized leave status (paragraph 14(d) of MCO 5100.19(E).

"EVERY MARINE RECRUIT A MARINE" MARINE CORPS ORDER 1050.1___AUTHORIZES A 5-DAY LEAVE EXTENSION OR SPECIAL LIBERTY CHIT TO MARINES ON LEAVE WHO RECRUIT AN ACCEPTABLE APPLICANT FOR ENLISTMENT IN THE MARINE CORPS OR MARINE CORPS RESERVE. CONTACT THE MARINE CORPS RECRUITER NEAREST YOU FOR DETAILS.

APPROVAL OF IMMEDIATE SUPERIOR/COMPANY COMMANDER

13. ☐ APPROVED ☐ DISAPPROVED	REMARKS (If disapproved)	SIGNATURE AND GRADE
14. ☐ APPROVED ☐ DISAPPROVED	REMARKS (If disapproved)	SIGNATURE AND GRADE

15. SIGNATURE (Officer authorized to grant leave)	16. GRADE AND COMPONENT	17. TITLE

MCTFS REPORTING INFORMATION

18. Hour and date of departure _____ _____	18. Hour and date of return _____ _____
_____ (Signature of Duty Officer/NCO/Indiv)	_____ (Signature of Duty Officer/NCO/Indiv)

20. EXTENSIONS Granted _____ days extension of leave. Your leave will now expire at _____ on _____

_____ (Signature of Granting Officer)	_____ (Unit)	_____ (Date)

21. HOSPITALIZATION

NAME AND ADDRESS OF HOSPITAL	TIME AND DATE ADMITTED	TIME AND DATE RELEASED

REMARKS/DIAGNOSIS

_____ (Signature of Physician)	_____ (Date)

22. UNIT DIARY COMPUTATION - INCLUSIVE DATES

NO. OF DAYS CHARGED AS LEAVE _____	FROM _____	THRU _____
UNIT DIARY NO. _____	UTR NO. _____	

FOR OFFICIAL USE ONLY

Adobe LiveCycle Designer

Enclosure (3)

Figure 6-4.

stations than the travel time you are allowed. Be sure to keep your travel orders in your possession until you report to your new duty station.

Liberty is a privilege that is granted only when it does not interfere with the duty and training of the command or with its prescribed state of readiness. Your CO will prescribe liberty limits, which members of the command may not exceed without written permission.

Off-Duty Education and Training

At almost every Marine Corps installation, off-duty education and training opportunities are available to help individuals improve and expand their abilities and skills as Marines and, at the same time, reap personal benefit. There are several hundred colleges and universities that offer off-duty classroom study on or near Marine Corps installations. These civilian school courses serve as a basis for improvement in your Marine Corps career and can frequently become part of a program leading to a college degree.

Financial assistance is available to those qualified Marines who elect to pursue off-duty or voluntary education through the Marine Corps Tuition Assistance Program, which will pay tuition and fees for college courses.

Tuition assistance (TA) offers financial assistance to those Marines who elect to pursue off-duty or voluntary education. TA rates vary and can be attained through your local education office or from command education office. It does not include books.

The Veterans Administration (VA) handles the educational benefits traditionally referred to as the GI Bill. The current program, authorized in wake of the September 11, 2001 attacks, is frequently called the "Post/911 GI Bill." The bill provides funding for approved courses at colleges, universities, and other schools and training center to eligible servicemen and women. Details on the bill, including eligibility requirements and benefits, are available at http://www.gibill.va.gov/.

In addition to the training received at service schools and on-the-job training, you may enroll in correspondence courses offered free through the Marine Corps Institute (MCI), MarineNet and Navy Knowledge Online websites. These latter courses are specifically designed to help you advance in rank (by accruing more earned points and achieving a higher composite score) and to assume additional responsibilities as a United States Marine.

Your education officer will provide you with more information on the off-duty educational opportunities that are available and the current GI Bill and VA benefits. The education officer also will help you select courses of study and establish a program that will meet your individual needs.

Family Members

An enlisted Marine is entitled to basic allowance for housing for legal family members when the government does not provide government quarters for the Marine and the family members at a duty station. All enlisted Marines with legal family members are required to make an application for basic allowance for housing on behalf of their family members. Although a Marine is not required to give a prescribed amount of money to family members, a government allotment is a sure and convenient means of ensuring that family members receive continuous monetary support. An enlisted Marine may receive basic allowance for housing for a spouse, legitimate or illegitimate minor child, and for certain other family members who rely upon the Marine for support. The regulations governing basic allowance for housing are complex and change frequently. If there is anyone for whom you have not claimed a dependent's allowance who is dependent upon you for support, you should immediately inform your chain of command. Likewise, you should immediately inform your chain of command of any change in the status of your family members. This is particularly important since your pay will be checked, and all payments made on behalf of your family members after their entitlement ceases will be deducted. A Marine may submit a request for waiver of recovery of the overpayment with proper justification to the CO. This request will then be forwarded to the CMC for a final determination.

A married Marine may, subject to the approval of his CO, be permitted to mess separately from an organization's general mess and be reimbursed a prescribed amount approximately equal to the cost to the government of the food consumed if eaten in the mess.

Family members are entitled to medical and dental benefits through the TRICARE medical plan, a health benefits plan that shares most of the costs of care from civilian doctors and hospitals when care is not provided through a military hospital or clinic. Family members are enrolled in the program through the Defense Eligibility Enrollment Reporting System (DEERS), which is accomplished by notifying the Information Personnel Administration Center (IPAC) whenever there is a change in the number or status of family members. Dental benefits also are provided for family members by TRICARE.

Legal Assistance

Most installations have legal assistance offices which are qualified to answer your questions about legal problems and advise and assist you in their solution. Legal assistance personnel are prohibited by regulations from revealing confidences of personnel obtaining legal assistance to the same extent that a civilian lawyer is prohibited by legal ethics from revealing confidences of their clients. Throughout the United States, numerous agencies exist to assist service families with their legal affairs. The Department of the Navy maintains liaison with these agencies. If you have a legal problem that requires the services of such an agency, your CO or legal assistance officer can advise you of the procedure to follow.

Each major base throughout the Marine Corps has a Staff Judge Advocate or a Legal Services Office that provides legal services to all active duty military members, their families and military retirees in the areas of military justice, legal assistance, research and civil law, administrative support, military magistrate (traffic court, civil processing and pretrial confinement), and income-tax preparation and filing.

Medals and Decorations

Medal of Honor. The highest military award given by our country was first authorized in 1861 and is given for acts of bravery above and beyond the call of duty.

Purple Heart. This was the first medal awarded by our country. It was first awarded in 1782 and was given for acts of bravery. Later, it was given for wounds only.

Other medals awarded for bravery in combat are:
- **Navy Cross.**
- **Silver Star.**
- **Distinguished Flying Cross.**
- **Navy and Marine Corps Medal** (peacetime or combat not involving actual conflict with the enemy).
- **Bronze Star.**
- **Air Medal.**
- **Navy and Marine Corps Commendation Medal.**
- **Navy and Marine Corps Achievement Medal.**

Ribbons were authorized in 1905 for wear on certain uniforms in lieu of medals. In addition to decorations, they represent service medals awarded for service performed in certain geographic areas during specified time periods. Stars and other devices worn on service medals and ribbons represent battles or campaigns in which the individual Marine participated. Stars, leaves or numerals on personal or unit decorations denote additional awards of the appropriate decoration to the individual Marine. Marksmanship badges are awarded for degrees of proficiency with small arms.

Personal Finances

The Marine Corps recognizes that it is sometimes necessary to go into debt in order to provide the essentials in life, but prompt settlement of indebtedness is expected.

The most modern and effective method to provide Marines with pay information is through an established MyPay account (https://mypay.dfas.mil/mypay.aspx). The MyPay website allows Marines to access and manage their pay information, view LES, last payment information and Forms W2; set up allotments; change their direct deposits and so forth. The most recent LES may be found 24 hours a day on MyPay.

Charge cards and time-payment plans offered through commercial businesses and finance companies have become a popular method of acquiring personal items of service or merchandise. However, they are misused often and can be costly to the consumer because of the higher rates of interest to be paid back. When it becomes necessary to borrow money to purchase the essentials of life, it is wiser to go to a bank or your local credit union to take advantage of the lower interest rates and personal savings plans that are available to each member.

The need for a personal savings plan is important to every Marine. It should reduce the need or amount to borrow. Also, money that you have saved will earn interest for you. You should save money for the less costly things that you may later wish to purchase or just to have money available for those unforeseen "emergencies" that may arise.

One of the most effective methods of saving money is by means of an allotment. An allotment is a regular sum of money automatically deducted from your pay monthly and paid by the government to a payee whom you designate. Allotments are made through your MyPay account only for purposes allowed by regulations. Information pertaining to allotments to family members who are authorized dependency allowances may be obtained through your the local disbursing office. Allotments may also be registered for relatives not authorized to receive dependency allowances. An allotment to a bank may be for the support of family or relatives. A savings allotment may be sent directly to a savings institution, such as a bank (savings or checking account) or credit union (savings or loan account). U.S. Savings Bonds may be purchased in a regular amount each month and paid for by an allotment. So may monthly life insurance premiums, including premiums on commercial insurance when the insurance is on the life of the grantor.

A newer option is the TSP (Thrift Savings Plan), a defined contribution retirement savings plan. It offers the same kind of benefits as a 401(k) retirement account, and the amount you and your employer put into the account is determined by you. The TSP has a Roth option that further protects your investment from tax penalties.

The Navy-Marine Corps Relief Society and the American Red Cross provide interest-free loans to qualified servicemen and women and often require payment through an allotment. The Navy-Marine Corps Relief Society is a nonprofit, charitable organization that provides financial, educational, and other assistance to members of the naval services of the United States and their eligible family members and survivors when in need. Their services include interest-free loans or grants to deal with emergency needs, education loans and grants, lifetime benefits, and information assistance.

A Marine who is married and has to support a family on pay and allowance must forgo many of the luxuries and pleasures that could be afforded as a single person. The Marine is expected to practice the economy necessary to provide adequate support for family members. If the family members are subject to real privation and hardship because of sickness or other emergency, the American Red Cross or the Navy-Marine Corps Relief Society may provide financial assistance. It must be understood that these organizations do not have enough money to help those who are capable of meeting their emergencies without assistance.

Leave and Earnings Statement

A LES is a monthly statement found among various types of pay information contained in the MCTFS and on the Marine's MyPay account. The LES is prepared at the Defense Finance and Accounting Center in Indianapolis, Indiana, and it can be viewed through the member's MyPay account. It is the Marine's responsibility to review the information contained therein to determine whether or not it is accurate and to report any inconsistencies to his chain of command.

Each Marine should become familiar with the LES in order to use it effectively. The LES provides information concerning your identification and service; the total amounts of pay that you are entitled to each month; the total amount of allotments you have; your total amount of deductions, such as Serviceman's Group Life Insurance (SGLI); income tax, social security payments, etc.; a record of your past pay amounts; monthly and annual tax information; a record of your leave used and accrued; and a remarks section that will show information pertinent to your pay. The LES contains a generalized legend to explain information appearing on the face of the form.

CHAPTER 7

Military Security

Military security is achieved by Marines through several organizational measures, including the establishment of an Interior Guard. In addition, regular indoctrination and training orient individual Marines toward enhanced awareness of security threats and actions necessary to counter those threats. These and other measures are tailored to the specific situation and location. However, general rules exist to be followed everywhere and form the basis for maintaining military security wherever Marines are located, both on and off duty.

Interior Guard

Wherever you are stationed as a Marine, ashore or afloat, your CO generally establishes and maintains an Interior Guard. This guard is charged with the preservation of order, protection of property, and the enforcement of orders and regulations. Interior Guards are to be distinguished from the various types of guards employed to protect and defend tactical areas and from guards in riot duty and other special situations. Such guards are specially organized and equipped to provide security commensurate with the requirements of the local situation.

The Interior Guard may be composed of one or more main guards, as the commander directs. In addition, the Interior Guard includes any special guards established by the senior commander or commanders of subordinate units. One Officer of the Day (OOD) supervises each main guard established ashore. On board ship, the Officer of the Deck performs the Interior Guard duties of the OOD. In large commands ashore, where there is more than one main guard, a Command Duty Officer (CDO) may be assigned to supervise the entire guard.

Main Guard. Generally, the main guard consists of a number of sentries on post, supervisory and administrative personnel, and a reserve. The CO prescribes the number of sentry posts. The necessary sentries to stand these posts normally are organized into three reliefs, each directly supervised by a Corporal of the Guard (COG). The main guard is commanded by the Commander of the Guard, who is assisted by the Sergeant of the Guard (SOG). Whenever the CO determines that a Commander of the Guard is not required, that position in the guard structure can be eliminated. On board ship, no Commander of the Guard is assigned. In such cases the SOG performs the duties prescribed for the Commander of the Guard in addition to those of the current position. The main guard always maintains a reserve, generally constituted from one or more of the off-duty reliefs of the guard.

Special Guards. Special Guards are detailed when it is impractical to use sentries from the main guard to guard property or an area. The commander establishing the Special Guard prescribes the composition. The senior commander of a troop organization embarked aboard ship and not a part of the authorized complement thereof (designated as "Commanding Officer of Troops") establishes a Special Guard for the control of personnel and equipment as the CO of the ship may approve or direct.

The functions of interior guards vary with the desires of the COs of individual posts and with the nature of the particular posts and stations. For example, sentries at a base for combat units generally have challenging posts, while stations such as Quantico have few if any challenging posts.

When you are on duty with an Interior Guard, you are one member of a distinct organization with definite orders to carry out. The Marines with authority over an Interior Guard are the CO and the OOD. The OOD is the CO's direct representative and is in charge of the security of the post, station, installation, or unit during the tour of duty.

There are four classes of personnel in an Interior Guard. These classes are: (1) the Commander of the Guard, (2) the SOG, (3) the Corporals of the Guard, (4) the privates, PFCs, and lance corporals of the guard.*

Usually there are three relief sections in each Interior Guard. Since a corporal is assigned to each relief section, there are three Corporals of the Guard. There are enough privates, PFCs, and lance corporals to provide three reliefs for each post the Interior Guard is assigned, plus a certain number of supernumeraries, depending on the size of the guard. These supernumeraries are held in reserve in case of an unexpected need to relieve a guard.

*These titles address specific billets and do not necessarily denote rank.

Duties of Guard Personnel

When you are assigned to Interior Guard duty, you will find that there are certain set duties that must be performed. The following discussion outlines the principal duties and responsibilities of the Commander, Sergeant, Corporals, and Privates of the Guard.

Commander of the Guard

The Commander of the Guard is the officer or NCO who ensures proper instruction, discipline, and performance of duty of the main guard. He performs the following tasks:

• Carries out the orders of the CO, Command Duty Officer (when assigned), OOD and, in emergencies, the senior line officer present only. The Commander of the Guard will report to the OOD any additional orders that the Commander of the Guard or other authorized persons have issued.

• Ensures that all members of the guard are correctly instructed in their orders and duties and that they understand and are properly executed. Questions the NCOs of the Guard and sentries about the instructions they may have received from the previous guard.

• Inspects the guard when directed by the OOD, but in any case inspects each relief at least once while on post. The Commander of the Guard ensures that the sentries, their arms, and their equipment are in proper condition and that the special orders for each post are posted in their proper location.

• Informs the SOG of his location at all times.

• Except during emergencies, may sleep as duties permit.

• When an alarm is sounded, expeditiously forms the reserve, if necessary. If the situation is serious, notifies the OOD immediately. Should a sentry call "The Guard" or discharge a weapon, a strong patrol/reaction force will be sent to that post.

• Details personnel to raise and lower the national flag at Morning and Evening Colors. Ensures that the national flag is kept in good condition and never handled except in the performance of duty. The Commander of the Guard will report to the OOD when the flag is not in serviceable condition.

• Ensures that reliefs are posted on schedule.

• Unless otherwise ordered, may permit members of the guard, not on post, to leave the guardhouse for short periods of time.

• Informs the OOD immediately of any

dangerous, suspicious or unusual occurrences.

• Notifies the OOD when any person is apprehended by the guard and will detain such person at the guardhouse for appropriate action by the OOD.

• Ensures the security of prisoners under charge of the guard. Before each relief is posted, requires the Corporals of the Guard of the old and new reliefs to verify together the number of prisoners. Will be guided in the performance of duties in connection with correction centers/facilities and brigs by the *Corrections Manual*.

• When formal relief is prescribed, examines the log of the SOG and causes any errors therein to be corrected and effects the relief of the SOG before being relieved. Once ready, reports to the OOD with the new Commander of the Guard for relief.

• Maintains a Commander of the Guard log which contains a concise account of the tour of duty.

Sergeant of the Guard

The SOG assists the Commander of the Guard in ensuring proper instruction, discipline and performance of duty of the main guard. The SOG performs the following tasks:

• The SOG performs the duties of the Commander of the Guard, if no Commander of the Guard has been assigned.

• Carries out the orders of the CO, CDO (when assigned), OOD, Commander of the Guard, and, in emergencies, the senior line officer present only.

• Ensures that the property under charge of the guard is cared for and accounted for properly.

• Assigns members of the guard to reliefs. The COG for each relief assigns that relief to posts and prepares a list of such assignments. The SOG receives a copy of such lists and, based upon them, prepares a guard roster. The guard roster sets forth the name, rank, post, and relief to which each member of the guard is assigned. The SOG prepares the guard roster in duplicate,

retains one copy and submits the other to the Commander of the Guard or the OOD, as appropriate, for approval. Once approved, no changes will be made to the guard roster without permission of the approving authority.

• Ensures that all reliefs are turned out for posting at the proper time.

• Ensures that the COGs understand their duties thoroughly and carries them out promptly and efficiently.

• Inspects the guard when directed by the OOD but must inspect each relief at least once during each watch.

• When absent from the guardhouse, the SOG directs the COG of the relief on post to perform guardhouse duties until the SOG returns. The SOG will notify the COG of his location at all times.

• When the COG of the relief on post is absent from the guardhouse, the SOG temporarily assumes the duties or designates another member of the guard to do so.

• Ensures that the guardhouse and its grounds are maintained in proper police.

• Informs the Commander of the Guard immediately of any dangerous, suspicious or unusual occurrence.

• Notifies the Commander of the Guard when any person is apprehended by the guard.

• Forms the guard whenever necessary.

• When formal relief is prescribed, effects the relief of the Corporals of the Guard.

• Maintains the SOG log and enters therein concise accounts of all important and pertinent events that transpire during the tour of duty and that affect the guard. Exercises care in preparing the log, which is an official record of the command. Under the last entry, signs name and grade. Upon finishing, reports to the old Commander of the Guard (old OOD, if no Commander of the Guard is assigned) with the new SOG for relief and posting.

Corporal of the Guard

The COG directly supervises the members

of the guard assigned to that relief. The COG performs the guardhouse duties of the SOG when the SOG is absent from the guardhouse. In particular, the COG performs the following tasks:

• Supervises the members of the guard assigned to that relief. Performs the guardhouse duties of the SOG when the latter is absent from the guardhouse.

• Carries out orders from the CO, CDO (when assigned), OOD, Commander of the Guard (when assigned), SOG, and, in emergencies, the senior line officer present only.

• Assigns sentries on that relief to posts. Prepares, in duplicate, a list showing the number of relief, each member's name, grade, and assigned post. Retains one copy and gives the other to the SOG.

• Knows and understands the special orders of every sentry on the relief. The COG forms the relief in sufficient time to accomplish the following: issue guard property, inspect appearance, fitness for duty, condition of arms, issue ammunition, and supervise loading of weapons (if authorized). The COG instructs each member concerning orders and duties, ensuring understanding. When completed, the COG reports to the SOG that the relief is ready to be posted or, if directed, posts the sentries without so reporting. Upon returning to the guardhouse with the old relief, the COG supervises unloading of weapons (if loading has been authorized), collects guard property (if necessary), and dismisses the old relief. Upon completion, the COG reports to the SOG with the old COG for relief and posting.

• Maintains the COG post in the guardhouse near the entrance or as may be directed on board ship. When required to depart the post in the performance of duties, the COG notifies the SOG, who will assume those duties or designate another member of the guard to do so. Either the SOG, the COG of the relief on post, or a member of the guard designated to perform the duties of the COG shall be present at the guardhouse at all times. The COG allows no one to enter the guardhouse without authority.

• Goes at once to, communicates with, or sends a patrol to any sentry who calls for the COG.

• Forms own relief promptly for posting or when the guard is turned out. If own relief is on post when the guard is to be formed, the current COG and oncoming COG relief remain on post. Ensures that sleeping arrangements for all members of the current relief can be easily located and turns them out quickly without confusion.

• Reports immediately to the SOG all violations of regulations and unusual occurrences.

• Awakens or alerts the COG of the next relief in time to form the oncoming relief and post it at the proper time.

• When a sentry calls "Relief," the COG relieves the sentry and posts a supernumerary or a member of the off-duty reliefs, if the COG determines that relief is necessary. If the sentry is to be relieved for a short time only, the COG posts the sentry again as soon as the necessity for the relief terminates.

• Notifies the SOG when any person is detained or apprehended by the guard. Escorts all persons apprehended to the guardhouse for appropriate action by the OOD.

Marines of the Guard

When you are a private, private first class, or a lance corporal member of the guard, you normally are assigned to a relief by the SOG. The COG for your relief usually assigns you to your post. You cannot be changed from one relief to another during the same tour of guard duty except by proper authority. Rules that govern your conduct while serving as a member of the guard are:

Rule 1. All members of the guard memorize, understand, and comply with the General Orders for sentries. In addition, they understand and comply with the regulations relating to General Orders and with special orders applying to their particular posts.

Rule 2. Supernumeraries understand the special orders for all posts on which they could be posted and comply with those for the particular post if posted thereon as a sentry.

Rule 3. Members of the guard not on post remain in the immediate vicinity of the guardhouse except when granted permission to leave by the Commander of the Guard. Reliefs of a running guard placed on an off-duty status may leave the guardhouse as directed by the CO.

Orders for Sentries

When you go on a tour of Interior Guard duty, your orders as a sentry will fall into two classes: general orders and special orders.

General Orders

The general orders do not change. There are 11 general orders, and they are the same wherever and whenever you are on Interior Guard duty. You are required to know and memorize these general orders and be able to recite them whenever you are called upon to do so.

The 11 general orders are listed below with explanations as necessary. The orders themselves are in bold-face type.

1. To take charge of this post and all government property in view.

• The number, type (fixed or patrol), and limits of a sentry's post constitute part of the special orders. The post's limits are defined to include every place to which the sentry must go to execute the special orders. Within these limits, the sentry has authority over all persons on the post. (See Navy Regulations.)

• A sentry reports immediately to the COG every unusual or suspicious occurrence noted.

• A sentry halts and detains all persons on or near the post whose presence or actions are subject to suspicion. Apprehends all persons involved in a disorder occurring on or near the post and all persons discovered or suspected of committing a crime or violating regulations. All persons apprehended or detained are turned over to the COG.

• The firing of a weapon at another person by an armed sentry is considered justified under certain conditions only. (See the section in this chapter titled "Use of Deadly Force.")

2. To walk my post in a military manner, keeping always on the alert and observing everything that takes place within sight or hearing.

• Special orders will prescribe the manner in which a sentry shall walk (stand, ride, or sit) the post and carry a weapon. Such manner is dependent upon the type of post (fixed or patrol) and the specific duties involved, but sentries will always conduct themselves in a military manner and remain vigilant and attentive to their duties.

3. To report all violations of orders I am instructed to enforce.

• A sentry reports a violation of orders to the COG at the first opportunity and to any Officer or NCO of the Guard inspecting them. The sentry apprehends the offender if necessary.

4. To repeat all calls from posts more distant from the guardhouse than my own.

• To call the COG for any purpose other than relief, fire, or disorder, a sentry will call, "Corporal of the Guard, Post Number ..." When sentry posts are located within hearing distance of each other, a sentry receiving a call from a post more distant from the guardhouse than one's own, repeats the call to the next post loudly, distinctly and exactly as received.

5. To quit my post only when properly relieved.

• If a sentry requires relief because of sickness or other reason, the Marine calls, "Corporal of the Guard, Post Number ..., relief."

• If a sentry is not relieved at the expiration of the tour or at mealtime, the Marine does not abandon the post but calls the COG for instructions.

- When so ordered, a sentry on the last relief of a post leaves at the proper time, returns to the guardhouse, and reports to the COG.
- A sentry may leave the prescribed limits of a fixed or patrol post to protect government property in view or to apprehend an offender, but only if these duties cannot be accomplished within the prescribed limits of the post. A sentry must inform the COG before leaving the post under these circumstances, unless immediate action is essential.

6. To receive, obey, and pass on to the sentry who relieves me all orders from the Commanding Officer, Officer of the Day, and Officers and Noncommissioned Officers of the Guard only.

- During his tour of duty, a sentry is subject to the orders of the CO, CDO, and Officers and NCOs of the Guard only. In emergencies, however, the senior line officer present may give orders to sentries. In addition, any officer or NCO is authorized to report violations of regulations by members of the guard.
- A sentry will give up a weapon only when ordered by a person from whom he lawfully receives orders while on post. Unless necessity thereof exists, no person will require a sentry to surrender a weapon while that sentry is on post.

7. To talk to no one except in the line of duty.

- When persons make proper inquiries of a sentry, courteous but brief answers will be given. Long conversations will be discouraged. When challenging or holding conversations with a person, a sentry armed with a rifle will take the position of port arms. If armed with a pistol, the sentry will take the position of "raise pistol" when challenging and will remain at "raise pistol" while conversing.

8. To give the alarm in case of fire or disorder.

- In case of fire, the sentry calls immediately, "Fire, Post Number …," and sounds the alarm if one is available. If possible, without endangering anyone or the performance of the duties, the sentry extinguishes the fire. If not, the sentry directs the responding fire personnel to the fire. The sentry notifies the guardhouse of this action as soon as possible.
- In case of disorder, the sentry notifies the COG immediately and then takes proper corrective action. If the assistance of the guard is required, the sentry calls, "The guard, Post Number …".
- When authorized by the CO and if the danger is great, the sentry discharges a weapon three times in rapid succession into the air before calling. In time of war, sentries give warning of enemy attacks as directed by the CO.

9. To call the COG in any case not covered by instructions.

- Whenever a sentry encounters a situation not covered by general or special orders or about which the sentry is in doubt, the sentry will call the COG for instructions.

10. To salute all officers and all colors and standards not cased. Sentries render salutes as prescribed in Navy Regulations and other portions of this manual with the following exceptions:

- No salute is rendered by a member of the guard who is engaged in the performance of a specific duty, the proper execution of which would prevent saluting.
- A sentry armed with a pistol does not salute after challenging. The sentry stands at "raise pistol" until the challenged person has passed. While at "raise pistol" and holding a conversation, the sentry does not salute but remains at "raise pistol" until the person has passed.
- A sentry armed with a rifle at "sling arms" does not salute after challenging or when holding a conversation. The sentry stands at "port arms" until the person has passed.
- A sentry in conversation with an officer will not interrupt the conversation to salute unless the officer salutes a senior, in which case the sentry will also salute.

• A sentry armed with a rifle (except at "sling arms") salutes by presenting arms. "Present arms" is only executed when halted. If armed with a rifle at "sling arms" or pistol (except after challenging), the sentry halts and renders the appropriate salute. (Colors and standards are cased when furled and enclosed in a protective covering.)

11. To be especially watchful at night and, during the time for challenging, to challenge all persons on or near my post and to allow no one to pass without proper authority.

• If a sentry observes a person approaching the post during the time for challenging, they call, "Halt: Who goes there?" while the person is still far enough away for the sentry to take effective measures should the person rush the sentry after being challenged. Before challenging, the sentry places himself in the most advantageous covered and/or concealed position from which to identify, detain, or apprehend the person or party. In effecting identification, the sentry may require the challenged person or one of a party to move as necessary to effect positive and prompt recognition. Normally upon receiving an answer to the challenge, the sentry will command, "Advance, (repeats the answer to the challenge, such as 'Officer of the Day') to be recognized." The sentry halts the person advanced again at a point where recognition can be effected.

• Positive recognition of all persons claiming authority to pass is the sentry's main consideration. The sentry must ascertain that those challenged are, in fact, the persons they represent themselves to be and have authority to be there before permitting them to pass. If the sentry is not satisfied as to their identity, the sentry will detain the person or party and call the COG.

• The sentry will permit only one of a party to approach for the purpose of recognition. On receiving an answer that indicates the party is friendly and may be authorized to pass, the sentry will command, "Advance one to be recognized." When that one has been recognized, the sentry directs them to bring up the rest of the party and to identify each individual as they pass.

• If two or more persons or parties approach the sentry's post from different directions at the same time, they will be challenged in turn and required to halt and remain halted until advanced. A sentry never permits more than one person to advance at the same time. The senior person or party is the first advanced.

• If a person or party is advanced already and in conversation with a sentry, the latter will challenge any other person or party that may approach. If the new person or party challenged is senior to the one already on the post, the sentry will advance the new person; otherwise, the sentry will advance no one until the first person or party leaves.

• Answers to a sentry's challenge intended to confuse or mislead the sentry are prohibited, but the use of an answer as "Friend" is not to be construed as misleading. It is the usual answer made by officers or patrols when the purpose of their visit makes it desirable that their official capacity should not be announced.

Special Orders

Special orders apply to particular personnel of the Interior Guard. They are promulgated by the CO (or commander of a unit establishing a special guard) to prescribe special duties for main and special guard sentries not contained in the general orders. They also prescribe duties and instructions for other personnel of the Interior Guard who are not contained in this chapter or the *Corrections Manual*. Each member of the Interior Guard is required to understand and comply with special orders which apply to them. Copies of special orders for the guard are posted conspicuously in the guardhouse for reference by all members of the guard. A copy of the special orders for each sentry post should be posted thereon. The special orders for each sentry post should describe and diagram (if practicable) the post's location and limits.

Reporting Posts

A sentry reports the post to an officer as follows: "Sir, Private—reporting post number—all secure. My post and orders remain the same; there have been no unusual occurrences during my watch (or anything that has to be reported)."

Use of Weapons While Assigned to Interior Guard

It is possible that sometime during your assigned tour of Interior Guard duty, it will be necessary for you to use the weapon with which you are armed. The following instructions will govern your actions in the use of your particular weapon.

Nightsticks

A sentry equipped with a nightstick shall confine the use of the nightstick to that portion of the body below the shoulders. The head will not be struck except as a last resort to protect human life.

Firearms

Armed personnel on duty will be governed by command restrictions as specified in their special orders.

Firearms will be used to protect human life, to prevent the destruction or theft of valuable government property and to give an emergency alarm when there is no other method of giving an immediate alarm.

Use of Deadly Force

Deadly force is defined as that which a person uses with the purpose of causing or which he knows, or should reasonably know, would create substantial risk of causing death or serious bodily harm. Deadly force is justified only under conditions of extreme necessity and only as a last resort when all lesser means have failed or cannot reasonably be employed. Use of deadly force will be in accordance with DOD Directive 5210.56.

Additional Instructions Involving Firearms.

a. In view of the dangers inherent in handling weapons, proper upload and download procedures will be followed at all times. It is the command's responsibility to ensure that the required training takes place and is regularly reinforced.

b. All local policies, practices, and directives relating to the arming of law enforcement and security personnel and the conditions under which they may use deadly force are in accordance with applicable DOD, CJCSI, and DN instructions.

c. All personnel assigned to perform law enforcement or security-type duties receive instructions on applicable regulations relating to the use of force and enticement to commit an illegal act. In addition, periodic instruction will be given to all personnel assigned such duties to ensure that they continue to be thoroughly familiar with all restrictions on the use of force. Such instruction should be situation and operationally oriented. Practical demonstrations should be incorporated that apply the general guidelines and rules of these instructions as to the specific situations in which armed law enforcement and security personnel are likely to find themselves at a particular command.

d. All law enforcement and security personnel are fully instructed in the use and safe handling of the weapons/equipment with which armed in accordance with the provisions of appropriate manuals and orders pertaining to the variety of other weapons/equipment associated with law enforcement and security duties.

e. All property or information will be specifically designated as vital or of substantial importance to the national security. Property shall be specifically designated as vital to the national security only when its loss, damage, or compromise would seriously damage the national defense mission.

f. All prisoner escorts/guards will be specifically authorized on an individual basis as to the use of deadly force to prevent the escape of a designated prisoner when it appears reasonably necessary to do so. Designation of such prisoners will be in accordance with these instructions.

Guard on Board Ship

General

The same general regulations and routine for performing guard duty and guard mounting ashore are carried out aboard naval vessels but with such modifications as may be necessary to conform to service afloat. Guard duty is performed by such personnel as the CO of the ship may direct.

The CO of the ship operates in a manner similar to the COs of shore stations with respect to the establishing and functioning of Interior Guard afloat.

The Officer of the Deck on a naval vessel performs duties with respect to the guard that are similar to those of the OOD ashore. The ship's Guard of the Day functions under and is responsible to the Officer of the Deck.

The CO of the ship prescribes such sentry posts as he deems necessary to the safe operation of the ship.

The Officer of the Deck, when necessary, gives special orders to sentries and, when such orders are of an important nature, informs the Executive Officer of the ship.

Sentries at the gangways salute all officers going on or coming off the ship, and all such sentries salute when passing or being passed by officers close aboard in boats.

Challenging by sentries at gangways or on board ship is dispensed with at the discretion of the CO of the ship.

Reliefs are posted informally by direct order for the individual to take an assigned post.

Troop Units Embarked Aboar Naval Vessels

The senior commander of troop organizations embarked on the ship is designated by higher troop unit commanders as "Commanding Officer of Troops" for that ship.

The CO of Troops is responsible for the management of discipline and efficiency of the command. The officer establishes guard details necessary for the control of Marines and equipment. These details must be in accordance with the policy of the ship and approved by the ship's CO.

All orders to troop organizations embarked aboard ship are, insofar as practicable, given through the CO of Troops. (See Navy Regulations.)

The CO of Troops details an OOD as a direct representative. The OOD supervises the guard and is responsible to see that Interior Guard regulations are carried out, ship regulations are enforced, and that special instructions and orders of the ship's CO are obeyed. The OOD also may detail Officers of the Guard when necessary.

Countersigns

The secret challenge and the secret password prescribed by the principal headquarters of a command facilitates mutual identification between sentries and persons challenged.

By Whom Authorized

If a countersign is prescribed, it is devised by the highest headquarters within a zone or area. The authority to designate a countersign may be delegated to subordinate units when necessary for their immediate use. However, these units notify higher headquarters of such action without delay. Only one countersign will be in effect within a command during a specified period.

Selecting the Countersign

The choice of words or sounds for the countersign is made with care. If possible, words are selected which are difficult for the enemy to pronounce. To minimize the possibility of an unauthorized person guessing the password, the word selected for the secret challenge must not suggest the word selected for the password (e.g., the secret challenge "atomic" suggests the password "bomb").

Using the Countersign

The initiative for use of the countersign rests with the challenging sentry. Positive recognition of all persons claiming authority to pass is the sentry's main consideration. If the sentry does not visually recognize the challenged person or party, the countersign is used to effect positive recognition. If there is any doubt of the challenged person's authority to pass, even if the password is given, the individual is detained for further action by the COG. If the sentry recognizes the challenged person or party prior to using the countersign, and there is no doubt that the person or party has authority to pass, the sentry will not use the countersign.

Mutual identification is essential. If the person challenged does not recognize the secret challenge, the password should not be given.

When a secret challenge and password are prescribed, the secret challenge is given by the sentry after the person is advanced to be recognized. The person challenged should then give the password. Both the secret challenge and the password are given in a low tone to prevent them from being heard by others. For example, a sentry observes a person approaching the post during the time for challenging. When the person is still far enough away for the sentry to take effective measures should the person rush the sentry after being challenged, the sentry commands, "Halt! Who goes there?" After receiving an answer (such as "Captain Jones, Company B, 6th Marines") indicating the person is friendly and may be authorized to pass, and the person having reached a point where the secret challenge spoken in a low tone can only be heard by the person, the sentry again commands, "Halt!"

Then the sentry gives the secret challenge in a low tone (e.g., "Snowflake"). After receiving the correct password from Captain Jones (e.g., "Rooster") and otherwise satisfying oneself that the captain is authorized to pass, the sentry says, "Advance, Captain Jones," and salutes if appropriate. If Captain Jones is one of a party challenged and is the person advanced according to established procedures, the sentry then tells Captain Jones to bring up the Marines and identify each individual before passing.

Terrorism Awareness and Counteraction

Terrorism

Terrorism is the calculated use of violence or threat of violence to attain goals that are political, religious, or ideological in nature. It involves a criminal act that is often symbolic in nature and intended to influence an audience beyond the immediate victims. Therefore, terrorists want publicity and want to take credit for their crimes.

Types of Attack

Terrorist attacks take many different forms. These include:

- Bombings.
- Arson.
- Hijacking/Vehicle thefts.
- Skyjacking/Aircraft thefts.
- Ambushes.
- Kidnappings.
- Hostage-taking.
- Robberies and Expropriations.
- Psychological Terror.
- Biological and Chemical Attack.
- Assassination.

Terrorism Counteraction

There are no purely preventative measures that can ensure 100 percent protection against terrorism. However, as Marines we must apply all known measures to protect ourselves from attack. Some common rules to follow in order to avoid terrorist attack are:

Rule 1. Vary transportation methods, routes, and times.

Rule 2. Park in well-lighted areas with multiple exits.

Rule 3. Lock unattended vehicles.

Rule 4. Report unusual activities to local security officials.

Rule 5. Avoid traveling alone.

Rule 6. Travel only on busy, well-traveled thoroughfares whenever possible.

Rule 7. Take proper security precautions at home during travel.

Rule 8. Attend periodic threat-awareness briefings and hostage-survival training.

Rule 9. Avoid establishing a pattern of attendance at certain events, locations, etc.

Rule 10. Keep a low profile; avoid calling attention to yourself.

Rule 11. Seek knowledge of the local situation and be aware of your surroundings.

Rule 12. Be sensitive to the possibility of surveillance.

Force Protection for Marines

What is force protection? Active and passive measures taken to deter and defeat threats to Marines, their family members, DOD civilians, and facilities and equipment. The following list gives a good checklist for keeping yourself and your family members safe, both in the United States and overseas.

Anti-terrorism/Force Protection Individual Protective Measures

At All Times

- Vary eating establishments.
- Alternate shopping locations.
- Do not establish any sort of pattern.
- Avoid crowded areas.
- Be especially alert exiting bars, restaurants, etc.
- Know how to use the local phone system.
- Know emergency phone numbers for police, ambulance, and hospital.
- Know location of the U.S. Embassy and other safe locations where you can find refuge or assistance.

Bomb Incidents

Be suspicious of objects found around the house, office, or vehicle.

Check mail and packages for:

- Unusual odors.
- Too much wrapping.
- Bulges, bumps, or odd shapes.
- No return or unfamiliar return address.
- Incorrect spelling or poor typing.
- Items sent "registered" or marked "personal."
- Protruding wires or strings.
- Unusually light or heavy packages.

Isolate suspect letters or packages. Do not immerse them in water. Doing so may cause them to explode.

Clear the area immediately.

Notify your chain of command.

Security While Traveling

At Airport Terminals

- Use concealed bag tags.
- Spend as little time as possible in airports.
- Pass through the airport-security checks quickly.
- Once through security, proceed to a lounge or other open area away from baggage lockers.
- If possible, sit with your back against a wall.
- Remain alert. Be a "people watcher."

At Hotel

- Do not give room number to strangers.

- Choose an inside hotel room.
- Sleep away from streetside windows.
- Leave lights on when room is vacant.
- Pull curtains.
- Arrange knock signals.
- Answer telephone "hello." Do not use name and rank.
- Look before you exit.
- If confronted, have a plan of action ready.
- Occasionally exit/enter through the rear entrance.
- Keep your room key in your possession at all times.

From Domicile to Duty
- Alternate parking places.
- Lock car when unattended.
- Look for tampering.
- Look under your auto.
- Be alert when opening door.
- Keep gas tank at least half full.
- If possible, alter routes and avoid choke points.
- Plan "escape" route as you drive.
- Watch mopeds/cycles.
- Do not pick up hitchhikers.
- Drive with windows up and doors locked.
- Remember: Remain alert.

CHAPTER 8

First Aid

First aid is the immediate treatment administered to a casualty of injury or illness before the services of a doctor or Corpsman can be obtained. Although the medical department has the finest equipment and its personnel have been trained in the most modern methods of saving lives and easing pain, there may be a time when your life or that of another Marine will depend on your knowledge of first aid. You can save a life if you know what to do and what not to do and if you act quickly and calmly. If you are injured, you can save your own life by caring for your own injuries or by directing others toward proper care. Remember, where medical help is not readily available, apply self-aid and then seek professional help or care. The basic rules for first aid given in this chapter are to help you to help yourself and your fellow Marines when it is necessary.

Your primary responsibility when in battle is to continue fighting when someone is wounded. Do not jeopardize the mission, your life, or that of others by stopping to aid a wounded Marine. By continuing to fight, you will make it possible for the Corpsman to advance with the troops and give emergency treatment. When you are on the battlefield, your first job is to fight.

You have been issued an Individual First Aid Kit (IFAK) containing simple but effective medical items. Learn the contents and use of each item in your kit, and keep it with you at all times.

As in all other matters of military technology and practice, the treatment of casualties on the battlefield, their evacuation, care in the field and removal from the battlefield have improved tremendously. This chapter identifies the basic information and tasks required of the individual Marine. Be prepared to do your part.

Tactical Combat Casualty Care

TCCC is a three stage approach to casualty management, ensuring the appropriate medical care is given at the correct time and place during combat missions.

Care Under Fire (CUF) is the care rendered by the first responder at the scene of the injury while he and the casualty are still under effective hostile fire. Available medical equipment is limited to that carried by the Marine or by the Corpsman (or service equivalent) in his aid bag.

Tactical Field Care (TFC) is the care rendered by the first responder once he and the casualty are no longer under effective hostile fire. It also applies to situations in which an injury has occurred, but there has been no hostile fire. Available medical equipment is still limited to that carried into the field by unit personnel. Time to evacuation to a medical treatment facility may vary considerably.

Tactical Evacuation Care (TACEVAC) is the care rendered once the casualty has been picked up by an aircraft, ground vehicle, or boat. Additional medical personnel and equipment that may have been pre-staged may be available in this phase of casualty management.

USMC Individual First Aid Kit

The IFAK provides the individual Marine or sailor with the right type and amount of consumable medical supplies to perform self and buddy aid. It shall also provide the Marines and sailors the capability to treat non-potable water for personal consumption. Marines and other U.S. military personnel carry the IFAK at all times for individual use. When caring for another person, be sure to use that person's kit, reserving your own for possible later use. Additional kits may be stowed in vehicles, boats, and aircraft for use as needed. The contents of the USMC IFAK (See Figure 8-1) are:
- Individual Equipment Pouch, 1 each.
- Pouch, Tourniquet: Combat Application Tourniquet (C.A.T.) tourniquet pouch, 2 each.
- Insert, Minor First Aid Kit, 1 each.

Minor First Aid Kit Components:
- Bacitracin Antibiotic Ointment 0.9 gram, 8 each.
- Bandage, adhesive, 3/4" by 3," 10 each.
- Bandage, adhesive, 2" by 4," 5 each.
- Card, casualty response, Two-side.
- Sharpie, Mini Black.
- Tablets, water purification chlorine, Micropur MP1 strip, 10 tabs.

Trauma Kit Components:
- Bandage, Gauze, cotton rolled 7/8" by 2," 1 each.
- Chest Wound Kit, Sterile.

Figure 8-1. USMC IFAK.

- Dressing, Burn, First Aid 45" by 45" by 63."
- Dressing, compression: flat-folded H-bandage; 8" by 10" abdominal pad, 1 each.
- Dressing, Hemostatic: combat gauze XL; 6.5" by 5" by 11."
- Dressing, Burn, First Aid: burntec hydrogel burn dressing; 4" by 6," 1 each.
- Glove, Patient, Examining: black talon exam gloves.
- Shield, Eye, Surgical: combination eye garter.
- Tape, Combat Medic Reinforced, 2" by 100."
- Tourniquet, Nonpneumatic, 2 each.

Care Under Fire Guidelines

You cannot begin to apply the lifesaving steps until you win the firefight at hand. Prosecuting the mission and caring for the casualties may be in direct conflict. What is best for the casualty may NOT be what is best for the mission. Suppression of hostile fire will minimize the risk of both new casualties and additional injuries to the existing casualties. The firepower contributed by medical personnel and the casualties themselves may be essential to tactical fire superiority. Steps for CUF are:

Step 1. Return fire and take cover.

Step 2. Direct or expect casualty to remain engaged as a combatant if appropriate.

Step 3. Direct casualty to move to cover and apply self-aid if able.

Step 4. Try to keep the casualty from sustaining additional wounds.

Step 5. Casualties should be extricated from burning vehicles or buildings and moved to relative safety. Do what is necessary to stop the burning process.

Step 6. Stop **life-threatening** external hemorrhage if tactically feasible:

- Direct casualty to control hemorrhage by self-aid if able.

- Use limb tourniquet for extremity hemorrhage.

- Apply the limb tourniquet clearly proximal to (closer to the body than) the bleeding site(s). If the site of the life threatening bleeding is not readily apparent, place the tourniquet "high and tight" (as proximal as possible) on the injured limb and move the casualty to cover.

Step 7. Move the casualty to cover if not already done.

Step 8. Airway management is generally best deferred until the TFC phase.

In combat, the three preventable causes of death on the battlefield are life-threatening extremity bleeding, a collapsed lung from a chest wound (tension pneumothorax), and obstruction of the airway. Since life-threatening bleeding from an extremity is the number one preventable cause of death, every combatant must train to apply tourniquets quickly, if the tactical situation permits. The Combat Application Tourniquet™ (C.A.T.) is a small, lightweight tourniquet that uses a windlass rod to occlude arterial blood flow in an extremity that can be applied rapidly on oneself or to another casualty. (See Figure 8-2.) Do not put a tourniquet directly over the knee or elbow and do not put a tourniquet directly over a holster or a cargo pocket that contains bulky items. Ensure

that the tourniquet is not covered by clothing or objects; it should be clearly seen by anyone assuming the responsibility of care for the casualty. Non-life-threatening bleeding should be ignored until the TFC phase. If in doubt, treat the bleeding and reassess when out of harm's way.

One-Handed C.A.T Tourniquet Application

Step 1. Insert the injured limb through the loop in the band and position tourniquet 2–3" above the bleeding site. If the most proximal bleeding site is not readily identifiable, place the tourniquet as high as possible on the limb.

Step 2. Pull band TIGHTLY and fasten it back on itself all the way around the limb, but not over the rod clips. Band should be tight enough that tips of three fingers cannot slide between the band and the limb. If the tips of three fingers slide under band, retighten, and resecure.

Step 3. Twist the rod until bleeding has stopped.

Step 4. Snap the rod inside a clip to lock it in place. Check for bleeding and distal pulse to see if bleeding has stopped. If bleeding is not controlled consider tightening the tourniquet or applying a second tourniquet above and side-by-side to the first. Reassess.

Step 5. Route the band over the rod and between the clips. Secure with the grey securing strap. Record time of application.

Figure 8-2. The Combat Application Tourniquet™.

Two-Handed C.A.T. Tourniquet Application

Step 1. Route the band around the limb, pass the red tip through the slit of the buckle, and position tourniquet 2–3" above the bleeding site. If the most proximal bleeding site is not readily identifiable, place the tourniquet as high as possible on the limb.

Step 2 to 5. Follow one-handed C.A.T. Tourniquet application instructions.

Tactical Field Care Guidelines

Distinguished from CUF by (1) a reduced level of hazard from hostile fire and (2) more time available to provide care based on the tactical situation. Time to evacuation may vary from minutes to hours to days. The sequence of priorities in TFC assumes that any obvious life-threatening bleeding has been addressed in the CUF phase. If this is not the case—address the massive bleeding first. Reassess the effectiveness of previous efforts to control bleeding. Unconscious casualties should have their airways opened using the jaw thrust technique (see Figure 8-3) with the casualty flat on the back. This simple maneuver moves the tongue, which frequently proves to be the primary obstruction. The jaw thrust is best for cases where head, neck, or facial trauma is suspected. From a position over the head of the casualty, place a thumb on each cheekbone, extending the forefinger and middle fingers along the jaw. Lift the jaw so that it is thrust forward. Steps for TFC are:

Step 1. Establish a security perimeter in accordance with unit tactical standard operating procedures and/or battle drills. Maintain tactical awareness.

Step 2. Casualties with an altered mental status should have weapons and communications equipment taken away immediately.

a. Altered mental status refers to an abnormal responsiveness, awareness, orientation, or behavior.

Figure 8-3. Jaw thrust technique.

b. It can affect speech, thought, mobility, memory, attention span, or alertness. It can range from slight confusion to complete unresponsiveness (coma).

c. An armed combatant with an altered mental status may use his weapons inappropriately. Anyone exhibiting altered state of consciousness must be relieved of weapons and explosives before proceeding with TFC.

d. Possible causes of altered mental status include Traumatic Brain Injury (TBI), shock, hypoxia, and pain medications.

Step 3. Massive Hemorrhage. Assess for unrecognized hemorrhage and control all sources of bleeding.

a. If not already done, use a recommended limb tourniquet to control life-threatening external hemorrhage on the arms or legs or for any traumatic amputation.

b. Apply directly to the skin 2–3" above the bleeding site.

c. If bleeding is not controlled with the first tourniquet, apply a second tourniquet side-by-side with the first.

d. For compressible (external) hemorrhage that is not on the arms or legs, use Combat Gauze as the hemostatic dressing of choice. It can adjust to any size

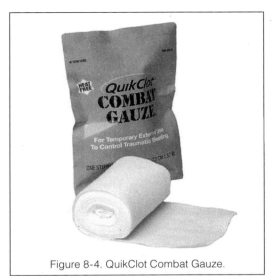
Figure 8-4. QuikClot Combat Gauze.

or shape wound, including penetrating wounds. (See Figure 8-4.)

- Expose injury by opening or cutting away clothing.
- Remove excess blood from wound while preserving any clots that may have formed, if possible.
- Locate the source of the most active bleeding.
- Remove Combat Gauze from package and pack it tightly into the wound directly over the site of the most active bleeding. (More than one roll of Combat Gauze may be required to control the bleeding). Combat Gauze may be re-packed or adjusted in the wound to ensure proper placement.
- Apply direct pressure quickly with enough force to stop the bleeding and hold direct pressure for at least 3 minutes.
- Reassess for bleeding control. Once applied, Combat Gauze is not to be removed (except by proper medical authority). If bleeding continues, reinforce with another roll of Combat Gauze and hold pressure.
- Leave the gauze in place and secure with a trauma dressing.

- Document, place empty package near wound, and transport casualty.

Step 4. Airway Management.

a. Conscious casualty with no airway problem identified:
- no airway intervention required.

b. Unconscious casualty without airway obstruction:
- Chin lift or jaw thrust maneuver.
- Nasopharyngeal airway, if available.
- Place casualty in recovery position.

c. Casualty with airway obstruction or impending airway obstruction:
- Allow a conscious casualty to assume any position that best protects the airway, to include sitting up.
- Clear the airway of obvious foreign material from the mouth and throat cavity. Blood or vomit accumulations may be wiped away.
- Chin lift or jaw thrust maneuver.
- Nasopharyngeal airway, if available.
- Place an unconscious casualty in the recovery position.
- If the previous measures are unsuccessful, refer to medical support immediately.

d. Cervical spine stabilization is not necessary for casualties who have sustained only penetrating trauma.

e. Always remember that the casualty's airway status may change over time and requires frequent reassessment.

Step 5. Respiration/Breathing.

a. In a casualty with progressive respiratory distress and known or suspected torso trauma, consider a tension pneumothorax and refer to a combat lifesaver or medical support as soon as possible.

b. All open and/or sucking chest wounds should be treated by immediately applying a chest seal from the IFAK to cover the defect. If a vented chest seal is not available, use a non-vented chest seal or any occlusive dressing taped on all four sides. Encourage the casualty to lie on the injured side if possible. Monitor the casualty for respiratory distress. If it develops, you should suspect a tension pneumothorax. Treat this by burping or temporarily removing the dressing. If that does not relieve the respiratory distress, refer to medical support.

Step 6. Circulation/Bleeding.

    a. Reassess prior tourniquet application:

    - Expose the wound and determine if a tourniquet is needed; if bleeding is not controlled, then tighten tourniquet if possible.

    - Any tourniquet that was applied over the casualty's uniform should be replaced with one applied directly to the skin, 2–3" above the bleeding site.

    - If the first tourniquet does not control bleeding after tightening, then add a second tourniquet side-by-side with the first.

    - Expose and clearly mark all tourniquets with time of application. Use a permanent marker to mark on the tourniquet and the casualty card.

    b. Always have medical personnel evaluate every tourniquet placed on a casualty to see if it is really needed, and if so, if it is working effectively!

Step 7. Assess for hemorrhagic shock (altered mental status in the absence of brain injury and/or weak or absent radial pulse).

    a. If the casualty is not in shock:

    - No IV fluids are immediately necessary.

    - Fluids by mouth are permissible if the casualty is conscious and can swallow.

    - Reassess the casualty frequently for the onset of shock.

    b. If the casualty is in shock or develops shock, refer to medical support. The early signs of shock: restlessness, thirst, pale-skin, rapid heartbeat; may be excited or may be calm and appear very tired; may be sweating even though the skin feels cool. Advanced signs of shock: may breathe in small, fast breaths or gasp even when the airway is clear; may stare vacantly into space; skin may have a blotchy or bluish appearance, especially around the lips.

    - Maintain adequate respiration: ensure upper airway remains clear; position the body to ensure adequate drainage of any obstruction.

    - Loosen constrictive clothing: neck and waist and at other areas where it tends to bind the casualty. Loosen but do not remove shoes. Remove constrictive jewelry.

    - Reassure the casualty: take charge, remain calm, self-confident, and gentle. If the casualty asks questions regarding the seriousness of the injury, explain that a medical officer will have to determine the extent of injury. Ill-timed or erroneous information can increase a casualty's anxiety.

    - Splint fractures: if the casualty has a fracture, apply a splint.

    - Position the casualty: unless contraindicated, most casualties should be placed in the Recovery Position. Roll the casualty on to one side resting the side of the face on the hand. Bend the upper leg at the knee so the casualty's body weight rests on the knee.

    - Keep casualty warm: aggressively treat for hypothermia.

    - Any casualty who has lost a lot of blood or who is in shock will need to be kept warm, regardless of the weather.

    - Relieve pain: proper dressing and bandaging of wounds, splinting of fractures, and positioning of a casualty are best methods for relieving pain.

Step 8. Prevention of hypothermia.

    a. Minimize the casualty's exposure to the elements. Keep protective gear on or with the casualty if feasible.

    b. Replace wet clothing with dry if possible. Get the casualty onto an insulated surface as soon as possible.

    c. Apply the Ready-Heat Blanket from the Hypothermia Prevention and Management Kit (HPMK) to the casualty's torso (not directly on the skin) and cover the casualty with the Heat-Reflective Shell (HRS).

d. If an HPMK is not available, the combination of Blizzard Survival Blanket and Ready-Heat blanket may be used.

e. If items mentioned above are not available, use dry blankets, poncho liners, sleeping bags, or anything to retain heat and keep the casualty dry.

Step 9. If a penetrating eye injury is noted or suspected:

a. Perform a rapid field test of visual acuity (How many fingers held up? Able to read writing from a piece of paper?

b. Cover the eye with a rigid eye shield (NOT a pressure patch) ensuring the foreign body is not touched.

c. Ensure that the 400 mg moxifloxacin tablet in the combat pill pack is taken by mouth if the casualty can swallow. Otherwise, refer to medical support for IV or IM antibiotics.

Step 10. Inspect and dress known wounds.

a. Any wound should be treated with antibiotics without delay.

b. Refer all casualties with combat wounds to medical support for the appropriate medication to prevent the development of infection.

c. All wounds should be kept as clean and dry as possible.

d. Seek further medical attention for wounds that show a delay in healing or signs of infection.

Step 11. Check for additional wounds.

Step 12. Pain relief on the battlefield:

a. For mild to moderate pain that will not keep the casualty out of the fight:
- Tactical Combat Casualty Care (TCCC) Combat pill pack: Tylenol
- 500-mg bilayer caplet, 2 by mouth every 8 hours.
- Meloxicam - 15 mg by mouth once a day.

b. If the casualty's pain is severe enough to interfere with his ability to fight, refer to medical support for treatment.

Step 13. Splint fractures and recheck pulses.

a. Pulse, motor and sensory checks before and after splinting.

b. Use rigid or bulky materials; try to pad or wrap if using rigid splint. Splint in position found; do not try to reset fracture.

c. Immobilize one joint above and below the fracture with the splint.

d. Secure splint with ace wrap, cravats, belts, duct tape.

e. Try to splint before moving the casualty.

Step 14. Antibiotics: recommended for all open combat wounds.

a. If the casualty can swallow: Moxifloxacin, 400 mg by mouth once a day.

b. If the casualty cannot swallow (shock, unconsciousness): refer to medical support for treatment.

Step 15. Burns.

a. Facial burns, especially those that occur in closed spaces, may be associated with toxic or thermal injury to the airways and lungs. Aggressively monitor the casualty's airway status and refer to medical support as soon as possible.

b. Cover the burn area with sterile dressings from IFAK. For extensive burns (greater than 20% of total body surface area), keep patient covered and warm to protect the burned areas and prevent hypothermia.

c. Do not pull clothes away from the burned area. Instead, cut or tear the clothes and gently lift them off. Do not try to remove pieces of cloth that stick to the skin.

d. Never break blisters or touch the burn.

e. Refer any casualty with extensive or severe burns to medical support as soon as possible.

Step 16. Communication.

a. Communicate with the casualty if possible.

b. Communicate with tactical leadership ASAP and throughout treatment. Provide casualty status and evacuation requirements.

c. Communicate with the evacuation system to arrange TACEVAC.

d. Communicate with medical personnel on evacuation assets and relay mechanism of injury, injuries sustained, signs/symptoms, and treatments rendered.

Step 17. Documentation.

a. Document clinical assessments, treatments rendered, and changes in the casualty's status on a TCCC Casualty Card (DD Form 1380).

b. Forward this information with the casualty to the next level of care.

Step 18. Cardiopulmonary resuscitation (CPR): Resuscitation on the battlefield for casualties of blast or penetrating trauma who have no pulse, no ventilations, and no other signs of life will not be successful and should not be attempted. However, casualties with torso trauma or polytrauma who have no pulse or respirations during TFC should have bilateral needle decompression performed to ensure they do not have a tension pneumothorax prior to discontinuation of care. Seek assistance from medical personnel.

Step 19. Prepare for evacuation.

a. Complete and secure the TCCC Card (DD 1380) to the casualty.

b. Secure all loose ends of bandages and wraps.

c. Secure hypothermia prevention wraps/blankets/straps.

d. Secure litter straps as required. Consider additional padding for long evacuations.

e. Provide instructions to ambulatory patients as needed.

f. Stage casualties for evacuation in accordance with unit standard operating procedures.

g. Maintain security at the evacuation point in accordance with unit standard operating procedures.

Splints

Fractures. A fracture is a broken bone. One or more of the following signs may be present:

- Tenderness over the injury.
- Pain with movement.
- Inability to move injured part.
- Deformed shape.
- Swelling and discoloration.

If you are not sure, treat the injury as a fracture. Fractures should be immobilized to prevent further injury, to reduce pain, and to help reduce shock. Do not attempt to reset a fracture. All fractures of long bones should be splinted "where they lie" before movement or transportation of any kind is attempted.

There are two kinds of fractures discussed in this *Guidebook*: (1) closed fracture Figure 8-5: a break in the bone with skin remaining intact and (2) open fracture Figure 8-6: a broken bone that breaks the overlying skin, the bone may protrude through the skin. (See Figure 8-5 and Figure 8-6.)

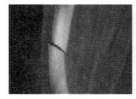 

Figure 8-5. Closed fracture. Figure 8-6. Open fracture.

Open fractures can be caused by a broken bone piercing the skin or by a bullet, which pierces the flesh and breaks the bone. Standard leg and arm splints are the most desirable forms of splints when available and when trained personnel are available for their application. However, first aid in the field may require you to improvise with splints from any material that is handy.

Be careful. Handle the person's body with the greatest care. Rough or careless handling causes pain and increases the likelihood of shock. The cracked ends of the bone are razor sharp and can cut through muscle, blood vessels, nerves and skin. Do not move a person with a fracture unless absolutely necessary. If you must, be gentle and keep the fractured part from moving. If there is a wound with a fracture, treat by applying pressure and a clean dressing as with any other wound.

Broken leg or hip. The quickest way to splint a broken leg is to tie it to the uninjured leg. Tie the legs together in at least two places, above and below the break. You can use a belt, cartridge belt, strips of cloth or handkerchiefs tied together. Do not move a person with a broken leg unless there are safety concerns. Grasp the casualty by the shoulders and pull in a straight line. Do not roll or move the body sideways.

Splints for broken leg, thigh, or hip (Figure 8-7). If you have time, you can make a good splint for the lower limb by using two long sticks or poles. Roll the sticks into a folded blanket from both sides. This forms a trough in which the leg rests. Secure the splints to the body at several places. For fractures of the lower leg, splints should extend from above the knee to below the foot. If the thigh or hip is broken, the inside splint should extend to the crotch and the outside splint should extend to the armpit. Always be sure that the ends of the sticks are well padded.

Figure 8-7. Splint for a broken leg or thigh (upper left); splint for arm fracture where elbow can't be bent (upper right); splint for fracture of lower arm (lower left); splint for fracture of upper arm (lower right).

Splint for a broken arm (Figure 8-7). When possible, keep a broken arm from moving by support with splints. Splints should extend from the joint below to the joint above

the fracture. Temporary splints are made from boards, branches, bayonets, scabbards, etc. Always pad splints with soft material to protect the limb from pressure and rubbing. Secure splints to the body part at several places above and below the fracture but not so tightly as to stop the flow of blood. It is helpful to apply two splints, one on either side of the limb. If an injured elbow is bent, do not try to straighten it. If straight, do not bend it.

Injured arm or shoulder. A sling is the quickest way to support a fractured arm or shoulder, a sprained arm, or an arm with a painful injury. Use a sling only after any fracture has been splinted.

Broken back. It is often impossible to determine if a person has a broken back. Be suspicious of any injury, especially if the back has been struck sharply or bent or if the person has fallen. The sharp bone fragments may cut the spinal cord if they are moved. This would cause permanent paralysis of the body and the legs, and possibly death.

Do not move the casualty with a possible broken back except in extreme emergency and then only on a hard board, door, or stretcher. Do not raise the head. Do not twist the neck or back.

Broken neck. Handling a broken neck is extremely dangerous. Bone fragments may cut the spinal cord just as in a broken back. Moving the head or neck may cause death. Keep

Figure 8-8. Protection for broken neck.

the head and neck straight and motionless by placing large stones or packs on each side of the head to support it. (See Figure 8-8 on previous page.)

Place a rolled blanket around the head and neck for support and padding, but do not place anything under the neck. If the casualty must be moved, get help. One person supports the casualty's head and keeps it in line with the body while others lift. Put the casualty on a hard stretcher or board. Keep the casualty face up.

Remember that it is always better to be on the safe side. Splint it if there is any question about a broken bone.

Tactical Evacuation Care Guidelines

Normally, TACEVAC would be managed by a medical person. It is possible that casualty care during evacuation may fall to you, especially in an immature theater or on a remote operation. If this happens, continue to care for casualties as you have been trained.

1. The care you can give a casualty during evacuation is the same as TFC.

2. For casualties with chest and abdominal trauma watch closely for tension pneumothorax, especially if evacuating by air or crossing mountainous terrain.

3. Watch for renewed bleeding from any wound. If it occurs, control it.

4. Keep the casualty warm.

5. Document the care you give.

6. Continue to reassess the casualty and keep the casualty warm.

Treat a Heat Injury

There are three types of heat injury: heat cramps, heat exhaustion, and heatstroke. Individual risk factors that can lead to a heat injury include poor fitness, large body mass, minor illness, drugs (cold and allergy, blood pressure), supplements, alcohol use, prior heat injury, skin disorders, and age >40. Prevention of heat-related casualties requires careful planning that recognizes the limits of tolerance for heat exposure according to the acclimatization, physical conditioning, and tactical environment of all hands. Of key importance, leaders at all levels must provide for adequate living and working conditions and personal hygiene. Leaders must pay close attention to the need for food and beverages to replenish electrolytes and water in the body. When operating in the field or working in garrison, pay attention to changing conditions and the wet bulb globe temperature, take frequent breaks, and do not overexert. Drink several cups of water or juice before beginning work, add fluid breaks frequently, and resume hydration after work or operations are complete. Always work or operate with partners.

Heat Cramps

Heat cramps are most likely related to electrolyte imbalance (sodium, potassium, calcium, and magnesium). Sweating profusely may result in a condition called hyponatremia (low-sodium).

Symptoms include profuse sweating and/or painful muscle spasms (legs, arms, abdomen). Skin usually is moist, pale and warm. Core temperature may be normal or slightly elevated.

Treatment:
• Rest in a cool environment; loosen uniform or clothing; remove head gear.
• Give casualty water, sports drink, or other drinks with salt.
• Massage and stretch affected muscles.
• If cramps are severe, take the casualty to medical facility.

Heat Exhaustion

Heat exhaustion is caused by excessive body heat overloading the body-control mechanisms. It results in excessive loss of body water and salt through prolonged sweating.

Symptoms include headache, fatigue, excessive sweating, dizziness, nausea/vomiting, weak and rapid pulse, normal to elevated temperature, or dilated pupils. The skin is pale, cool, moist, and clammy.

Treatment:

- Lay the casualty on their back in a cool, shaded area and loosen the clothing.
- If conscious, give the casualty cool water to sip–2 quarts over 60 minutes. Replace fluids and salt.
- Actively cool casualty by fanning and wetting the head and upper torso with water.
- Handle as a litter case and evacuate to medical facility as soon as possible.

Heatstroke

Heatstroke is caused by a failure of the body's heat-regulating mechanism that causes the body to become overheated. Sometimes called "sunstroke." This is a true medical emergency!

Symptoms include: sweating may cease, hot and dry skin, headache, dizziness, vomiting, fast pulse, mental confusion, combative, collapsed, or unconsciousness. The face may appear flushed or red.

Treatment:

- Rapid and immediate cooling; remove clothing; remove head gear.
- Wet the casualty, wrap in cool, wet/iced sheets and fan vigorously. Stop cooling if casualty starts shivering.
- Treat for shock as necessary, once temperature is lowered.
- Call for transport immediately.

Treat a Cold Injury

When the body is subject to severely cold temperatures, blood vessels constrict and body heat is gradually lost. As body temperature drops, tissues are easily damaged or destroyed.

All cold injuries are similar, varying only in degree of tissue injury. Cold injuries are classified into three categories: hypothermia, cold/dry (freezing), and cold/wet (nonfreezing). Hypothermia is defined as core body cooling below 95° F. Cold/dry and cold/wet injuries are localized to extremities and exposed skin. Cold/dry injury causes freezing of cells and tissues and is known as frostbite. Cold/wet injury is classified as nonfreezing cold injury and includes chilblain and trench foot. It is not unusual for both hypothermia and local cold injuries to occur simultaneously. Cold stress is imposed by the combination of environmental, mission, and individual risk factors. Environmental risk factors include temperature, wind, rain, immersion, and altitude. Mission risk factors include the work intensity; duration of cold exposure; and the availability of adequate shelter, clothing, and food. Individual risk factors include physical fitness, body composition, fatigue, race, gender, and health (including prior history of cold injury, use of medications, alcohol, nicotine, drugs of abuse, and poor nutrition).

Hypothermia

Defined as a core temperature below 95° F (35° C).

Symptoms include shivering, followed by a feeling of sleepiness, slurred speech, unsteady gait, confusion, and behavior change. Shivering may cease, unconsciousness may follow. Shock becomes evident as the casualty's eyes become glassy, respiration becomes slow and shallow and the pulse becomes weak or absent. Early signs are "the umbles" (stumbles, mumbles, fumbles, grumbles).

Treatment:

- Observe breathing and heartbeat.
- Warm the casualty as soon as possible. It may be necessary to treat other injuries before the casualty can be moved to a warmer place.
- Replace wet or frozen clothing, cover head.
- If the casualty is in a warm place and is conscious, the most effective method of warming is immersion in a tub of warm water.
- If a tub is not available, apply external heat. Body heat from the rescuers, called "buddy warming," is also effective. Placing the casualty under a blanket or in a sleeping bag is not sufficient. (Do not place artificial heat next to bare skin.)
- If the casualty is conscious, give warm liquids to drink. (Never give alcoholic

beverages or allow the casualty to smoke.)

• Dry thoroughly if water is used to rewarm the casualty. Blot skin dry; do not rub.

• As soon as possible, transfer the casualty to a medical facility, keeping the body warm en route.

Nonfreezing Cold Injury

Chilblains (also known as pernio or kibe). Superficial cold injury typically occurring after 1 to 5 hours in cold-wet conditions, at temperatures below 50° F (16° C). Small lesions develop on skin that are swollen, tender, itchy, and painful. Rewarming results in skin becoming inflamed, red and hot to the touch, swollen, and itching or burning sensation that may last for several hours after exposure.

Trench foot. Cold injury sustained by tissues exposed to cold-wet conditions for prolonged periods of time. It can occur in any tissue but is most common in the foot. It initially appears as a swollen, edematous foot with a feeling of numbness. The initial color is red but soon becomes pale and bluish if the injury is more severe. Peripheral pulses are hard to detect. Trench foot is accompanied by aches, increased pain sensitivity, and infections.

Treatment for nonfreezing cold injury:

• Prevent further exposure.
• Remove wet shoes, socks, and gloves.
• Remove constrictive clothing.
• Expose the affected area to warm, dry air. Wash and dry extremities gently.
• Keep the casualty warm, elevate limbs, and cover with layers of loose, warm, dry clothing.
• Do not rupture blisters or apply salves and ointments.
• If the skin is broken, gently wrap with a sterile sheet to protect the sensitive tissue from pressure and additional injury.
• Transport to a medical facility as soon as possible.

Frostbite

Frostbite occurs when the tissue temperature falls below 32° F. Depending upon the temperature, altitude, and wind speed, the exposure time necessary to produce frostbite varies from a few minutes to several hours. The areas commonly affected are the face and extremities.

Frostbite is classified with four degrees of injury based upon initial indications after freezing and rewarming:

• *First-degree frostbite ("frostnip").* Usually produced by a short-duration exposure to cold air or contact with a cold object. The skin appears white or has yellowish plaque at the site of injury, no blister or tissue loss, and feels numb. Skin thaws quickly, becoming red with surrounding swelling. Healing occurs in seven to 10 days.

• *Second-degree frostbite.* Involves the surface and underlying layer of skin; initially appearing similar to first-degree injury, with deeper frozen tissues. Thawing is rapid but results in a superficial blister with clear fluid more than several hours after thawing; no permanent loss of tissue. Healing occurs in three to four weeks.

• *Third-degree frostbite.* Includes all layers of skin and subcutaneous tissue. Frozen skin is stiff with restricted mobility. After tissue thaws, skin swells rapidly and blood-filled blister develop. The swelling restricts mobility, and skin loss occurs slowly through sloughing. Healing is slow, may have permanent tissue loss.

• *Fourth-degree frostbite.* Frozen tissue including full thickness, underlying tissues, and bones. No mobility when frozen. Thawing restores passive mobility, but muscle function is lost. Poor skin reperfusion after thawing, no blisters or swelling develops. Early signs of dead tissue are present, injury evolves slowly over weeks resulting in sloughing and auto amputation.

Treatment: minor frostbite.

• Bring the casualty indoors, if possible.
• Warm hands by placing them under the arm pit, against the abdomen or between the legs.
• Warm feet by placing in the arm pit or against the abdomen of a buddy.

- Gradually rewarm the body to normal temperature.

Treatment: severe frostbite.
- Move to a warm shelter; prevent hypothermia.
- Cover with loose, sterile dressing; non-compressive, non-adhesive.
- Do not allow walking on affected feet. If walking is required, do not thaw the extremity prior to walking.
- Do not give alcohol or cigarettes because of their vasoconstrictive properties.
- Separate fingers and toes with gauze.
- Do not drain blisters.
- Splint and elevate affected limbs to reduce swelling.
- Protect fragile tissues during transport.
- Avoid excessive heat—casualty unable to determine if temperature is too hot.
- Do not rub the affected tissue.
- Prevent thawing and refreezing of tissue.
- Provide early transport to medical facility.

Preventing Cold Injuries

- Risk factors: fatigue, dehydration, malnutrition, lack of experience in cold weather, wind chill, female, black race, and tobacco users.
- Seek shelter as soon as possible.
- Avoid dehydration; avoid alcoholic beverages.
- Stay calm; avoid touching metal; do not lie or sleep directly on snow.
- Use protective clothing; sleeping bags; stay as dry as possible.
- Move fingers and toes and face or exercise, especially with a partner.
- Keep clothing, gloves and boots loose for circulation.
- Remain alert for signs of frostbite, such as numbness, tingling, skin discoloration.
- Engage in training exercises to provide practical experience.

Treat a Snake, Insect or Animal Bite

Poisonous snakes

Poisonous snakes are found throughout the world, primarily in the tropics and temperate regions. Within the United States there are four kinds: rattlesnakes, copperheads, moccasins, and coral snakes. Poison is injected from the venom sacs through grooved or hollow fangs that, depending on the species, are either long or short. The venoms of different snakes cause different effects. Pit viper venom destroys the tissues into which it is injected and destroys blood cells. The cobra, adder, and coral snakes inject powerful venoms that affect the central nervous system (neurotoxins), causing respiratory paralysis. Sea snakes have venom that has both effects. The most definitive care for envenomation is anti-venom.

Treatment: In treating snakebites, the aim is to reduce circulation of blood through the bite area, delay absorption of venom, prevent aggravation of the local wound, maintain vital signs, and transport as soon as possible to the care of medical personnel. First aid in most instances will be mainly supportive.
- Locate the bite site; if on hands or feet, remove any watches, rings, bands, or other constricting devices.
- Place the limb at a neutral level in relation to the casualty's heart.
- Leave the fang marks exposed.
- Apply a splint, immobilizing the limb.
- Check pulse and respirations frequently.
- Calm and reassure the casualty, who often will be anxious. Keep the casualty lying down, quiet, and warm. The casualty should not be given alcohol or any other stimulant to drink.
- Transport immediately.
    - Do NOT cut or incise the bite site.
    - Do NOT apply ice or heat to the bite site.
    - Do NOT apply oral (mouth) suction.
    - Do NOT remove dressings or elastic wrap.

- Do NOT try to kill the snake for identification as this could lead to more injuries. Consider taking a picture from at least 6 feet away.

- Do NOT allow the casualty to eat or drink anything.

Insect Bite

The sources of insect bites remain wide and varied: bee, wasp, and ant stings; centipede, millipede and caterpillar bites; black widow and brown recluse spider bites; scorpion and sea animal stings.

Treatment: Insect bites often cause one or more itchy and sometimes painful red bumps. A small hole often is in the middle of the bite, perhaps with the end of the stinger sticking out. Apart from this local irritation, a bite is usually not dangerous provided the casualty is not allergic to insect bites. Bee and wasp stings are more likely to cause allergic reactions than other kinds of insect bites.

• Remove the stinger by scraping across the skin with a credit card, knife blade, or similar object. Do not use tweezers to grasp the stinger, this only injects the remaining venom into the casualty. Do not attempt to press out the stinger as this will only increase the poison spread under the skin.

• Immediately after the casualty has been stung, wash the bite with soap and water, then cool the skin with ice, water, or a cool cloth. Relax the affected area and if possible elevate it to prevent excessive swelling.

• If necessary, use a painkilling cream or gel or an antihistamine to soothe the itch. If the casualty is allergic to insect bites, call for medical assistance immediately and treat for shock.

• Anyone requiring medical treatment or who simply feels unwell following a bite or sting should be relieved of all duties, if the tactical situation permits.

Sea Animals

A number of sea animals are capable of inflicting very painful wounds by biting, stinging, or puncturing. Except under rare circumstances, stings and puncture wounds are not fatal. Major wounds from sharks, barracuda, moray eels, and alligators should be treated initially by controlling the bleeding.

Animal Bites

Apart from treatment of wounds and bleeding, animal bites include the threat of rabies. Rabies is carried by a number of animals in the wilderness, including skunks, raccoons, foxes, and bats. Assume that any animal that has bitten a person is rabid.

Treatment:

• Move away from the animal and establish security to prevent additional bites.

• Clean the wound thoroughly and aggressively with soap or iodine solution.

• Keep the wound open. Do not attempt to close it with closure strips or butterfly bandages.

• Dress and bandage the wound.

• Keep the patient well hydrated.

• Monitor carefully for infection.

• Evacuate immediately whether or not you believe the animal was rabid.

Other First Aid Measures

Belly wound. Do not give food or water because anything oral will pass through the intestine and spread germs through the belly. Do not replace protruding organs. Cover the protruding organs with a loose, clean, wet bandage. Pour clean water from a canteen on the bandage prior to applying it. Cover the wound with a sterile dressing and fasten securely. Treat for shock.

Jaw wounds. Wounds of the face and neck need special treatment to avoid choking on blood. Bleeding from the face and neck is usually severe because of the many blood vessels. Allow casualty to be in position of comfort. Stop the bleeding by applying pressure with a sterile dressing. Apply a dressing to protect the wound. If the jaw is broken, tie the bandage under the chin and over the head to provide support. Make sure you do not prevent the blood from draining out of the mouth. To prevent choking on blood, the person may sit up with his head held forward and down, or he may lie on his back with the head turned to one side or on his side. These positions will allow the blood to drain from the mouth instead of going down the windpipe. Treat for shock.

Electrical shock. Electrical shock from contact with a "live" wire occurs frequently. Being struck by lightning is not as common. Do not place yourself in danger by touching an electrocuted casualty while the power is on. Turn off the power at its source; at home, the switch is usually near the fuse box. In case of high-voltage electrocution, such as that caused by fallen power lines, immediately notify the appropriate authorities (such as military or civilian engineers). All materials will conduct electricity if the voltage is high enough, so do not enter the area around the casualty or try to remove wires or other materials with any object, including wooden ones, until the power has been turned off by knowledgeable personnel.

In the event that you verify high voltage is not present, you may use a dry wooden pole, dry clothing, dry rope, or some other material that will not conduct electricity, to remove the person from the wire or the wire from the person.

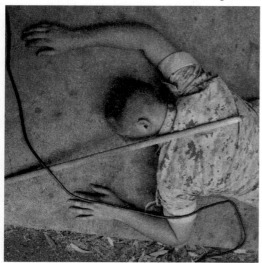

Figure 8-9. Removing an electrical wire from electric shock victim.

If a pole is not handy, simply drag the patient off the wire by means of a loop of dry clothing. Do NOT touch the wire or the person with your bare hands, or you will be shocked also. (See Figure 8-9.)

It is important to have the patient seen by a doctor or medical personnel. All casualties of electric shock require medical assessment because the extent of injury may not be apparent. Until you obtain medical aid, keep the patient quiet and calm.

Carbon monoxide poisoning. Carbon monoxide has no odor and kills without warning. Symptoms include: dizziness, headache, ringing (noise) in ears, and throbbing in temples. Skin, lips, and nail beds are often bright red. These symptoms occur rapidly and in quick succession. Poisoning from this gas occurs most often from breathing motor vehicle exhaust gas. This happens frequently from running an engine with the garage doors closed or from sitting in a vehicle with the windows closed and the motor running. Faulty mufflers are also a major cause of carbon monoxide poisoning. The same gas is formed by stoves in poorly ventilated shelters, where it is equally dangerous. If someone is overcome by carbon monoxide, move the casualty into fresh air immediately. Commence mouth-to-mouth resuscitation efforts, if indicated.

Transportation of the Sick and Wounded

Knowing how to move seriously injured persons is one of the most important parts of first aid. Careless or rough handling not only may increase the seriousness of an injury but may even result in death. Unless there is a good reason for moving an injured person immediately, do not transport until a litter or ambulance is available. Sometimes, when the situation is urgent and you know that no medical facilities are available, you will have to move the casualty yourself. Always give necessary first aid before attempting to move a person who is wounded. If the casualty has a broken bone, never attempt to move until you have splinted the bone.

Improvised litters. Using a litter not only makes it easier to carry the casualty but also makes the journey safer and more comfortable. If the distance is long or if the person has a fractured leg, hip, back or skull, the casualty should only be moved on a litter. A litter can be improvised from many different things (litter bed: blanket, shelter half, tarpaulin, or other material; strong branches, tent poles, rifles, skis, etc.). (See Figures 8-10 (below) and 8-11 (on next page.)

Carries. There are several ways by which a casualty may be moved without using a litter. Use the carry that is easiest for you and which is best fitted to the situation.

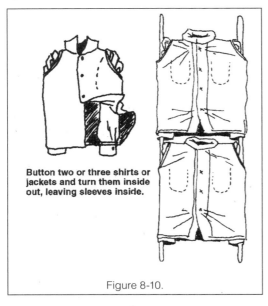

Button two or three shirts or jackets and turn them inside out, leaving sleeves inside.

Figure 8-10.

1. One person drag with a line.
    a. Advantages: There is no equipment required. Just grab the casualty by the loop on the flak jacket, if possible. During this move, only one rescuer is exposed to hostile fire.
    b. Disadvantages: This carry may be slow, and it is not an optimal body position to sustain for very long.
2. Two person drag with a line.
    a. Advantages: This move is much faster than the one person drag.

b. Disadvantages: This move exposes two rescuers to hostile fire.
3. Two person drag with lines.
    a. Advantages: You can shoot while dragging. This move is much faster to cover, and it is much easier than dragging without lines.
    b. Disadvantages: The two person drag with lines also exposes two rescuers to hostile fire.
4. SEAL Team Three Carry.
    a. Advantages: May be useful in situations where drags do not work well. It's also less painful for the casualty than dragging.
    b. Disadvantages: It may be slower than dragging and may be more difficult, especially with an unconscious casualty. Unfortunately, this move also exposes two rescuers to hostile fire.
5. Hawes Carry.
    a. Advantages: This carry requires only one rescuer and may be useful in situations where a drag is not a good option. It's much better than the outdated fireman's carry.
    b. Disadvantages: It's hard to accomplish with the rescuer's and casualty's gear in place. It's also difficult when the casualty is bigger than the rescuer. It's often much slower than dragging, and it creates a high profile for both casualty and rescuer, which exposes them both to hostile fire.

Common Emergencies

In addition to the first aid kit that every Marine carries, special first aid kits are often available. These are for use in common emergencies, such as cuts, burns, and eye injuries. First aid kits found in many motor vehicles contain tourniquets, swabs, adhesive tape, and dressings of several sizes. Familiarize yourself with them. Directions are included with each kit.

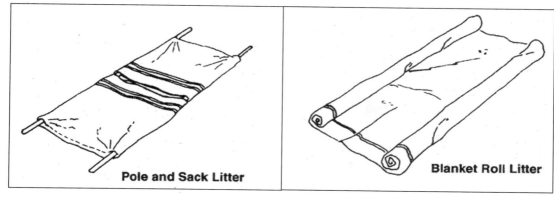

Pole and Sack Litter

Blanket Roll Litter

Figure 8-11. Litter made with poles and jackets.

Minor wounds. Small wounds, such as cuts, usually do not bleed very much and will stop bleeding once a dressing has been applied. Infection is the principal danger, and any break in the skin should be protected. Do not touch a wound or allow clothes to touch it. Keep it clean. Apply a dressing over the wound. There are various sized dressings. Pick a size that adequately covers the wound. Be careful not to touch the inside of the dressing.

Burns. Small burns frequently occur and, unless properly protected, can become infected. Large burns must be treated by medical personnel. Small burns can be handled at the first aid level. Severe sunburn requires similar first aid measures. Cover the burned area with burn ointment and a sterile or clean dressing of suitable size.

Foreign body in eye. If a particle is in your eye, do not rub the eye. Close it for a few minutes and tears may wash away the object. If tears have not washed away the particle, try flushing it out with water. Your eyelids must be held open widely with your fingers while flushing. If this does not work, have someone treat the eye as shown in Figure 8-12. When a foreign body cannot be dislodged or the eyeball is scratched, obtain medical attention immediately. When an acidic or caustic solution enters the eye, immediately flush with a large volume of water and seek medical attention.

Foreign bodies in ear, nose, and throat. Never probe into the ear with a pin, wire, or stick if an object is in the ear. Seek medical attention.

An insect in the ear may be killed with a few drops of oil or water. Other objects also may be flushed out this way. However, if the object is something that swells when wet (such as a bean), do not put water into the ear. Probing into the nose merely will jam the foreign body tighter. Try to loosen it by gently blowing the nose. If this does not work, seek medical attention. Objects in the nose usually are not dangerous. When a foreign body becomes lodged in the throat, try to cough it up. Coughing takes precedence over removal by fingers because the latter method can result in the item being pushed farther down the throat. To remove a foreign object from the throat of another person, strike

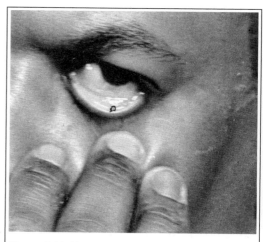

Figure 8-12. To remove an object from the lower lid or eyeball, have someone pull down the lower lid and remove the object with a clean handkerchief.

sharply between the shoulder blades with one hand, while you support the chest with the other. If this does not work, stand behind the casualty and wrap your arms around the waist. Grasp your wrist and place the thumb side of your fists against the casualty's abdomen, above the navel and just below the rib cage. Give a quick thrust inward and upward to the casualty. The obstruction should pop out like a champagne cork. Repeat the procedure, if necessary. This procedure is called Abdominal Thrust and is illustrated in Figure 8-13.

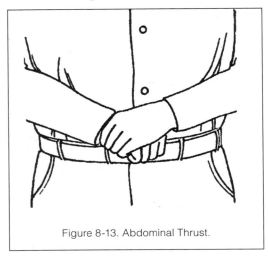

Figure 8-13. Abdominal Thrust.

Care of the feet. Prevention of foot trouble is the best first aid for feet. Keeping feet clean, thoroughly drying the feet after bathing, especially between toes, helps prevent athlete's foot. For itching or redness between the toes, apply foot powder twice daily. If this does not improve, seek medical attention. Do not try to treat it yourself. Do not cut a callus or corn; doing so increases the risk of a serious infection. Seek medical attention. To avoid ingrown toenails, keep toenails clean and short; cut them straight across. Dust feet with foot powder after bathing and before a march. Foot powder absorbs perspiration and prevents chafing. Wear clean socks every day, if possible. Do not wear socks that have holes, are poorly darned, or do not fit properly. Break in boots before wearing them on a march.

Poisonous plants. Poison ivy, poison oak, and poison sumac cause skin irritation. The faster you receive first aid after exposure, the milder the reaction will be. Learn to recognize the plants, so you will know when you have touched them and can start first aid before a rash appears. Poison ivy is a creeper having three leaves on each stem. The leaves are shiny, pointed, and have prominent veins. Poison oak and poison sumac are shrubs or small trees. If you discover that you have been exposed to a poisonous plant, wash the parts of the body affected promptly and thoroughly, using cold water and strong soap. The rash starts with redness and intense itching followed by little blisters. If a rash already has developed, do not wash it. Avoid scratching for it will make the condition worse by spreading it to other areas of the body. These areas can easily become infected. Seek medical attention.

Unconsciousness. It is often impossible to find the cause of unconsciousness. Check for breathing and a pulse first. Bleeding, heat stroke, or head injury may have been the cause. If you cannot find the cause, keep the casualty lying down. Do not move the casualty unless absolutely necessary and do so very carefully. If cold, make the casualty warm. If the casualty has suffered the effects of excessive heat, give first aid accordingly. Do not pour liquids into the mouth of an unconscious person because you may cause choking. If vomiting occurs, turn the patient onto their stomach (if not contraindicated by injuries) and turn the head to one side. Check to make sure the patient does not inhale the vomitus. Take off equipment, loosen clothing, and call for emergent medical support.

If the casualty has merely fainted, consciousness will be regained in a few minutes. Let the casualty lie quietly. Loosen the clothing. Apply a wet, cold cloth to the face. If the casualty is about to faint, have them put their head between their knees. If the casualty has fainted, place them to the ground on their back. Carefully ensure that the casualty does not fall and cause injury.

What Is Combat and Operational Stress?

Stress is any challenge to the body or mind and can occur at any time. Sources of stress may be financial, relationship or work related. The effects of stress may present immediately or may be delayed. Stress presents a danger and if the stress is recognized and managed accordingly it presents an opportunity for growth. Stress is a necessary component of our lives, it can promote growth and provide motivation for being at our best. However, too much stress can cause functional impairment. The chart in Figure 8-14 shows the Stress Continuum designed to help identify levels of stress in units and individuals. The Stress Decision Matrix Figure 8-15 (on next page) is a tool to assist in identifying a Marine in distress and executing the required actions.

Combat and Operational Stress First Aid (COSFA): The Seven Cs

If you are experiencing combat or operational stress, or know of a Marine who is, COSFA is the primary method to begin recovery for you or the affected Marine. The seven Cs of COSFA (see Figure 8-16 on next page) should be implemented immediately when there are signs and symptoms of stress injury (orange zone):

1. Check–assess: observe and listen.
2. Coordinate–get help, refer as needed.
3. Cover–get to safety as soon as possible.
4. Calm–relax, slow down, refocus.
5. Connect–get support from others.
6. Competence–restore effectiveness.
7. Confidence– restore self esteem.

Stress first aid starts in the orange zone. Marines experiencing the yellow zone for a long period of time are at higher risk for orange zone stress injuries. Also, a single overwhelming event, such as the loss of a close peer, can instantly jump a Marine from the green zone into the orange zone.

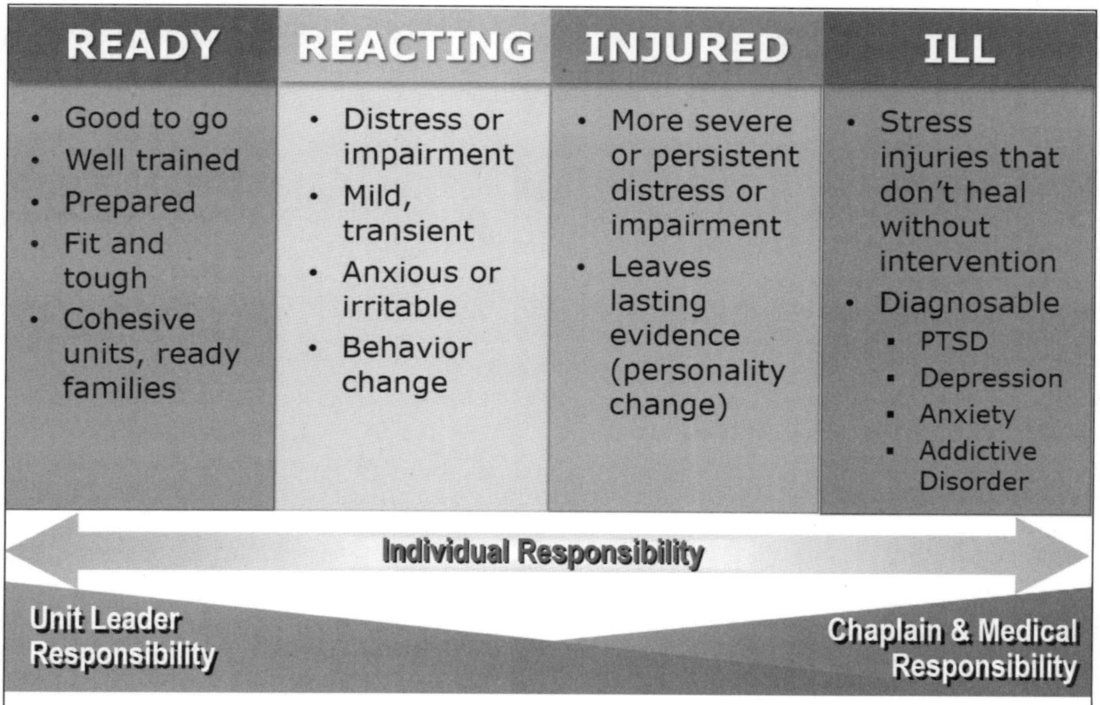

READY	REACTING	INJURED	ILL

• Good to go
• Well trained
• Prepared
• Fit and tough
• Cohesive units, ready families
	• Distress or impairment
	• Mild, transient
	• Anxious or irritable
	• Behavior change
		• More severe or persistent distress or impairment
		• Leaves lasting evidence (personality change)
			• Stress injuries that don't heal without intervention
			• Diagnosable
			  ▪ PTSD
			  ▪ Depression
			  ▪ Anxiety
			  ▪ Addictive Disorder

Individual Responsibility

Unit Leader Responsibility

Chaplain & Medical Responsibility

Figure 8-14. Stress Continuum.

Green Zone (Ready):
• Continue to monitor for signs of distress or loss of function

Marine Under Stress

IDENTIFY   TAKE ACTION

Does the distress look **MILD OR TEMPORARY**?   Yes →

Yellow Zone (Reacting):

• Difficulty relaxing and sleeping
• Loss of interest in social or recreational activities
• Any change from normal personality
• Difficulty performing normal duties
• Hyperactive startle responses to noises
• Unusual and excessive fear, worry, or anger
• Recurrent nightmares or troubling memories

• Ensure adequate sleep & rest
• Manage home-front stressors
• Discussions in small units
• Mentor back to full duty and function
• If problem worsens, discuss with Senior Mentor/Team Members or Extenders

No ↓

Does the distress look **SEVERE OR PERSISTENT**?   Yes →

Orange Zone (Injured):

• Inability to fall asleep or stay asleep
• Withdrawal from social or recreational activities
• Uncharacteristic outbursts of rage or panic
• Nightmares or memories that increase heart rate
• Inability to control emotions
• Loss of usual concern for moral values
• Serious suicidal or homicidal thoughts

• Keep safe and calm
• Rest & recuperation 24-72 hours
• Mentor back to full duty and function
• Refer to medical or chaplain

No ↓

Does it look like it's significantly impacting **CAREER OR RELATIONSHIPS**?   Yes →

Red Zone (Ill):

• Stress problems that degrade performance
• Stress problems that last for more than several weeks post-deployment
• Stress problems that don't get better over time
• Stress problems that get worse over time

• Refer to medical
• Ensure treatment compliance
• Mentor back to duty if possible
• Reintegrate with unit

Figure 8-15. Stress Decision Matrix.

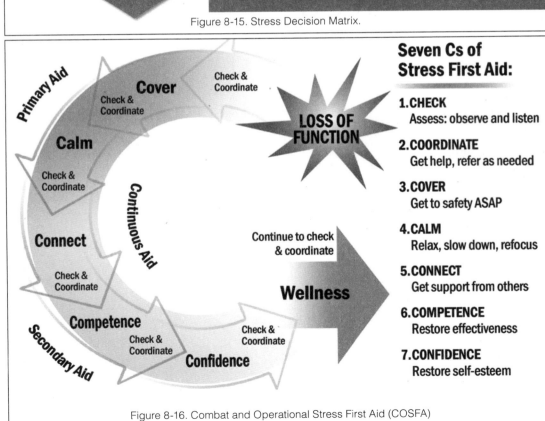

Seven Cs of Stress First Aid:

1. **CHECK**
Assess: observe and listen

2. **COORDINATE**
Get help, refer as needed

3. **COVER**
Get to safety ASAP

4. **CALM**
Relax, slow down, refocus

5. **CONNECT**
Get support from others

6. **COMPETENCE**
Restore effectiveness

7. **CONFIDENCE**
Restore self-esteem

Figure 8-16. Combat and Operational Stress First Aid (COSFA)

Orange zone injuries are serious, require immediate attention, and may not resolve without help. Leaders and peers must recognize the signs early and ensure the appropriate help is received. The sooner you can safely calm the Marine down (indicated by heart rate and breathing rate), the greater the chances for quick and full recovery. "Coordinate" requires assessing that a Marine needs additional help. Marines in distress may require the attention of unit leadership in coordination with the chaplain, medical officer, Corpsman, and sometimes family members. "Connect" refers to the restorative power of being with trusted buddies and unit members; unit cohesion and quality time are therapeutic. Isolation should be avoided. All efforts should be geared toward avoiding unnecessarily evacuating a Marines in distress out of the unit or combat theater. "Confidence" refers to regaining a sense of self-efficacy and personal competence as soon as possible, being good-to-go, which can be built through resumption of normal activities in the unit. A severe stress event may inhibit an individual from functioning effectively. It is of utmost importance for unit leadership to restore "competence" in a Marine that has experienced a severe stress event. Unit leadership should ensure that Marines receive the help they deserve; free from retribution or harassment. Unit leadership must create an environment where it is okay to receive help for both combat and operational stress, just as with any physical injury. The goal of COSFA is to return the Marine to the green zone where he is prepared, ready, and remains with the unit as an effective, well-functioning Marine.

CHAPTER 9

Physical Fitness

"Even the bravest cannot fight beyond his strength."
- Homer

The Marine Corps Physical Training Program Purpose and Philosophy

As professional warrior-athletes, every Marine must be physically fit, regardless of age, grade, or duty assignment. Fitness is an essential component of Marine Corps combat readiness. Furthermore, physical fitness is an indispensable aspect of leadership. The habits of self-discipline and personal commitment that are required to gain and maintain a high level of physical fitness are inherent to the Marine Corps way of life and must be a part of the character of every Marine. Marines who are not physically fit are a detriment and detract from the combat readiness of their unit.

The core of the Marine Corps Physical Fitness Program (MCPFP) and key to its success is the Force Fitness Instructor (FFI), assigned throughout the total force down to the company and squadron level, with the end state of optimizing the physical fitness of their unit, and creating a more knowledgeable and capable force. The FFI will serve as the commander's subject matter expert (SME) on nutrition, physical fitness, and injury prevention. The FFI will advise the commander on the design and implementation of a structured physical fitness training program that is uniquely tailored to the unit's Training and Exercise Employment Plan (TEEP). The FFI will assess and baseline the physical fitness of the unit and individual Marines and design a comprehensive program to facilitate progressive improvement. The FFI will also facilitate integration of resources such as the Marine Corps Martial Arts Program (MCMAP), the Marine Corps Water Survival Training Program (MCWSTP), Semper Fit, High Intensity Tactical Training (HITT), strength coaches, and Navy medicine to support the commander's physical fitness training objectives and unit mission.

Components and Principles of Physical Fitness

There are many ways to define fitness. Oftentimes the definition will depend on the goals of a particular program. For the Marine, the obvious goal is combat preparedness. As such, training must focus on preparation for the unforeseen and unforeseeable requirements of combat. To capitalize on the components of physical fitness that can benefit training efforts, the following categories of exercises should be included in both individual and unit physical training programs:

a. **Cardio-Respiratory Endurance**. Cardio-respiratory endurance refers to the efficiency with which the body's circulatory and respiratory systems deliver oxygen and nutrients needed for sustained physical activity. The two types of endurance training needed for a Marine to meet the physical demands of combat are aerobic and anaerobic.

  1. Aerobic activity, meaning "in the presence of oxygen," is categorized by physical demands that are sub maximal and continuous in nature (lasting more than three to five minutes). Examples of aerobic activity are road marching and long distance running.

  2. Anaerobic activity, meaning "without oxygen," is categorized by physical demands that are high intensity and of shorter duration (lasting less than two to three minutes). Examples are most forms of weight lifting and sprinting.

b. **Muscular Strength.** Muscular strength is the greatest amount of force any given muscle or group of muscles can exert in a single effort. Muscular strength is often associated with training with weights or machines. To the contrary, however, a Marine's ability to effectively handle his body weight must be prerequisite to integrating resistive exercises using weights or machines. Strength training can be broadly separated into two categories, general and specific.

  1. General strength training strengthens the entire muscular system by focusing on a full body workout. In this type of training, muscle groups are exercised without a specific task or functional goal in mind. General strength training contributes greatly to combat preparation and overall health.

  2. Specific strength training strengthens individual muscles or groups of muscles by focusing on a specific task. In this type of training, individual muscles or muscle groups are exercised in isolation. Specific strength training may be useful to assist in preparation for particular martial tasks. For example, Marines desiring to climb a rope better would climb ropes while wearing body armor and focusing their training on only those muscles involved in rope climbing.

c. **Muscular Endurance.** Muscular endurance is the ability of a muscle or group of muscles to perform repeated movements at a sub maximal effort for a sustained period of time.

d. **Stamina.** Stamina is defined as the body's ability to process, store, and deliver energy throughout a period of prolonged, stressful effort.

e. **Power.** Power is the ability of a muscle or group of muscles to apply force rapidly. Mathematically, power is expressed as a work/time ratio. For example, a Marine climbing a wall takes an abnormally long time to elevate his body to the second deck. On the other hand, a Marine climbing stairs elevates his body the same distance in a short amount of time. Both Marines have done the same amount of work, yet the Marine climbing the wall has a lower power rating than the Marine opting to take the stairs.

f. **Speed.** Speed is the ability to minimize the time it takes for the body to execute a movement.

g. **Coordination.** Coordination is the ability to combine a series of different movements into one movement pattern.

h. **Agility.** Agility is the ability to perform a series of movements in rapid succession and in opposing directions.

i. **Balance.** Balance is the ability to control the body's center of gravity while either stationary or in relation to the movement of its base.

j. **Flexibility.** Flexibility is a joint's ability to move freely through a full and normal range of motion. During such movement, a muscle or group of muscles will relax, stretch and lengthen.

k. **Nutrition.** Nutrition is the makeup of the individual's daily caloric needs in relation to operations, physical training and performance.

Because of the unique nature of the Marine Corps' mission, physical training must prepare the individual Marine to maintain a high level of fitness throughout the length of his career. There are several different principles of physical fitness to consider when developing an effective physical training program:

a. **Progression.** The intensity (how hard) and duration (how long) of exercise must gradually increase over a period of time in order to maximize potential gains and minimize the risk of injury.

b. **Regularity.** Regular exercise, rest, and sleep are vital to a healthy body. There are no easy or occasional methods to develop fitness. Individuals must exercise regularly in order to achieve the desired training effect. Daily exercise is preferred and encouraged. Regularity is not only a vital aspect in exercise, it is important in recovery and diet. The lack of regular exercise, rest, and proper nutrition can do more harm than good. To realize any training effect, programs must be conducted at least three times per week.

c. **Overload.** Overload is the basis for all exercise training. In order for physical fitness to improve, exercise must exceed the body's normal workload. Unless the body is taken beyond its "comfort zone" by running either faster or longer, or putting more workload on the muscles, then physical fitness will not improve. Only when the various systems of the body are overloaded will they become able to handle greater load.

d. **Variety.** Providing a variety of training reduces boredom and increases motivation and progress. The most successful programs usually include conditioning activities, competitive events, and military physical skill development. Physical training should emphasize unit and fitness training, rather than training solely for the physical fitness test (PFT).

e. **Recovery.** Recovery is the most important principle of physical fitness. Gains from physical training are realized during recovery. There are two types of recovery—active and passive. A moderate to light training day, following a hard training day, is an example of active recovery. Days off during a training cycle are examples of passive recovery. Too many days or weeks of high intensity training can inadvertently lead to overtraining and injury. Recovery is essential for allowing the systems overloaded during training to adapt and become stronger.

f. **Balance.** To enhance its effectiveness, a program should include activities that address all fitness components equally. Programs that overemphasize any single component has the potential to suppress other components. Examples of overemphasizing a single component of fitness may be found within the weight lifter or long distance runner communities. Many weight lifters lack cardio-respiratory endurance and many long distance runners lack muscular strength. Balanced training programs ensure that all the components of physical fitness are properly addressed.

g. **Specificity.** Training that is specific in nature yields specific gains. For example, a fitness goal of "getting in shape" is non-specific; rather, a more particular fitness goal would be "getting in shape by improving cardio-respiratory endurance (through running, swimming, aerobics) and muscle tone (by reducing fat through proper eating habits and weight lifting)." Nevertheless, physical training programs must contain specificity, while remaining cognizant of balance.

h. **Synergy of Training.** Properly designed physical training programs develop a high level of physical fitness, mental toughness and discipline throughout the unit, while simultaneously building character and leadership within the individual. Training in this manner enhances the synergy of the mind, body, and spirit of the Marine.

Phases of Daily Physical Training

Every physical training evolution should flow in the following sequence: dynamic warm-up, abdominal and lower back core strength training, conditioning event, cool-down, flexibility training, and recovery.

a. The dynamic warm-up exercises facilitate gradual distribution of blood flow to the muscles, preparing both the cardiovascular and musculoskeletal systems for the exercise session. The increased blood flow to the muscles produces a warming effect, increasing the elasticity of the muscles and connective tissue. This effect is believed to produce fewer injuries than preworkout static stretching alone.

b. Core strength development is crucial for combat fitness. Marines often train the abdominal region but not the lower back, leading to lack of muscular balance and resulting injury. Core specific strength training ensures balance and an increase in core strength. Core strength training may be conducted either before or after the conditioning event.

c. The conditioning event is whatever physical training exercises, circuit training, cross training, or agility training that has been selected as the individual's or unit's workout of the day.

d. The period immediately following the conditioning event is known as the cooldown. Much like the dynamic warm-up prepares the body for an exercise session, the cool-down facilitates a gradual relaxation in which an individual's heart rate is designed to decrease.

e. By incorporating frequent flexibility training, a Marine prevents injuries, increases his natural range of motion and increases the flow of blood to muscles. The benefits of flexibility training far outweigh the alternative. If need be, the training event should be reduced by 10 to 15 minutes in order to facilitate proper and comprehensive flexibility training. There are several flexibility training techniques and methods that are applied to combat conditioning.

1. Active stretching occurs when the only force required to conduct the stretch is supplied by the individual. For example, if an individual raises his leg to the front as high as possible, agonist muscles (hip flexor and quadriceps) are supplying the force of the stretch while antagonist muscles (glutes and hamstrings) are stretching.

2. Passive stretching involves the use of a partner or device (belt, rope, or towel) to provide force for the stretch. Using a passive stretching device is both an excellent and efficient means of conducting flexibility training.

3. Static stretching is the most convenient method of stretching. The method refers to the constant tension being held at the end position of the stretch. The amount of time spent in the end position of a static stretch should vary from 30 to 60 seconds. The only requirements for static stretching are proper form and technique.

4. A dynamic stretch is one that involves mimicking the range of motion that will be required to conduct the conditioning event. Specifically, dynamic stretching uses movement specific to the activities about to be performed. Marines may use this type of stretching to prepare for calisthenics or obstacle course evolutions. For example, prior to obstacle course training, Marines performing slow, full range of motion high stepping to the front and laterally may prepare their respective muscles for leaping and bounding over obstacles.

5. Proprioceptive neuromuscular facilitation (PNF) is considered the gold standard of flexibility training. Throughout PNF stretching, the same or opposing muscles contract and relax. This causes a neural response that prevents the contraction of the muscle being stretched, resulting in reduced resistance and increased range of motion. An added benefit to PNF stretching is that this method can increase one's muscular strength due to the isometric or concentric contraction of the muscle being stretched. PNF stretching is best done with the help of a partner; however, a passive stretching device will work as well. PNF stretches should be held for 30 to 60 seconds.

6. Ballistic stretching uses bouncing movements in which a joint's range of motion is moved beyond normal limits. As such, the muscle or group of muscles is not stretched and held at its end position. Ballistic stretching is the least desirable form of flexibility training for Marines due to its tendency to damage and injure the muscles and surrounding tissues. Irregularly bouncing, jolting, and snapping movements may damage muscles and joints and should generally be avoided.

f. Again, gains from physical training activities are realized during the recovery phase. Recovery will last from the last repetition of the current conditioning event until the first repetition of the next conditioning event.

Physical Training Circuits, Cross Training, and Agility Training

Physical training circuits should be developed with designated stations that encompass combat conditioning agility training, exercises, and standard martial tasks. For example, a station based drill on the LZ filled with various exercises and martial arts techniques would include each of the functional areas of combat conditioning circuit training.

Cross training consists of multiple exercises performed in a specific order that will significantly affect the body. These cross training events can be highly varied, short in duration, and very intense, promoting a high fitness level among Marines and ideally preparing them for the unexpected rigors of combat. For example, three rounds of 10 buddy squats, 15 pull-ups, and a 400-meter run would take a relatively small amount of time to complete; however, it would likely produce a relatively high degree of intensity.

Agility training assists in the development of coordination, or the ability to maneuver on the battlefield. This may be accomplished by incorporating cone drills, agility ladders, and mini-hurdles. Additionally, training may be integrated into immediate action drills, command and control drills, fire and movement drills, and bayonet engagements.

Physical Conditioning Exercises

The exercises depicted are divided into five categories: individual conditioning exercises, buddy exercises, buddy carries, movement exercises, and strength training exercises. These physical training events/exercises can be completed with minimal equipment by any Marine anywhere and are not necessarily inclusive of all equipment and methods that can be used to develop physical capacity.

a. Individual conditioning exercise includes core strength conditioning and calisthenics. These exercises are designed to increase the Marine's level of fitness, using only the Marine's body weight.

b. Buddy exercises include calisthenics, core strength conditioning and stabilization exercises that, in order to be conducted, require a partner. Buddy exercises are designed to increase teamwork, as well as provide additional weight or resistance during exercises in order to increase the muscular strength and endurance required to accomplish martial tasks.

c. Buddy carries and movement exercises are designed for movement on the battlefield while under fire, moving to the objective or while evacuating a casualty to cover or an aid station. These movements may be executed individually or as a squad.

d. Strength training exercises are important in providing Marines with a rounded physical training program, while providing skill transfer for martial tasks. These strength training exercises focus on the use of austere equipment rather than weight training as one would find in a gym.

1. Weighted ammo can or five-gallon water can training provides a means of strength training for operational units. Both types of cans are easily deployed and cost effective. Moreover, if cans cannot be obtained, sandbags, bricks, large rocks, and similar items may be used as well. In addition to fighting, Marines should be capable of training in every clime and place.

2. Sandbag medicine ball training also provides skill transfer for martial tasks, while potentially increasing one's range of motion and strength. Single sandbags filled with varying amounts of sand, shaped appropriately, and duct taped will provide field expedient medicine balls that can be used in garrison or in the field.

3. Sandbag kettlebells are performed with one-half to three-quarters full sandbags that have been formed with a handle to represent a kettlebell. Training with sandbag kettlebells will help develop strength, power, and explosiveness.

When programming drills, circuits, or routines, trainers must have an understanding of the body's movement during a particular exercise. The four basic movements include pushing, pulling, overhead, and squatting. Drills and routines must be designed in a specific order. For example, four pushing movement exercises executed in a row greatly increases muscular fatigue and are not ideal in most situations. Most routines should alternate between pushing and pulling, overhead and squatting movements. This emphasizes the principle of balance by alternating working muscle groups and provides specific muscle groups a brief period of recovery. Additionally, alternating movements tends to intensify the workout by making the body work harder to send blood and oxygen to multiple muscle groups throughout the body during a routine.

There are three categories of exercise that assist in programming workouts. The first category of exercise is weighted, in which any weight other than the body is used during the exercise. Examples of weighted exercises include buddy squats and sandbag swings. The second category of exercise is body weighted, in which only one's body weight is used during the exercise. Examples of body weighted exercise include push-ups, pull-ups, and body squats. The third category of exercise is aerobic, in which the focus of the exercise is aerobic conditioning. Examples of aerobic exercises include running, swimming, hiking, and rowing.

An Assortment of Physical Conditioning Exercise Illustrations and Descriptions

Core Strength Exercises

Front Plank. This position can begin from any of the side plank or front leaning rest positions. The Marine will begin on the elbows while keeping the upper arm perpendicular to the torso creating a 90 degree angle. (See Figure 9-1.) Once in this position the Marine will suck the stomach in and keep the back straight. The hips will remain up and in alignment with the shoulders; the head will be in a neutral position. (See Figure 9-2.) The exercise will be held for a specified time.

Side Planks. There are two positions of the side plank: left and right. This position may begin from the front plank or the front leaning rest position. The Marine will turn on one side while making only two points of contact with the deck: the forearm and foot. The upper arm will remain perpendicular with the ground. (See Figure 9-3.) The head will remain neutral while the hips will be up away from the deck, forward and in alignment with the shoulders. The shoulders will be rolled back and the position will resemble that of a modified position of attention. (See Figure 9-4.) The exercise will be held for a specified time.

Back Bridge. The Marine will begin in the front leaning rest or front plank. The Marine will shoot one arm underneath the opposite armpit and turn to his back. (See Figure 9-5 on next page.) The hips will be raised while the Marine maintains three points of contact with the deck: each foot and the upper back. (See Figure 9-6 on next page.) This exercise will be held for a specified time.

Back Bridge With Leg Extension. The Marine will begin in the back bridge position. The Marine will extend either leg to a 45-degree angle and point the toe upward. (See Figure 9-7 on next page.) The Marine will continue to

Figure 9-1.

Figure 9-2.

Figure 9-3.

Figure 9-4.

Figure 9-5.

Figure 9-6.

Figure 9-7.

Figure 9-8.

bridge the hips upward ensuring that the thighs are parallel but not touching. (See Figure 9-8.) Each leg should be held for a specified time.

Abdominal Crunch. The Marine will begin by lying on the deck with hands behind or to the side of the head. Fingers will not be interlocked and the elbows will remain pointing outboard. At no time during the exercise will the Marine pull up on the head. The knees will be bent and feet shall remain in contact with the deck at all times. (See Figure 9-9 on next page.) On order, the Marine will suck the stomach in and force the lower back into the deck. The Marine will use the abdominal muscles to raise the shoulders off the deck. (See Figure 9-10 on next page.) On order, the Marine will lower the torso back to the starting position.

Combination Crunch. The Marine will begin by lying on the deck with hands behind or to the side of the head. Fingers will not be interlocked and the elbows will remain pointing outboard. At no time during the exercise will the Marine pull up on the head. The thighs will be elevated and the knees bent at 90 degrees at all times. (See Figure 9-11 on next page.) On order, the Marine will suck the stomach in and force the lower back into the deck. The Marine will use the abdominal muscles to raise the shoulders and hips off the deck until neither the shoulder blades nor lower back are in contact with the deck. (See Figure 9-12 on next page.) On order, the Marine will lower the torso and hips to the starting position.

Free Foot Sit-Ups (Sit and Reach). The Marine will begin by lying on the deck with arms straight and extended perpendicular to the torso. The Marine will keep the knees bent and feet in contact with the deck at all times. (See Figure 9-13 on next page.) On order, the Marine will suck the stomach in and force the lower back into the deck. The Marine will use the abdominal muscles to raise the torso off the deck and into the seated position. The arms will remain perpendicular to the deck throughout the entire exercise. (See Figure 9-14 on page 117.) On order, the Marine will lower the torso back to the starting position.

Figure 9-9.

Figure 9-10.

Figure 9-11.

45- to 90-Degree Leg Raises. The Marine will begin by lying on the deck with hands behind or to the side of the head. Fingers will not be interlocked and the elbows will remain pointing outboard while the legs are straight and elevated at 90 degrees. (See Figure 9-15 on next page.) The Marine will keep the legs elevated and straight at all times. On order, the Marine will suck the stomach in and force the lower back into the deck. The Marine will use the abdominal muscles to lower the legs to 45

Figure 9-12.

Figure 9-13.

degrees. (See Figure 9-16 on next page.) The lower back will be pressed to the deck throughout the entire exercise. On order, the Marine will use the abdominals to raise the legs back to the 90-degree angle.

Bicycle. The Marine will begin by lying on the deck with hands behind or to the side of the head. Fingers will be interlocked and the elbows will remain pointing outboard while the legs are straight and elevated at approximately 45 degrees. At no time will the head be pulled during the exercise. The exercise will be executed to a four-count cadence. On the command one, the Marine will bring the left knee in toward the shoulders while raising the right elbow and shoulder blade off the deck toward the knee. (See Figure 9-17 on page 118.) On two, the Marine will return to the starting position. On the command three, the Marine will bring the right knee in toward the shoulders while raising the left elbow and shoulder blade off the deck toward the knee. (See Figure 9-18 on

Figure 9-14.

Figure 9-15.

page 118.). On four, the Marine will return to the starting position.

Slide Side Reach. The Marine will begin by lying on the deck with hands off the deck and to the side of his body at a 45 degree angle. The Marine will keep the knees bent and feet in contact with the deck at all times. The exercise will be executed to a four-count cadence. On the command one, the Marine will crunch to the left side, forcing the left hand through the opening between the hamstring and calf. (See Figure 9-19 on next page.) On two, the Marine will return to the starting position. On the command three, the Marine will crunch to the right side, forcing the right hand through the opening between the hamstring and calf. (See Figure 9-20 on next page.) On four, the Marine will return to the starting position.

Hyperextensions. The Marine will begin by lying on the stomach in the beginner (arms to the side), intermediate (hands overlapped under the chin), or advanced (arms extended past the head and parallel to the deck) position. (See Figure 9-21 on next page). On order, the Marine will raise the torso while keeping the toes on the deck. (See Figure 9-22 on next page.) On order, the Marine will lower, not drop, the torso to the starting position.

Reverse Hyperextensions. The Marine will begin by lying on the stomach with the hands overlapped and under the chin. (See Figure 9-23 on page 119.) On order, the Marine will raise the feet and thighs off the deck while keeping the legs straight. (See Figure 9-24 on page 119.) On the down command the Marine will lower, not drop, the legs to the deck.

Figure 9-16.

Figure 9-17.

Figure 9-18.

Figure 9-19.

Figure 9-20.

Figure 9-21.

Figure 9-22.

Combination Hyperextensions. The Marine will lie on his stomach in the beginner (arms to the side) intermediate (hands overlapped under the chin), or advanced (arms extended past the head and parallel to the deck) position. (See Figure 9-25 on next page.) On order, the Marine will raise the torso and thighs, while simultaneously lifting the legs straight and off the deck. (See Figure 9-26 on next page.) On order, the Marine will lower, not drop, the torso and thighs to the starting position.

Swimmer Hyperextensions. The Marine will begin by lying on the stomach with the arms extended past the head and parallel to the deck. The exercise will be executed to a four-count cadence. On the command one, the Marine will raise his left arm and the right leg. (See Figure 9-27 on next page.) On two, the Marine will lower, not drop, the arm and leg to the starting position. On the command three, the Marine will raise the right arm and left leg. (See Figure 9-28 on next page.) On four, the Marine will lower, not drop, the arm and leg to the starting position.

Figure 9-23.

Figure 9-24.

Figure 9-25.

Figure 9-26.

Figure 9-27.

Figure 9-28.

Hyperextension Twist. The Marine will begin by lying on the stomach with the arms bent and hands overlapped under the chin. The exercise will be executed to a four-count cadence. On the command one, the Marine will raise the left elbow up and to the rear toward the right hip. (See Figures 9-29 and 9-30 on next page.) On two, the Marine will return to the starting position. On the command three, the Marine will raise the right elbow up and to the rear toward the left hip. On four, the Marine will return to the starting position. The feet will remain on the deck throughout the exercise.

Bodyweight Exercises

Push-Ups. The Marine will begin by lying on the stomach with the hands shoulder width apart. The "V" between the thumb and forefinger will be in line with the shoulder. The elbows will not point away from the torso more than 45 degrees. Throughout the entire exercise the Marine will keep the stomach sucked in and the back straight. The hips should be in line with the shoulders. (See

Figure 9-29.

Figure 9-30.

Figure 9-31.

Figure 9-32.

Figure 9-31.) The exercise can be executed to the commands up and down or four-count cadence. On order, the Marine will press to the up position and hold. At this time the Marine will suck the stomach in and keep the back straight. The arms will be straight and elbows locked out; the hips will remain up and in alignment with the shoulders; the head will be in a neutral position. (See Figure 9-32.) On order, the Marine will lower the torso and lower body to the deck, maintaining the previously described alignment. To ensure proper form, the exercise should not be executed at a high tempo.

Power-Ups. The Marine will begin in the kneeling position with the stomach sucked in and the back straight. Forearms will be perpendicular with the deck; the hands will be placed approximately shoulder-width apart and the "V" between the thumb and forefinger will be slightly below and in line with the shoulder. (See Figure 9-33 on next page.) On order, the Marine will extend the arms and fall forward to the deck. The stomach will remain sucked in and the back flat throughout the entire exercise. Upon contact with the ground, the elbows will not point away from the torso more than 45 degrees. (See Figure 9-34 on next page.) On order, the Marine will rapidly extend the arms, explosively pushing away from the deck and returning to the kneeling position. (See Figure 9-35 on next page.) To ensure proper form, the exercise should not be executed at a high tempo.

Dive Bombers. The Marine will begin in a modified push-up position with the hips raised higher than the chest and feet more than shoulder width apart. (See Figure 9-36 on next page.) On order, the Marine will lower the chest to the deck in a parabolic motion (see Figure 9-37 on next page) and extend upward until the arms are straight, the elbows locked out, and the chest is higher than the hips. (See Figure 9-38 on page 122.) On order, the Marine will reverse the motion (see Figure 9-39 on page 122) and return to the starting position (see Figure 9-40 on page 122). The exercise should resemble the Marine attempting to push himself under a fence, or similar obstacle, and returning to the side from which he began.

Figure 9-33.

Figure 9-34.

Figure 9-35.

Dips. The Marine will perform this exercise on a dip bar or between two stable surfaces of approximately the same height. The Marine will begin with the arms fully extended and the elbows locked out. (See Figure 9-41 on page 123.) On order, the Marine will slowly lower the body until the bend of the elbow is slightly less than 90 degrees or where the shoulders are lower than the elbows. (See Figure 9-42 on page 123.) On order, the Marine will return to the starting position by extending the arms until the elbow has locked out. (See Figure 9-43 on page 123.)

Burpees. The Marine will begin in a standing position. On order, the Marine will drop down into a squatting position, placing both hands flat on the deck approximately shoulder width apart. (See Figure 9-44 on page 123.) The Marine will shoot both legs backwards (see Figure 9-45 on page 123) and perform a push-up without resting on the deck (see Figure 9-46 on page 123). While maintaining hand placement on the deck, the Marine will bring the legs back to the squatting position (see Figure 9-47 on page 123) and perform a vertical leap for maximal height. This exercise most closely resembles an eight count bodybuilder executed at a much faster rate.

Figure 9-36.

Figure 9-37.

Figure 9-38.

Figure 9-39.

Figure 9-40.

L Pull-Ups. The Marine will begin by mounting a pull-up bar and arriving at a "dead hang." The Marine may grip the pull-up bar with the palms facing either outboard or inboard. The Marine will raise the lower body until the legs have formed a 90-degree angle with the torso, or the body forms an "L." (See Figure 9-48 on page 124.) On order, the Marine will execute a pull-up while maintaining the legs in the "L" position. (See Figure 9-49 on page 124.) On order, the Marine will lower himself back to the starting position. (See Figure 9-50 on page 124.)

Knees to Elbows. The Marine will begin by mounting a pull-up bar and arriving at a "dead hang." The Marine may grip the pull-up bar with the palms facing either outboard or inboard. (See Figure 9-51 on page 124.) On order, the Marine will raise the lower body until the knee caps and elbows are touching. (See Figure 9-52 on page 124.) On order, the Marine will slowly lower the legs, returning to the starting position. (See Figure 9-53 on page 124.)

Rope Climb. The rope climb is a movement that all Marines should be able to perform. There are three primary means of climbing a rope; one involves mostly upper body strength, while the remaining two are significantly more energy efficient. The hand-over-hand method does not require the use of the legs or feet. (See Figure 9-54 on page 125.) The "wrap" method involves the rope being wrapped around one leg and over the foot while simultaneously being locked into place by constant pressure exerted by the opposite foot. (See Figure 9-55 on page 125.) The "J-hook" method involves the rope being threaded under one foot and overtop the opposite foot. (See Figure 9-56 on page 125.)

Body Squat. The Marine will begin in the standing position with the feet shoulder width apart. The stomach will be sucked in and the back flat. Hand placement may be behind or to the side of the head. Fingers will not be interlocked and the elbows will remain pointing outboard. Alternatively, the arms may be held outstretched from the body, parallel with the deck. The head will be erect at all times. (See Figure 9-57 on page 125.) On order, the Marine will bend at the knees, keeping the stomach sucked in and the back straight. The knees will not move forward past the toes. Although the optimal bend in the knee will result in slightly less than a 90-degree angle, individual flexibility will determine the Marine's ability to perform a deep squat. The lumbar curve of the lower back will be maintained throughout the course of the exercise; weight will be distributed through the heels, while the chest and posterior are pushed out. (See Figure 9-58 on page 125.) On order,

Figure 9-41.

Figure 9-42.

Figure 9-43.

Figure 9-44.

Figure 9-45.

Figure 9-46.

Figure 9-47.

Figure 9-48.

Figure 9-49.

Figure 9-50.

the Marine will return to the starting position by extending the hips and straightening the legs. (See Figure 9-59 on next page.) To ensure proper form, the exercise should not be executed at a high tempo.

Lunges. The Marine will begin in the standing position with the feet shoulder width apart. The stomach will be sucked in and the back straight. Hand placement may be behind or to the side of the head. Fingers will not be interlocked and the elbows will remain pointing outboard. Alternatively, the hands may be placed on

Figure 9-51.

Figure 9-52.

Figure 9-53.

Figure 9-54.

Figure 9-55.

Figure 9-56.

the hips. The head will be erect at all times. (See Figure 9-60 on next page.) The exercise will be executed to a four-count cadence. On the command one, the Marine will step forward. The heel of the foot will make contact with the deck first, followed by the rest of the foot. The step should be wide enough to keep the knee from moving forward of the toes. The rear foot will provide balance during the exercise. On two, the Marine will lower the hips until the rear knee almost makes contact with the deck. Both the lead and rear legs will be bent to approximately

Figure 9-57.

Figure 9-58.

Figure 9-59.

Figure 9-60.

Figure 9-61.

Figure 9-62.

90 degrees. (See Figure 9-61.) On the command three, the Marine will rise up and begin to push off with the lead foot. The heel will be the last portion of the lead foot to break contact with the deck. On four, the Marine will have returned to the starting position. (See Figure 9-62.) The Marine will then alternate legs and repeat the exercise as prescribed above. To ensure proper form, the exercise should not be executed at a high tempo.

Split Squat. The Marine will begin the exercise with one leg forward. The stomach will be sucked in and the back straight. Hand placement may be behind or to the side of the head.

Figure 9-63.

Figure 9-64.

Figure 9-65.

Fingers will not be interlocked and the elbows will remain pointing outboard. Alternatively, the hands may be placed on the hips. The head will be erect at all times. (See Figure 9-63 on previous page.) This exercise may be executed to the commands down and up or as a four-count cadence. On order, the Marine will lower the hips straight down. The shoulders and hips will travel on the same imaginary line throughout the entire movement, as if the torso was affixed to a pole. The rear leg will be the working leg and the lead leg will provide the balance throughout the exercise. (See Figure 9-64 on previous page.) On order, the Marine will rise up by extending the rear leg while keeping the stomach in and the back straight. The torso will continue to move as if it were affixed to a pole until the Marine returns to the starting position. (See Figure 9-65 on previous page.) The Marine will continue the exercise until the assigned repetitions are accomplished before switching legs.

Buddy Exercises

Vertical Sit-Ups. To begin, Marines will be seated with one Marine securing the other's feet by grasping the left calf with the left hand and right calf with the right hand. (See Figure 9-66.) At no time during the exercise will the Marine securing the legs use the forearms to simultaneously secure the left and right calves. Additionally, placing the hands or forearms above the calves or directly behind the knee is not authorized. The Marine whose feet and legs are secured will be executing the exercise. The Marine executing the exercise will lay on the deck with arms crossed over the chest or the hands behind or to the side of the head. Fingers will not be interlocked and the elbows will remain pointing outboard. The Marine will have knees bent and the stomach sucked in. On order, the Marine will press the lower back into the deck executing a sit-up. (See Figure 9-67.) Once in the sit-up position, the Marine will transition to the standing position. (See Figure 9-68 on next page.) While standing, the Marine will push the hips forward while maintaining a straight back and erect head and shoulders. On order, the Marine will lower himself to the deck

Figure 9-66.

Figure 9-67.

by first squatting down to the sit-up position and then lowering the torso back to the starting position. The Marine who is securing the feet and legs must maintain a secure hold throughout the exercise to provide balance and assistance.

Buddy Leg Raises. To begin, one Marine will lay on the deck with the legs straight and perpendicular to the deck. The other Marine will straddle the head and grasp the feet of the Marine on the deck. The Marine standing will have the feet approximately shoulder width apart; the Marine on the deck will grasp the ankles of the Marine standing. (See Figure 9-69 on next page.) On order, the Marine standing will lightly push the legs toward the deck in the left, right, or center forward angles of movement.

Figure 9-68.

The Marine on the deck will keep the stomach sucked in and the lower back pressed into the deck. Once the Marines legs and feet are assisted downward, the Marine lying down will not allow them to touch the deck, but rather, will stop the legs and feet approximately six inches off the deck. (See Figure 9-70.) The Marine will then return the legs and feet to the starting position by contracting the abdominal muscles. (See Figure 9-71.) The Marine pushing the legs and feet toward the deck must be conscious of avoiding a predictable movement pattern. The Marine on the deck will be forced to work harder to stabilize the core if he is not cognizant of the direction in which the legs and feet are going to be pushed.

Squad Push-ups. Marines will begin by lying on their stomachs with their hands shoulder width apart. The "V" between the thumb and forefinger will be in line with the shoulder. The elbows will not point away from the torso more than 45 degrees. Throughout the entire exercise, Marines will keep their stomachs sucked in and backs flat. Each Marine will place the shins and feet on the shoulders of the Marine behind him. (See Figure 9-72 on next page.) On order, each Marine will push off the deck into

Figure 9-69.

Figure 9-70.

Figure 9-71.

a fully locked push-up position. At this time, Marines will suck their stomachs in and keep their backs straight. The arms will be straight and elbows locked out; the hips will remain up and in alignment with the shoulders; the head will be in a neutral position. (See Figure 9-73.) On order, all Marines will slowly lower themselves to the deck. (See Figure 9-74.) Anyone incapable of coming to a fully locked-out push-up position should be moved to the head or rear of the squad; Marines capable of performing such push-ups with relative ease should be moved to the center of the squad. It is recommended that no more than 10 Marines execute the exercise as a squad.

Buddy Squat. To begin, one Marine will begin in the fireman's carry position with the feet shoulder width apart. The stomach will be sucked in and the back flat. The Marine being carried will use the free hand to support the lumbar curve of the other Marine's lower back. (See Figure 9-75.) On order, the Marine will bend at the knees, keeping the stomach sucked in and the back flat. The knees will not move forward past the toes. Although the optimal bend in the knee will result in slightly less than a 90-degree angle, individual flexibility will determine the

Figure 9-72.

Figure 9-73.

Figure 9-74.

Figure 9-75.

Figure 9-76.

Figure 9-77.

Marine's ability to perform a deep squat. The lumbar curve of the lower back will be maintained throughout the course of the exercise; weight will be distributed through the heels, while the chest and posterior are pushed out. (See Figure 9-76 on previous page.) On order, the Marine will return to the starting position by extending the hips and straightening the legs. (See Figure 9-77 on previous page.) To ensure proper form, the exercise should not be executed at a high tempo.

Movement Exercises

Fireman's Carry. This movement exercise will begin with both Marines in the standing position. The Marine performing the carry will stand perpendicular to the Marine being carried. The Marine will execute a squat while reaching between the other Marine's legs with one arm and grasping the other Marine's wrist. The Marine being carried will lean forward until he lies across the other Marine's shoulders. (See Figure 9-78.) The Marine performing the carry will transition control of the wrist to the hand that is between the legs of the Marine being carried. Once in this position, the Marine performing the carry will rise to the standing

position. (See Figure 9-79.) Throughout the entire execution, the Marine being carried will place the palm of the free hand in the small of the back of the Marine performing the carry. On order, the Marine will rapidly carry the other Marine the designated distance. To prevent fatigue, Marines may change roles at the halfway point.

Under Arm Drag. This movement exercise will begin with Marines covered-down and facing the opposite direction of movement. The Marine standing behind the other Marine and closest to the starting line will execute the carry. The Marine performing the carry will thrust the forearms under the other Marine's armpits, until the Marine's back is touching the chest of the Marine performing the carry. The armpits should be positioned in the bend of the elbow or on the biceps of the Marine performing the carry. Once in this position, the Marine executing the drag will lock the hands without interlocking the fingers. (See Figure 9-80.) On order, the Marine will begin to move backwards in the direction of movement. The Marine that is being dragged will begin to move closer to the deck. The Marine executing the drag must lower his hips in order to remain upright throughout

Figure 9-78.

Figure 9-79.

Figure 9-80.

Figure 9-81.

Figure 9-82.

Figure 9-83.

the carry. (See Figure 9-81.) The feet of the Marine being carried will be splayed such that the instep of the foot is facing upward. At no time will the Marine being carried dig the heels into the deck or place the soles of the feet on the deck. Additionally, at no time will the Marine being carried assist the Marine executing the drag. To prevent fatigue, shorter distances (25 meters or less) are preferred and Marines may change roles at the halfway point.

Cross-Body Carry. This movement exercise will begin with both Marines in the standing position. The Marine performing the carry will stand perpendicular to the Marine being carried. The Marine performing the carry will wrap one arm over the near shoulder, around the head, and under the armpit of the Marine being carried. (See Figure 9-82.) The Marine performing the carry will lean forward slightly, bending at the hips and maintaining a straight back and slightly bent knees. The Marine being carried will lie across the back of the Marine performing the carry. The Marine performing the carry will reach over legs of the Marine being carried and place the free arm around the other Marine's legs, grasping the leg closest to the deck. The Marine performing the carry will

straighten up, lifting the other Marine off the deck, and adjust the Marine being carried such that he is parallel to the deck and positioned at or above the hips of the Marine performing the carry. (See Figures 9-83 and 9-84 on next page.) On order, the Marine will rapidly carry the other Marine the designated distance. To prevent fatigue, shorter distances (25 meters or less) are preferred, and Marines may change roles at the halfway point.

Buddy Drag. This movement exercise will begin with Marines covered-down and facing the direction of movement. The Marine standing in front of the other Marine and closest to the starting line will execute the carry. The Marine being carried will thrust both arms over the shoulders of the Marine performing the carry. Once in this position, the Marine being carried will lock the hands without interlocking the fingers. (See Figure 9-85 on next page.) The Marine performing the carry will ensure that his shoulders are seated in the armpits of the Marine being carried. The Marine performing the carry will grasp the wrists or forearms of the Marine being carried. (See Figure 9-86 on next page.) At no time will the forearms of the Marine being carried contact the neck or throat

Figure 9-84.

of the Marine performing the carry. Additionally, the feet of the Marine being carried will remain in contact with the deck; however, at no time will the Marine being carried place the soles of the feet on the deck. Further, at no time will the Marine being carried assist the Marine executing the drag. On order, the Marine will rapidly carry the other Marine the designated distance. (See Figure 9-87.) To prevent fatigue, shorter distances (25 meters or less) are preferred and Marines may change roles at the halfway point.

Piggy-Back. This movement exercise will begin with Marines covered-down and facing the direction of movement. The Marine standing in front of the other Marine and closest to the starting line will execute the carry. The Marine being carried will place the hands on the shoulders of the Marine performing the carry. The Marine performing the carry will lean forward slightly, bending at the hips and maintaining a straight back and slightly bent knees. The Marine being carried will jump onto the back of the Marine performing the carry and lock the hands, without interlocking the fingers, around the shoulders of the Marine performing the carry. The Marine performing the carry will reach

Figure 9-85.

Figure 9-86.

Figure 9-87.

over the legs of the Marine being carried and grasp the hamstrings or behind the knees. (See Figure 9-88.) The Marine performing the carry will straighten up, lifting the other Marine, and adjust the Marine being carried such that he is perpendicular to the deck and positioned at or above the hips of the Marine performing the carry. (See Figure 9-89.) At no time will the forearms of the Marine being carried contact the neck or throat of the Marine performing the carry. On order, the Marine will rapidly carry the other Marine the designated distance. To prevent fatigue, shorter distances (25 meters or less) are preferred, and Marines may change roles at the halfway point.

Bear Crawl. The Marine will begin by maintaining four points of contact with the deck: the hands and feet. The Marine will face the deck and move forward by placing the right hand and left foot forward. (See Figure 9-90 on next page.) Once both the hand and foot are on the ground, the Marine will move forward by placing the left hand and right foot forward. (See Figure 9-91 on next page.) The Marine will continue in this manner until the prescribed distance has been reached. The Marine performing the bear crawl will not stand up until the exercise has been conducted for the designated distance. At no time will the knees make contact with the deck.

Crab Walk. The Marine will begin by maintaining four points of contact with the deck: the hands and feet. The Marine will face away from the deck, maintain elevated hips and support the body with only the hands and feet. The Marine will move forward by placing the left hand and right foot forward. (See Figures 9-92 and 9-93 on next page.) Once both the hand and foot are on the ground, the Marine will move forward by placing the right hand and left foot forward. The Marine will continue in this manner until the prescribed distance has been reached. The Marine performing the crab walk will not stand up until the exercise has been conducted for the designated distance. At no time will the Marine rest on the heels or allow the hips to contact the deck. Exercise variations include performing the crab walk laterally, as well as in a linear fashion.

Figure 9-88.

Figure 9-89.

Figure 9-90.

Figure 9-91.

General Aerobic Training

Aerobic training is often linked to endurance training. Such training requires aerobic, or oxygenated, energy pathways to supply fuel to each of the working muscles. Terms often used to describe aerobic training include: cardiovascular, cardiopulmonary, or cardio-respiratory endurance training because aerobic training significantly challenges the heart (cardio), blood vessels (vascular), and lungs (pulmonary or respiratory). The purpose of aerobic conditioning is to improve the efficiency with which the body produces energy for working muscles by means of aerobic metabolism. Quite simply, cardio-respiratory endurance training will improve aerobic energy production and lead to positive long- and short-term changes within the Marine's body.

Figure 9-92.

Within the first few weeks of beginning a cardio-respiratory endurance program, a Marine's body will adapt to the various stresses placed upon it, resulting in a decreased heart rate whether resting or working, an increase in the amount of blood pumped by each heartbeat (stroke volume), and an increase in the amount of blood pumped by the heart in one minute (cardiac output). After engaging in a cardio-respiratory endurance program for more than 16 weeks, it is common for a Marine to possess

Figure 9-93.

an increased number of red blood cells, higher plasma volume in his blood, greater capillary density, weight loss, and a decreased resting heart rate.

To develop a proper cardio-respiratory endurance program, Marines must apply the combat conditioning principle of overload. By "shocking" his system and allowing adequate recovery, a Marine may improve aerobic fitness while simultaneously limiting the risk of injury and/or illness. Aerobic fitness requires three to five training sessions per week, at a moderate intensity, for a period of 20 to 60 minutes. Additionally, recent research indicates that aerobic exercise sessions may be separated into two or more sessions of at least ten minutes, resulting in significant cardio-respiratory endurance gains.

There are several different exercise modes that may enhance a Marine's cardio-respiratory endurance, including, but not limited to: running, jogging, walking, swimming, cycling, rowing, and striding on an elliptical trainer. By cross training, or providing multiple aerobic activities in a single exercise program, a Marine may increase his cardio-respiratory endurance through a varied, rather than boring, workout. Besides reducing boredom, the physical conditioning principle of variety allows for more enjoyable physical training sessions.

Developing Cardio-Respiratory Endurance

Beginning an aerobic training program by imitating a friend or following a fitness magazine's schedule may not necessarily be the best approach to developing cardio-respiratory endurance. Oftentimes, sample programs present idealized training that most people with jobs, families, and additional responsibilities cannot follow without significantly disrupting their lives. The most efficient training programs are individually tailored and incorporate long slow distance, pace, and interval training sessions.

a. **Long Slow Distance Training.** Long slow distance training is conducted at an intensity of approximately 50 to 85 percent of one's heart rate reserve (HRR). The HRR may be determined by subtracting the resting heart rate (the number of heartbeats per minute while at rest) from the maximal heart rate (220–one's age). Long slow distance training should be performed for a duration ranging from 30 minutes to several hours. The main benefit of this type of training is improved energy production due to an increase in the amount of capillaries transporting oxygen and nutrients to the working muscles, as well as an increase in the number of mitochondria in each muscle cell.

b. **Pace Training.** Pace training involves exercise sessions that are conducted at approximately the same pace in which one runs the semiannual PFT three-mile run or slightly faster. Pace training forces a Marine to push himself and challenges the Marine's body to adapt. Just as in strength training, the body will respond to the demands placed upon it; if a Marine always runs at the same pace, the body will not be stimulated to adapt and become more efficient. Unlike long slow distance training, pace training relies on a combination of aerobic and anaerobic energy production. Training with high intensity will often cause a rapid increase in breathing rate, as well as a burning or heavy sensation in the working muscles. Such sensations are caused by an increased production of lactate, a product of anaerobic energy production. After an appropriate cool-down period, Marines may effectively remove lactate from muscles by participating in a comprehensive flexibility session. The main benefits of pace training are the improvement of one's running economy and the understanding of how to run with high intensity.

c. **Interval Training.** Interval training consists of short, high intensity bouts ranging in duration from 30 seconds to several minutes. The purpose of interval training is to condition one's body to elevate performance and exercise at very high intensities. Much like sprinting at the end of a long distance run, interval training assists Marines in pushing beyond an already strenuous capacity. An interval session may consist of five to ten interval and recovery sessions. It is important to remember that interval training is very stressful. As such, after each interval session, an equal period of rest or low-intensity exercise should be allotted for recovery. Additionally, interval training should be limited to a small portion of one's overall cardio-respiratory endurance training program. Interval training in excess not only results in fatigue but carries a heightened risk of injury as well.

Benefits of Cardio-Respiratory Endurance Training

A properly designed cardio-respiratory endurance training program, consisting of three to five sessions per week, will provide a Marine with a strong aerobic fitness level. By combining long slow distance, pace, and interval training, a Marine will likely maximize his performance during day-to-day physical activities, as well as during the semiannual PFT.

Semi-annual Physical Fitness Test and Semi-annual Combat Fitness Test

For the most current information on the semi-annual Physical Fitness Test (PFT) and Combat Fitness Test (CFT), including male and female scoring and how to prepare for the tests visit the Marine Corps Force Fitness website at: https://www.fitness.marines.mil.

Negative Effects of Physical Training

Fatigue. In addition to muscular soreness and stiffness, the Marine who exercises for fitness will experience fatigue as a result of exertions. Fatigue is a feeling of tiredness that results from prolonged or intense physical or mental activity. Fatigue is a regulator in that it prevents us from damaging our body's systems by overexertion (too much work). The accumulation of training fatigue can result in long term decrements in performance with or without the associated physical or mental signs and symptoms of maladaptation. This is called overtraining. Overtraining limits a Marine's ability to increase physical performance and often results in degraded performance. It can take weeks or months to recover. Thus it is extremely important to be aware of indications of excessive fatigue. Fatigue may be neuromuscular, organic, or mental.

a. **Neuromuscular fatigue** is indicated by cramps, heaviness in the limbs and failure of the muscular system to perform. It is temporary and normally not dangerous. Examples of neuromuscular fatigue would be the cramps in the stomach muscles when you've done just about your maximum in situps or the heaviness felt in your legs at the end of a long run.

b. **Organic fatigue** is normally felt in the inner organs and is indicated by hyperventilation (uncontrollably high rate of breathing), heat illness (the failure of the body's cooling system to maintain the normal temperature range), and nausea or other illness.

c. **Mental fatigue** may be brought on by nervousness, low morale, depression, and lack of rest. Energy is spent on worry and through muscular tension. Chronic mental fatigue contributes to an inability to exert maximum physical effort. This lack of tolerance for effort is called the effort syndrome.

Fatigue is natural and normal. Everyone experiences it in one of its forms. It is important to be able to recognize fatigue because unchecked fatigue will lead to exhaustion and collapse. An example of exhaustion is the case of a runner who has gone far past the point of a good maximum effort, is starting to experience severe muscular pain and an inability to focus vision, is experiencing nausea, has a very high body temperature (104 degrees or higher), and is experiencing an uncontrollable shortness of breath. If that person continues to run, one or more body systems will fail and cause collapse. A good warning sign of overexertion is a strong pounding sensation in the temples of the individual with each pulse.

Sleep and Rest. Nature's way of eliminating fatigue is through sleep and rest. Our need for sleep and rest is obvious, and the Marine Corps plans accordingly. Even during basic training, which may be the most demanding experience a Marine faces, each recruit normally receives a full eight hours of sleep. The sleep is necessary in order for a recruit's body to recover from one training day and build its reserves of energy for the next.

a. Sleep is a state of unconsciousness produced by the body's central nervous system for the purposes of restoring and rebuilding its capabilities. The characteristics of sleep are relaxation of the muscles and of the mind. While all people do not require the same amount of sleep, eight hours are recommended for most young adults. Getting the proper amount of sleep is important. Too much sleep can cause you to be lazy. Too little sleep causes irritability and a reduction in the mental powers of reasoning and learning.

b. Rest is a relaxation of the mind and body. The characteristics of rest are a lessening of physical and mental activities. The amount of time required for rest depends upon a person's age, level of fatigue, and overall physical condition. An example of rest is the 10-minute break given during each hour of a forced march. Resting regularly during the day will increase both your effectiveness on the job and your enjoyment of your daily pursuits.

The Rewards of Physical Fitness

Physical fitness is not a gift; like the respect of your fellow Marines, physical fitness must continually be earned. It must be done by each individual Marine; no one can do it for you. Self-improvement requires a hard, determined effort; however, the reward is a strong, healthy body capable of accomplishing any mission, at any time, under any set of circumstances. This chapter presented basic concepts related to physical training for combat. For more information seek out a FFI, your NCOs, and visit www.fitness.marines.mil.

CHAPTER 10

Small Arms

The discussion in this chapter relates to general characteristics and principles of small arms.

A small arm is defined as a weapon which discharges small antipersonnel projectiles over relatively short ranges. Currently, weapons with a bore diameter of 1.181" (30mm) or less are classified as small arms. The size or bore diameter of some weapons is expressed in millimeters.

For example, the M16A4 rifle is a 5.56mm weapon and the M240 is referred to as a 7.62mm weapon. Small arms are also classified into three main groups. These are hand guns, shoulder weapons, and machine guns.

Component Parts of Small Arms

Every small arm has four basic components, which are barrel, breech mechanism (bolt), firing mechanism, and receiver.

Barrel

The barrel is a straight metal tube with the primary purpose of directing the projectile toward the target. The breech end is the end into which the cartridge is inserted. The part of the tube through which the projectile is pushed by the propelling gases is called the bore. The bore may contain rifling which is a system of lands and grooves. Lands are ridges between grooves, which give the projectile a stablizing spin to provide for greater accuracy.

The chamber is located just behind the bore and is shaped for a cartridge to fit snugly. When a high-pressure cartridge is fired, the cartridge case expands against the inner wall of the chamber forming a gas-tight seal. This action

is known as obturation. It is important because it prevents the escape of gases around the bolt. This protects the shooter and ensures accuracy of the weapon.

Types of Bolts

Breech Mechanism (Bolt)

The breech mechanism is a device which keeps the cartridge case in the chamber while obturation provides the gas-tight seal. (See Figure 10-1(a).) The following parts may be added to the basic bolt:

Figure 10-1(a).

- A portion of the firing device such as the firing pin.
- An extractor for removing the expended cartridge case from the chamber.
- An ejector for throwing the expended cartridge case from the weapon.
- A locking device for locking the bolt to the barrel. Three common locking methods are the following:
  - The rotating bolt (Figure 10-1(b).) has locking lugs which are rotated into locking recesses in the receiver or barrel to positively lock the weapon. The service rifle (M16A4/M4) rifle has this type of breech mechanism.
  - The interrupted screw-horizontal swinging breech (Figure 10-1(c).) is constructed so that the entire bolt swings into a locking recess.
  - The locking-block breech mechanism (Figure 10-1(d).) has a block that swings or is cammed into position in a locking recess in the bolt.

Firing Device

This is a device which causes ignition of the cartridge in the chamber. The firing mechanism normally includes a firing pin, hammer, sear, and trigger.

The firing pin strikes the primer of the cartridge causing ignition. There are two types of firing pins, moveable and fixed.

- A moveable firing pin is a steel rod that runs longitudinally through the bolt and is driven forward either by spring expansion or hammer action, or a combination of both. The three types of movable firing pins are free-floating, inertial, and percussion.
  - **Free-floating** is driven forward by a sharp blow of a hammer and is retracted by a cam action (the M16A4/M4). No spring force is used on either forward or rearward movement of the pin.
  - **Inertia** is shorter than the total distance it must travel to strike the primer of a cartridge. It is driven forward by a hammer. A spring, which is

Figure 10-1(b).

Figure 10-1(c).

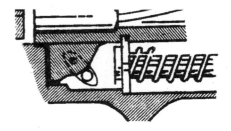

Figure 10-1(d).

compressed on the forward movement, retracts the pin.
  - **Percussion** is driven forward by the force of a compressed spring and is retracted by the camming action that cocks the weapon.
- No small arms employed by the Marine Corps uses a fixed firing pin.

Receiver

The receiver is a device secured to the barrel to contain certain other parts of the weapon. The receiver may fulfill any or all of the following purposes. It may house a bolt, a source of ammunition (such as a magazine) or a major portion of the firing mechanism. Further, it may provide a base for a rear sight or provide a means of securing a stock to the weapon.

Additional Parts

In addition to the basic components, small arms normally have other parts which are added for safety, accuracy, and convenience, such as the following examples:

- Safety devices to prevent premature or accidental firing.
- Sights used to aim the weapons.
- A means for holding ammunition in position ready for use, such as a magazine or belt.

A magazine is a container that holds a number of rounds and fits into the receiver. A built-in spring in the magazine pushes the round into position to permit chambering.

A belt is used in rapid-fire automatic weapons like the machine gun. The rounds are held together in flexible cloth or metal link belts. Once the first round is fired, the belt is automatically fed into the weapon, placing each round in such a position that it may be rapidly chambered and fired.

Cycle of Operation

Every small arm has a specific cycle of functioning. This cycle refers to the actions that occur each time a round is fired. The sequence or manner of accomplishing them may vary in weapons of different design. The following is an example of the M16/M4 cycle:

Firing

This is accomplished when the primer of the cartridge is struck by the firing pin. The explosive composition in the primer is crushed and ignites the propellant in the cartridge case, forcing the bullet out of the barrel.

Unlocking

The bolt is unlocked so that it may move. Weapons using high-pressure cartridges combine slow initial extraction with the unlocking of the bolt to overcome the effects of obturation. The cartridge-case head could be torn off if it was not loosened in the chamber before extraction.

Extracting

This action is the removal of the empty cartridge case from the chamber. This step must be timed to prevent a blowback of gases into the shooter's face. The extractor may be a small hooked piece of metal in the bolt, which grips the extracting groove or rim of the cartridge case and pulls the empty case to the rear.

Ejecting

This action is the removal of the expended cartridge case from the receiver. This step can be accomplished by placing an ejector in the receiver. The case is carried to the rear by the extractor until it strikes the ejector. The ejector causes the case to be removed from the receiver. Another way of accomplishing this step is to use a spring-loaded ejector in the face of the bolt. When the case clears the chamber, the spring expands, throwing the case from the weapon.

Cocking

Cocking is the positioning of the operating parts in readiness to fire another round. The hammer or firing pin is moved to the rear and held there until released.

Feeding

This action places a round in the receiver ready for chambering. In its simplest form, it is the insertion of a cartridge by hand. Feeding usually is accomplished by a spring in a magazine, a mechanism in the receiver or a series of cams and pawls.

Chambering

This is the action required to place the new round in the chamber. Again, in its simplest form, the shooter places the round into the chamber by hand. In some weapons, it takes place as the bolt strips the new round from the feed mechanism and forces it into the chamber.

Locking

This action secures the bolt to the barrel,

preventing the loss of gas pressure until after the bullet has left the muzzle. It is accomplished manually by the shooter or automatically by mechanical action of various parts.

Types of Operating Systems

The cycle of functioning is accomplished by one of three types of operating systems. They are classified according to their source of power.

Manual Operation

In manual operation, the source of power is the shooter. An example is the bolt-action rifle. The shooter chambers the round by pushing the bolt forward. After the round is fired, the shooter unlocks the bolt and pulls it to the rear. This causes extracting, ejecting, and cocking. Bolt-action rifles, most revolvers and some shotguns, are manually operated weapons.

Gas Operation

In gas-operated weapons, a portion of the expanding gas is tapped off through a port in the barrel. The gas is vented into a gas cylinder or into a tube as with the service rifle/carbine (M16A4/M4). The gases moving rearward act against the operating parts, which causes unlocking, extracting, and cocking. A feed mechanism then feeds the new round. The forward motion of the bolt chambers the round and locks the breech.

Recoil Operation

This system uses the rearward thrust (recoil) of the weapon to drive the barrel, bolt, and other operating parts to the rear. The bolt is locked to the barrel at the time of firing and remains locked, recoiling rearward with the barrel, until the bullet has left the muzzle and the gas pressure is reduced. After the bullet has left the muzzle, the bolt is unlocked from the barrel and continues to the rear. Various methods are used to unlock the bolt and actuate the other operating parts. The 9mm pistol has this type of operation.

Automatic and Semiautomatic Firing Systems

A weapon that functions automatically utilizes gas, blowback, or recoil operation. Automatic functioning does not mean that a weapon that functions automatically also fires automatically.

Semiautomatic Fire

This is the firing of one round each time pressure is applied to the trigger. The cycle of functioning is completed automatically; however, the trigger must be released and pressure reapplied to fire a subsequent round. The 9mm pistol is a weapon that is capable only of semiautomatic fire.

Automatic Fire

This is the continuous operation of a weapon while the trigger is held to the rear. It ceases to operate when the trigger is released, all ammunition is expended or a stoppage occurs. The M240 machine gun is an example of a weapon that is capable only of automatic fire.

Combination of Automatic and Semiautomatic Fire

Some weapons are designed to fire automatic or semiautomatic. These weapons have a selector which permits the shooter to choose the type of fire. The M4A1 carbine and the M27 infantry automatic rifle are examples of these type of weapons.

General Care and Cleaning

(Specific care and cleaning of the M16A4/M4 and M240B can be found in the chapters dealing with those weapons.)

The Marine today is armed with the finest infantry weapons devised by man, but unless given the proper care, they are no better than the clubs carried by cave men. Seventy-five percent of the stoppages that occur in a modern automatic or semiautomatic weapon can be traced back to improper care and cleaning.

In general, the care and cleaning of your weapon is a simple job, but here are a few things to remember under unusual conditions. Let us first take a look at some of the tools in Figure 10-2 that you use to care for your weapons:

1. Cleaner, lubricant, and preservative (CLP). When using CLP, always shake the bottle well before each use. In all but the coldest arctic conditions, CLP is the lubricant that should be used for the service rifle.

2. Rods. The rod is in three sections with a handle assembly.

3. Brushes. The brushes are bore, chamber, and general purpose.

4. Patch holder. The patch holder includes swabs, patches, pipe cleaners, and clean rags.

5. Swab (patch). A 1" or 2½" square piece of cloth used with the cleaning rod to clean the bore of a weapon. Swabs are packed in a plastic bag or cardboard box.

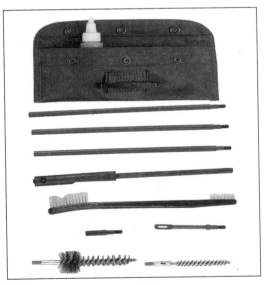

Figure 10-2.

Cleaning of Weapons

Steps to Cleaning your Weapon

1. Be sure the weapon is in Condition 4.
2. Disassemble weapon.
3. With a dry rag, wipe off all old oil and dirt.
4. Use your small arms cleaning brush to clean the corners, screw heads, etc.
5. Run a swab with CLP through the bore, following this with a wire brush, then by several dry swabs. Repeat this process until the dry swabs come out clean. Clean the chamber the same way.
6. Run a lightly oiled swab through the bore and chamber.
7. Clean the face of the bolt and inside of receiver with a general purpose brush, rag, and/or swab soaked with CLP applied. Clean off the CLP with dry rags and swabs. Repeat this process until all traces of carbon are removed.
8. Put a light coat of oil over all metal parts on your weapon, being careful not to over lubricate or trap perspiration from your hands under the oil, where it can start to rust.
9. If your weapon is magazine fed, inspect the interior of the magazine by depressing the follower. If the interior is dirty or rusted, disassemble, clean, and oil lightly. You can avoid many stoppages by always handling your magazines so that they will not become dirty or dented.
10. Reassemble your weapon, and conduct a function check.

REMEMBER:

Do

1. Clean the chamber with the same care as the bore.
2. Use a cleaning brush to clean the small, hard-to-reach parts.
3. Run the swab or brush all the way through the bore before you try to pull the rod back out.

Don't

1. Don't use unauthorized cleaning materials. They could damage your weapon.
2. Don't place a swab or plug in the muzzle of your weapon. The barrel will rust due to moisture trapped by the swab. Serious injury may result if you should forget to remove the swab or plug and attempt to fire the weapon.
3. Don't attempt to disassemble your weapon beyond authorized disassembly. You could damage certain parts beyond repair.

Cleaning Weapons Before Firing

Before you fire your weapon you should do the following:

1. Clean weapon as described above.
2. Make sure there are no obstructions, such as dirt, mud, or snow in the bore. Failure to observe this precaution may result in serious injury.
3. If your weapon is magazine fed, check to see that magazines are clean and operative.

Cleaning of the Weapon in the Field

Preventive maintenance in the field is performed when detailed disassembly and cleaning is not practical due to operational tempo or the level of threat. To perform limited field preventive maintenance—

1. Place the service rifle in Condition 4.
2. Break the service rifle down by removing the rear take-down pin and rotating the upper receiver and barrel forward.
3. Remove the bolt carrier group.

Note: Do not disassemble the bolt carrier group further.

Clean the bolt carrier group as follows:

1. Clean the upper and lower receiver groups without further disassembly.
2. Clean the bore and chamber. Lubricate the service rifle.
3. Reassemble the service rifle and perform a function check.

Care of Weapons in Arctic Climates

In the cooler regions of the earth, grease and oil thicken and cause much trouble. These materials, while fluid at normal temperatures, usually become thick or almost solid as the temperature drops below freezing. Consequently, they can slow down or stop the operation of weapons. For this reason, the proper type of lubricants must be used and then only in small quantities.

Much difficulty is caused by bringing cold weapons into a warm room or tent. When the cold metal of the weapon comes in contact with the warm, moist air, condensation takes place, leaving drops of moisture on the weapon. These drops of moisture will cause rust or will freeze when the weapon is taken outdoors. If possible, weapons should be stored in unheated sheds. Snow, blown or drifted into the weapon, will cause no harm as long as the temperature is below freezing. But when the weapon becomes heated by firing, the snow melts and the moisture spreads to other surfaces. When the weapon cools, the moisture will freeze and lock the mechanism tightly, preventing further operation. Occasional operation of the weapon by hand may keep its parts from freezing together.

Care of Weapons in Tropical Climates

In those tropical parts of the world where large water areas exist, there is a large amount of moisture in the air. Extra precautions must be taken to prevent your weapon from rusting. At all times it will be necessary to clean your weapons more than once a day.

Care of Weapons in Desert Climates

Due to the fact that there is little moisture in the air, rust is a small problem in the desert, but where vegetation does not cover the earth, a large quantity of dirt, dust, and sand is constantly swept through the air by wind. This material sticks to exposed oil and grease on your weapon. Grit of this nature caught between moving parts increases friction. A large amount will jam the moving parts and prevent their functioning. If the weapon does function under these conditions, the parts will become worn almost certainly, resulting in stoppage and requiring frequent replacement. Remember, in desert climates, use as little oil as possible and clean your weapons often.

Repairs

When you find a part broken or missing on your weapon, report it at once to your leadership. Your weapon should only be repaired by a qualified ordnance repairman. Do not attempt to detail strip or repair your weapon yourself.

Modern military weapons are expensive and made by precision methods. Without the proper skill and tools, attempts by you to repair your own weapon can be damaging to the weapon and dangerous to you.

Special Instructions

Due to the difference in operation and construction of some weapons, additional steps and precautions are required for their care that are not covered by this chapter. These special instructions are covered in the chapter on the particular weapon.

CHAPTER 11

Service Rifles

*Every Marine has been trained as a rifleman, for it is the rifleman who must close
with and destroy the enemy. Riflemen form the basis for success on the battlefield. Become
thoroughly acquainted with your rifle and treat it well. The success of your mission, your life,
and the lives of your buddies may someday depend on you and your rifle. This chapter tells
you the names and parts of your rifle, the way to strip it and put it back together,
the proper care to keep it operating, and how to reduce common stoppages.*

Description

The service rifle and carbine are light-weight, 5.56mm, magazine-fed, gas-operated, air-cooled, shoulder-fired rifles. The rifle and carbine fire in either semiautomatic (single-shot) mode or a three-round burst through the use of a selector lever. The M16A4 (Figure 11-1 on next page) has a maximum effective range of 550 meters for individual or point targets, and the M4 (Figure 11-2 on page 147) has a maximum effective ranges of 500 meters. The bore and chamber are chrome-plated to reduce wear and fouling. The handguards feature rail mounting systems for additional components.

An aluminum receiver helps reduce the overall weight of the rifle. The trigger guard is equipped with a spring-loaded retaining pin that, when depressed, allows the trigger guard to be rotated out of the way for access to the trigger while wearing heavy gloves. An ejection-port cover prevents dirt and sand from getting into the rifle through the ejection port. The ejection-port cover should be closed when the rifle is not being fired. It is automatically opened by the action of the bolt carrier. The muzzle compensator serves as a flash suppressor and assists in reducing muzzle climb

M16A4

Caliber	5.56mm
Weight	8.79 lbs. (approximately) with 30 rounds in a magazine
Length	39 5/8" with compensator
Mechanical Features	Rifling (right-hand 1/7 twist) Detachable carrying handle Integral accessory mounting RAS
Firing Characteristics	Muzzle velocity - 3,100 fps Chamber pressure - 52,000 psi Cyclic rate of fire - 800 rounds per minute (approximately)
Max Effective Rates of Fire	Semi - 45 rounds per minute Burst - 90 rounds per minute
Sustained Rate of Fire	12 to 15 rounds per minute
Max Effective Range	601.48 yd. (550 m) (individual point targets) 656.16 yd. (600 m) (area targets)
Max Range	3,936.96 yd. (3,600 m)
Fire Selector	SAFE, SEMI, BURST

Figure 11-1.

Note: Procedures to clear, disassemble, clean, assemble, perform a function check, handle, and carry are the same for the service rifle and carbine. Any difference in between the two weapons will be specifically mentioned and from here forward the M16A4 and M4 will be refered to as the "Service Rifle."

M4 CARBINE

Caliber	5.56mm
Weight	7.5 lbs. with 30 rounds in a magazine
Length	Buttstock closed - 29.75" Buttstock open - 33"
Mechanical Features	Rifling (right-hand 1/7 twist) Detachable carrying handle Integral accessory mounting rail
Firing Characteristics	Muzzle velocity - 2,970 fps Chamber pressure - 52,000 psi Cyclic rate of fire - 700-900 rounds per minute (approximately)
Max Effective Rates of Fire	Semi - 45 rounds per minute Burst - 90 rounds per minute
Sustained Rate of Fire	12 to 15 rounds per minute
Max Effective Range	546.8 yd. (500 m) (individual point targets) 656.16 yd. (600 m) (area targets)
Max Range	3,936.96 yd. (3,600 m)
Fire Selector	SAFE, SEMI, BURST

Disassembly and Assembly

Disassembly of the Service Rifle

Individual Marines are authorized only to field strip the service rifle. This is done only for cleaning or instruction. No force should be used in disassembling or assembling the weapon. When disassembling, the parts should be laid out left to right in the order they are taken out of the rifle and put back in the reverse order.

Clearing the Service Rifle

The first consideration in handling any weapon is to ensure that the weapon is clear. To clear the service rifle.

- Point the weapon in a safe direction. Attempt to point the selector lever to safe. If the weapon is not cocked, the selector lever cannot be pointed to safe position.
- Press the magazine release and remove the magazine.
- To lock the bolt open, pull the charging handle rearward. Press the bottom of the bolt catch and allow the bolt to move forward until it engages the bolt catch. Return the charging handle to forward position, ensuring it locks into place. Verify the selector lever is on safe.
- Visually check the receiver and chamber to ensure these areas contain no ammunition.
- With the selector lever on safe, allow the bolt to go forward by pressing the upper

Figure 11-2.

portion of the bolt catch. The weapon is now cleared and is at weapons Condition 4.

Disassembly

Main Group Disassembly

The service rifle is disassembled into three main groups. (See Figure 11-3.)

Before disassembling the service rifle:

- Ensure the weapon is in Condition 4.
- Remove the sling.

Upper Receiver

- Move the take-down pin from the left to the right as far as it will go to allow the lower receiver to pivot down from the upper receiver.
- Move the receiver pivot pin from the left to the right as far as it will go and separate the upper and lower receivers.
- Pull back the charging handle and bolt carrier approximately 3" and remove the bolt carrier group.
- Remove the charging handle by sliding it back and down, out of the upper receiver.

Bolt Carrier

To disassemble the bolt carrier:

- Remove the firing pin retaining pin.
- Push the bolt back into the bolt carrier to the locked position.
- Tap the base of the bolt carrier against the

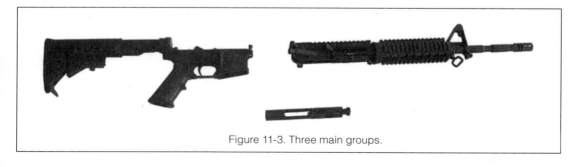

Figure 11-3. Three main groups.

palm of your hand so that the firing pin will drop out.

- Rotate the bolt cam pin one-quarter turn, and lift the bolt cam pin out.
- Withdraw the bolt assembly from the carrier.
- Press on the extractor's rear and use the firing pin to push out the extractor-retaining pin. Remove the extractor and spring (the spring is permanently attached to the extractor). (See Figure 11-4.)

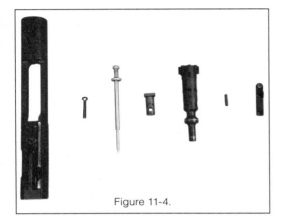

Figure 11-4.

Caution

Be careful not to damage the tip of the firing pin while pushing out the Extractor-retaining pin.

Note: The extractor assembly has a rubber insert within the spring. Do not attempt to remove it. If the spring comes loose, put the large end of the spring in the extractor and seat it. Push in the extractor pin.

Lower Receiver

To disassemble the lower receiver:

- Press in the buffer and depress the buffer retainer.

Note: It may be necessary to use the edge of the charging handle to depress the buffer retainer.

- Press the hammer downward and ease the buffer and action spring forward and out of the receiver. Separate the parts. (See Figure 11-5.)

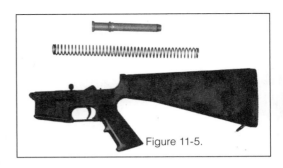

Figure 11-5.

- No further disassembly of the lower receiver is performed.

Note: In combat situations, the rifle may be partially disassembled in any sequence. However, combat situations are the exception not the rule. Under normal operating circumstances, disassemble the rifle in the sequence just performed. Any further disassembly of the rifle is to be performed by a qualified armorer.

Magazine Disassembly

The magazine should be disassembled regularly for cleaning to avoid the possibility of malfunction or stoppage of the service rifle caused by dirty or damaged magazines. To disassemble the magazine:

- **Gently** pry up and push the base plate out from the magazine.
- Jiggle the spring and follower to remove. Do not remove the follower from the spring. (See Figure 11-6.)

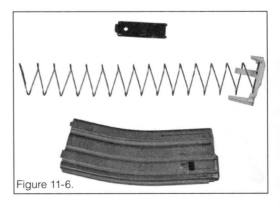

Figure 11-6.

Upper Receiver and Barrel Assembly

Upper receiver contains ejection port, ejection-port cover, housing for key and bolt carrier assembly, and bolt assembly and mounting surface for the carrying-handle assembly. Rifle-barrel assembly is air-cooled, contains compensator and front-sight assembly.

Lower Receiver and Buttstock Assembly

Provides firing control for the service rifle and carbine. M16A4 buttstock provides a storage space for basic cleaning materials. The buttstock of the M4 is collapsible and adjusts to 4 different positions.

Care and Cleaning of the Service Rifle

Cleaning Materials

The following cleaning materials are used in preventive maintenance. (See Figure 11-7.)
- CLP. Always shake the bottle well before use.
- Rod in three sections and a handle assembly.
- Patch-holder section, swabs, patches, pipe cleaners, and clean rags.
- Brushes: bore, chamber and general-purpose.

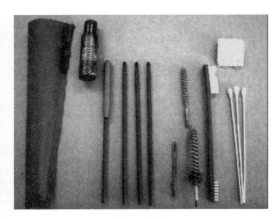

Figure 11-7.

Cleaning the Upper Receiver

Basic cleaning of the upper-receiver group should include the following:
- Attach the three-rod sections together, but leave each one about two turns short of being tight.
- Attach the patch holder onto the rod.
- Point the muzzle down and insert the non-patch end of the rod into the chamber. Attach the handle to the cleaning-rod section and pull a CLP-moistened 5.56mm patch through the bore.
- Attach the bore brush to the rod, but leave it two turns short of being tight. Put a few drops of CLP on the bore brush. Insert the rod into the barrel from the chamber end, attach the handle, and pull the brush through the bore. Repeat three times. Remove bore brush and attach the patch holder to the rod with a CLP moistened patch. Insert the rod into the barrel from the chamber end, attach the handle, and pull the patch through the bore.
- Inspect the bore for cleanliness by holding the muzzle to your eye and looking into the bore.
- Repeat the above steps until the patches come out of the bore clean.
- Attach the chamber brush and one section of the cleaning rod to the handle. Moisten it well with CLP and insert it into the chamber.
- Scrub the chamber and bolt lugs using a combination of a plunging and clockwise rotating action.

Note: Do not reverse direction of the brush while it is in the chamber.
- Clean the interior portion of the upper receiver with the general-purpose brush and CLP.
- Dry the bore, chamber, and the interior of the receiver with rifle patches, swabs, and clean rags until they come out clean. Then moisten all interior surfaces with CLP.
- Wipe the barrel, gas tube, and handguards clean with a rag.

Cleaning the Bolt Carrier Group

- Clean the outer and inner surfaces of the bolt carrier with a general-purpose brush.
- Clean the bolt carrier key with a pipe cleaner.
- Clean the locking lugs, gas rings, and exterior of the bolt with the general-purpose brush.
- Insert a swab into the rear of the bolt and swab out the firing pin recess and gas ports.
- Clean the extractor with the general-purpose brush, ensuring all the carbon is removed from underneath the extractor lip.
- Clean extractor pin, firing pin and firing pin retaining pin using the general-purpose brush and CLP.
- Clean charging handle assembly with the general-purpose brush and patches.

Cleaning the Lower Receiver

- Wipe dirt from the firing mechanism using a general-purpose brush, clean patch, pipe cleaners, and swabs.
- Clean the outside of the receiver with the general-purpose brush and CLP. Clean the buttplate and rear sling swivel, ensuring drain hole is clear of dirt.
- Wipe the inside of the buffer tube, buffer, and action spring.
- Wipe the inside of the magazine well with a rag.
- Wipe out the inside of the pistol grip and ensure that it is clean.

Cleaning the Magazine

- Clean the inside of the magazine with the general-purpose brush and CLP.
- Wipe dry.
- Keep the spring lightly oiled.

Inspection

While cleaning the rifle, and during each succeeding step in the preventive-maintenance process, inspect each part for cracks and chips and ensure parts are not bent or badly worn. Report any damaged part to the armorer. Inspection is a critical step to ensure the combat readiness of your rifle. It is performed normally during rifle cleaning (prior to lubrication); however, it can be performed throughout the preventive-maintenance process.

Lubrication

Lubrication is performed as part of the detailed procedure for preventive maintenance. Lubrication procedures also are performed in preparation for firing.

Lubricant

- In all but the coldest arctic conditions, CLP is the lubricant for the rifle. Remember to remove excess CLP from the bore and chamber before firing.
- "Lightly lube" means that a film of CLP barely visible to the eye should be applied.
- "Generously lube" means the CLP should be applied heavily enough that it can be spread with the finger.

Upper Receiver

- Lightly lube the inside of the upper receiver, bore, chamber, outer surfaces of the barrel, and surfaces under the handguard.
- Depress the front-sight detent and apply two or three drops of CLP to the front-sight detent. Depress several times to work lubrication into the spring.
- Lubricate the moving parts and elevation-screw shaft of the rear sight.

Bolt Carrier Group

- Generously lube the outside of the cam pin area, the bolt rings, and outside the bolt body.
- Lightly lube the charging handle and the inner and outer surfaces of the bolt carrier.

Lower Receiver

- Lightly lube the inside of the lower receiver extension.

- Generously lube the moving parts inside the lower receiver and their pins.

Reassembly

Reassembling the Rifle

- Return all cleaning gear into the buttstock of the rifle (M16A4 ONLY) and close the buttplate.
- Connect the buffer and action spring and insert them into the buffer tube/stock.
- Place the extractor and spring back on the bolt. Depress the extractor to align the holes and reinsert the extractor pin.
- Insert the bolt into the carrier. Do not switch bolts between rifles.
- Hold the bolt carrier with the bolt carrier key at 12 o'clock. Insert the bolt into the bolt carrier with the extractor at 12 o'clock.
- Rotate the bolt counter-clockwise until the cam pinhole aligns to the cam pin slot in the bolt carrier.

Warning: Ensure the cam pin is installed in the bolt group or the rifle may explode while firing.

- Insert the bolt cam pin through the bolt carrier and into the bolt. Rotate the cam pin one-quarter turn right or left. Pull the bolt forward until it stops.
- Drop in the firing pin from the rear of the bolt carrier and seat it.
- Replace the firing pin retaining pin. Ensure the head of the firing pin retaining pin is recessed inside the bolt carrier. The firing pin should not fall out when the bolt carrier group is turned upside down.
- Place the charging handle in the upper receiver by lining it up with the grooves in the receiver. Push the charging handle partially in.
- With the bolt in the unlocked position, place bolt carrier key into the groove of the charging handle. Push the charging handle and bolt carrier group into the upper receiver until the charging handle locks. Join the upper and lower receivers and engage the receiver pivot pin.

- Ensure the selector lever is on safe before closing the upper receiver. Close the upper and lower receiver groups. Push in the takedown pin.
- Install the rail covers.
- Attach the sling.
- Place the weapon in Condition 4.

Function Check

- Pull the charging handle to the rear and release. Ensure the selector lever is on safe and pull the trigger. The hammer should not fall.
- Place the selector lever on semi. Pull the trigger and hold it to the rear. The hammer should fall. Pull the charging handle to the rear and release. Release the trigger and pull again. The hammer should fall.
- Pull the charging handle to the rear and release. Place the selector lever on burst. Pull the trigger and hold it to the rear. The hammer should fall. Pull the charging handle to the rear three times and release. Release the trigger and pull again. The hammer should fall.
- Pull the charging handle to the rear and release. Place the selector lever on safe.

Reassembling the Magazine

To reassemble the magazine:
- Insert the follower and jiggle the spring to install.
- Slide the base under all four tabs until the base catches. Make sure the printing is on the outside.

Functioning

The cycle of functioning consists of eight basic steps: feeding, chambering, locking, firing, unlocking, extracting, ejecting, and cocking. More than one of these steps can take place at the same time. Functioning in the rifle may be either burst-controlled or semiautomatic through the use of the selector lever.

Cycle of Operation

There are eight steps in the cycle of operation for the service rifle:

Step 1. Firing. Firing is the ignition of the propellant within the cartridge case forcing the projectile out of the barrel.

Step 2. Unlocking. Unlocking is the rotation of the bolt until the locking lugs no longer align with the lugs on the barrel extension.

Step 3. Extracting. Extracting is the withdrawal of the cartridge case from the chamber by the extractor claw.

Step 4. Ejecting. Ejecting is the expulsion of the cartridge case by the ejector and spring.

Step 5. Cocking. Cocking is the resetting of the chamber.

Step 6. Feeding. Feeding is the stripping of a round from the magazine by the bolt.

Step 7. Chambering. Chambering is the pushing of the round into the chamber by the bolt.

Step 8. Locking. Locking is the alignment of the locking lugs on the bolt with the lugs on the barrel extension.

Burst Control Fire

With the selector lever set in the BURST position, the rifle will fire three-round bursts.

• As the trigger is squeezed, the cycle of functioning begins. The hammer is cocked as the bolt carrier recoils, but the center cam holds the disconnector down preventing it from engaging the lower hammer hook.

• The automatic sear, the bottom of which now is moved forward, catches the upper hammer hook, and holds it until the bolt carrier moves forward. As the bolt carrier moves forward, the rear portion strikes the top of the sear, releasing the hammer and causing the rifle to fire.

• The rifle will fire a three-round burst using the cycle of function described. On the fourth round, the burst control cam on the hammer retention pin causes the secondary disconnector to move upward and engage the lower hammer hook and thus interrupt the cycle of functioning.

• If the trigger is released, the hammer moves forward and is caught by the nose of the trigger. This will end the burst-control automatic cycle until the trigger is squeezed again.

• All other portions of the cycle of functioning remain the same.

Weapons Handling

Purpose. Weapons handling prepares a Marine to employ individual weapons safely and confidently, standardizes procedures used during training and combat to enhance safety, and ensures consistency for loading, unloading, and employing individual small arms.

Safety Rules

These safety rules apply to all weapons at all times and must never be violated.

Rule 1. Treat every weapon as if it were loaded.

Rule 2. Never point a weapon at anything you do not intend to shoot.

Rule 3. Keep finger straight and off the trigger until you are ready to fire.

Rule 4. Keep weapon on safe until you intend to fire.

Weapons Conditions

A weapon's readiness/safety status is described by one of four conditions. The steps in the loading and unloading process take the weapon through four specific conditions that indicate the weapon's readiness for live fire.

Condition 1. Safety on, magazine inserted, round in chamber, bolt forward, ejection port cover closed.

Condition 2. Not applicable to the service rifle.

Condition 3. Safety on, magazine inserted, chamber empty, bolt forward, ejection port cover closed.

Condition 4. Safety on, magazine removed, chamber empty, bolt forward, ejection port cover closed.

Commands

Load

"**Load**" is the command that takes a weapon from Condition 4 to Condition 3.

- Ensure the rifle is on safe.
- Withdraw the magazine from the farthest to reach magazine pouch with the support hand.
- Observe the magazine to ensure it is filled. Index the magazine by raising the grip on the magazine so the index finger touches the top round. Ensure that the top round is present and seated properly in the magazine. Lower the grip to the bottom of the magazine by striking the bottom of the magazine on your gear.
- Fully insert the magazine in the magazine well. The magazine catch will "click" as it engages, which can be felt or heard by the shooter. Without releasing the magazine, tug downward on the magazine to ensure it is seated.
- Fasten the magazine pouch.

Note: Steps used to load the weapon, as stated above, will be used if given the command to "reload."

Make Ready

"**Make Ready**" is the command to take a weapon from Condition 3 to Condition 1.

- Pull the charging handle to its rearmost position and release.
- Right-handed shooter using support hand: Grip the pistol grip with the firing hand and pull the charging handle with the support hand. (See Figure 11-8.)
- Left-handed shooter using left hand: Grip the handguards with the firing hand and pull the charging handle with the support hand.
- To ensure ammunition has been chambered, conduct a chamber check to ensure a round has been chambered.
- Bring your support hand back against the magazine well so that the slip ring rests in the "V" of the hand.
- Extend the fingers of your support hand and cover the ejection port (right-handed Marine) or extend your thumb over the ejection port (left-handed Marine).
- Grasp the charging handle with your index and middle fingers of your firing hand. Control the weapon by pointing the muzzle to the deck and applying tension against the stock with the heel of your hand.
- Pull the charging handle slightly to the rear and visually and physically inspect the chamber. For right-handed Marines, insert one finger of the support hand into the ejection port and feel whether a round is present. For left-handed Marines, insert the thumb of the right hand into the ejection port and feel whether a round is present.
- Release the charging handle and observe the bolt going forward.

Caution

Pulling the charging handle too far to the rear while inspecting the chamber can cause double feed or ejection of one round of ammunition.

- Tap the forward assist.
- Close the ejection port cover if time and the situation permits.
- Remove the magazine if one is present

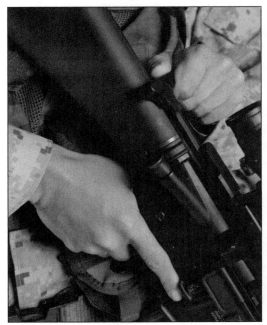

Figure 11-8.

and observe if ammunition is present. If time permits, count the rounds. Reinsert the magazine into the magazine well.

Note: The same procedure is used during both daylight and low visibility. A chamber check may be conducted at any time.

- Release the charging handle and observe the bolt going forward.
- Close the ejection port cover (if time and the situation permit).

Fire

"**Fire**" is the command used to specify when Marines may engage targets.

- On the command "Fire," aim the rifle, take the rifle off safe, and press the trigger.

Cease Fire

"**Cease Fire**" is the command to stop target engagement.

- Place your trigger finger straight along the receiver.
- Place the weapon on safe.

Unload

"**Unload**" is the command to use to take the weapon from any Condition to Condition 4.

- Ensure the weapon is on safe.
- Remove the magazine from the rifle and retain it on your person.
- Bring your support hand back against the magazine well so the slip ring rests in the "V" of the hand. While cupping the support hand under the ejection port, rotate the rifle so the ejection port is facing the deck.
- Pull the charging handle to the rear, and catch the round in the support hand.
- Lock the bolt to the rear.
- Put the weapon on safe if the selector lever would not move to safe earlier.
- Ensure the chamber is empty and that no ammunition is present.
- Depress the bolt catch, and observe the bolt moving forward on an empty chamber.
- Close the ejection port cover.
- Place any ejected round into the magazine, return the magazine to the magazine pouch, and close the magazine pouch.

Unload, Show Clear

"**Unload, Show Clear**" is the command used that will allow the chamber to be checked by a second individual prior to going to Condition 4. Perform the following to unload the rifle and show it clear to an observer (take the rifle to Condition 4):

- Ensure the weapon is on safe.
- Remove the magazine from the rifle and retain it.
- Bring your support hand back against the magazine well so the slip ring rests in the "V" of the hand. While cupping the support hand under the ejection port, rotate the rifle so the ejection port is facing the deck.
- Pull the charging handle to the rear and catch the round in the support hand.
- Lock the bolt to the rear.
- Put the weapon on safe if the selector lever would not move to safe earlier.
- Ensure the chamber is empty and no ammunition is present.
- Have a second party inspect the weapon to ensure no ammunition is present.
- Upon acknowledgement that weapon is clear, press the bolt catch and observe the bolt seating on an empty chamber.
- Close the ejection port cover.
- Place any ejected round in magazine; secure magazine in pouch.

The Observer

- Visually inspects the chamber to ensure it is empty, no ammunition is present, and the magazine is removed.
- Ensures the weapon is on safe.
- Acknowledges the rifle is clear.
- Observes Marine seat bolt on empty chamber.
- Places any ejected round into the magazine, returns the magazine to the magazine pouch, and closes the magazine pouch.

Fill a Magazine

The two methods for filling the magazine are

by hand for loose rounds or with the magazine filler for stripper clips of ammunition.

By Hand

1. Remove a magazine from the magazine pouch.
2. Place a round on top of the follower.
3. Press down on the round until the round is held between the follower and the feed lips of the magazine. (See Figure 11-9.)
4. Repeat Steps 1 and 2 until the desired number of rounds are inserted.
5. Tap the back of the magazine to ensure the rounds are seated against the back of the magazine.

Figure 11-9.

By Stripper Clip and Magazine Filler

1. Remove a magazine from the magazine pouch.
2. Slide the magazine filler into place.
3. Place a 10-round stripper clip into the narrow portion of the magazine filler.
4. Using thumb pressure on the rear of the top cartridge, press down firmly until all ten rounds are below the feed lips of the magazine. (See Figure 11-10.)
5. Remove the empty stripper clip while holding the magazine filler in place.
6. Repeat until the desired numbers of rounds are inserted.
7. Remove the magazine filler and retain it for future use.
8. Tap the back of the magazine to ensure the rounds are seated against the back of the magazine.

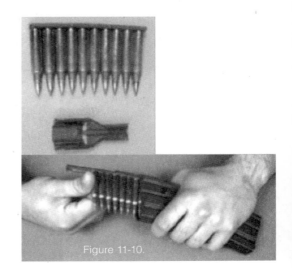

Figure 11-10.

Empty the Magazine

There are two methods of emptying the magazine. Whichever method is used, it will be followed by securing the magazine in the magazine pouch and retrieving any loose rounds.

Method 1. By hand. Using your thumb, push on the cartridge base of the top round, forcing it forward, and out of the magazine. Continue this procedure until the magazine is empty.

Method 2. With stripper clip. With the front of the magazine parallel to the deck, press the second round in the magazine with a stripper clip, relieving the tension on the top round, and allowing it to fall out of the magazine. Continue this procedure until the magazine is empty.

Weapons Carries

Tactical Carry. A Marine carries the rifle at the tactical carry if no immediate threat is present. The tactical carry permits control of the rifle while a Marine is moving, yet it still allows quick engagement of the enemy.

• Place the support hand on the rail system, firing hand around the pistol grip, trigger finger straight along the receiver, and firing

hand thumb on top of the selector lever.
• Place the buttstock along the side of the body at approximately hip level.
• Angle the muzzle upward approximately 45 degrees, in a safe direction.
• Position the muzzle in front of the eyes, slightly below eye level. (See Figure 11-11.)

Figure 11-11.

Two-point Sling Controlled Carry. A Marine carries the rifle at the sling controlled carry when no immediate threat is present, and the weapon:
• Is on safe.
• Hangs muzzle down in front of the body. The muzzle should point down, just to the outside of the feet, with the buttstock at approximately armpit level. The Marine maintains constant muzzle awareness.
• Is controlled with the firing hand grasping the pistol grip or buttstock. (See Figure 11-12.)

Figure 11-12.

Alert. A Marine carries the rifle at the alert if enemy contact is likely or anticipated. The alert also is used for moving in close terrain (e.g., urban, jungle). A Marine can engage the enemy faster from the alert than from the tactical carry. However, the alert is more tiring than the tactical carry and its use can be physically demanding. The weapon is on safe:
• Place his support hand on the rail system, his firing hand around the pistol grip, his trigger finger straight along the receiver, and his firing thumb on top of the selector lever.
• Place the buttstock in his shoulder.
• Lower the sights and angle the muzzle downward at 45 to 70 degrees based upon the need for mobility, observation, and muzzle awareness.
• Point the muzzle in a safe direction or the general direction of anticipated enemy contact. (See Figure 11-13 on next page.)

Figure 11-13.

Figure 11-14.

Ready. A Marine carries the rifle at the ready if contact with the enemy is imminent. The ready allows immediate target engagement, but it is very tiring to maintain over a long period of time. The weapon is on safe until the enemy is engaged. The Marine will perform the following:

• Marine places-
- Support hand on the rail system.
- Firing hand around the pistol grip.
- Trigger finger straight along the receiver.
- Firing thumb on top of the selector lever.
• Place the buttstock in his shoulder.
• Lower the sights to just below eye level so that a clear field of view is maintained for target identification. (See Figure 11-14.)
• Point the muzzle in a safe direction or the general direction of imminent enemy contact.

Strong-side sling arms—transport muzzle up with web sling. To assume this transport from the tactical carry, perform the following steps:

Step 1. Release your hold on the pistol grip.

Step 2. Lower the buttstock and bring the service rifle to a vertical position.

Step 3. Grasp the sling above your support forearm with your firing hand.

Step 4. Guide the service rifle around your firing shoulder with your support hand.

Step 5. Apply downward pressure on the sling with your firing hand. This stabilizes the service rifle on your shoulder.

Step 6. Release the rail system. (See Figure 11-15 on next page.)

Weak-side sling arms transport muzzle down with web sling. This transport can be used in inclement weather to keep moisture out of the rifle's bore. To assume this transport from the tactical carry, perform the following steps:

Step 1. Release your hold on the pistol grip.

Step 2. Lower the buttstock of the service rifle, and bring the service rifle to a vertical position.

Figure 11-15.

Figure 11-16.

Step 3. Rotate the service rifle outboard until the pistol grip is pointing toward your body.

Step 4. Reach over the support forearm and grasp the sling with your firing hand.

Step 5. Rotate the muzzle down with your support hand, while sliding your firing hand up the sling. Place the sling on the support shoulder.

Step 6. Grasp the sling with your support hand and apply downward pressure on the sling. This stabilizes the service rifle on your shoulder.

Step 7. Release the rail system. (See Figure 11-16.)

Perform Unknown Condition Transfer

There are times when time or the tactical situation does not permit a show clear transfer of the service rifle. The procedure is conducted when a Marine takes possession of a service rifle and the condition of the service rifle is unknown (e.g., a service rifle from a casualty).

To properly take charge of a service rifle when its condition is unknown, the Marine must perform the following procedures:

1. Ensure that the service rifle is on safe.

2. Remove the magazine and observe or verify that ammunition is present. If time permits, count the rounds.

3. Conduct a chamber check to determine or verify the condition of the weapon.

Corrective Action

If the rifle fails to fire, a Marine performs corrective action. Corrective action is the process of identifying the cause of the stoppage, clearing the stoppage, and returning the weapon to operation.

Step 1. Take cover as the tactical situation dictates. Seek cover (if situation permits).

Step 2. Observe the indicators of the stoppage/malfunction.

Malfunctions and stoppages are two different occurrences that can happen to the rifle which causes the rifle not to fire.

Malfunction. A malfunction occurs when a part of the rifle fails to operate according to the specification. Anytime a rifle has a malfunction it will need to be fixed by an armorer or a qualified individual.

Stoppage. A stoppage occurs when something interrupts the cycle of operation (hence stoppage). A stoppage can easily be fixed by the Marine and does not require an armorer or qualified individual to fix it.

Indicators. Once the rifle ceases firing, you must visually or physically observe the ejection port to identify the problem before they can clear it. The steps taken to clear the weapon are based on observation of one of the following three indicators:

  a. Bolt is forward or ejection port cover is closed.

  b. Brass is obstructing chamber area.

  c. Bolt is locked to the rear.

Step 3. Perform corrective action for the stoppage/malfunction.

Bolt is Forward or Ejection Port Cover is Closed

This type of stoppage can occur when a weapon fails to feed the round from the magazine or feeds it improperly. When the bolt is completely forward or the ejection port cover is closed the following procedure is used to return the weapon to Condition 1:

1. Seek Cover. (If the situation permits.)
2. Tap. Tap the bottom of the magazine.
3. Rack. Pull the charging handle to the rear and release it.
4. Bang. Sight in and attempt to fire.

Brass is Obstructing The Chamber

This can indicate a double feed or a failure to eject. Double feed is a stoppage that occurs when two rounds are forced into the chamber at

the same time. Failure to eject is a stoppage that occurs when the expelled brass casing does not sufficiently eject out of the chamber. Procedure to return the weapon back to Condition 1 when brass is observed obstructing the chamber (see Figure 11-17):

Figure 11-17.

1. Seek Cover. (If the situation permits.)
2. Attempt to remove the magazine.
3. Attempt to lock the bolt to the rear.
4. If the bolt will not lock to the rear, rotate the rifle so the ejection port is facing down; hold the charging handle to the rear as far as it will go and shake the rifle to free the round(s). If the rounds do not shake free, hold the charging handle to the rear and strike the butt of the rifle on the ground or manually clear the round.
5. Conduct a reload.
6. Sight in and attempt to fire.

Bolt Locked to the Rear

Although a dry weapon is not considered a true stoppage or mechanical failure, a Marine must take action to return the weapon to operation. (See Figure 11-18 on next page). The appropriate procedure to get the weapon to Condition 1 from observing this indicator is:

1. Seek Cover. (If the situation permits.)
2. Conduct a dry reload.
3. Sight in and attempt to fire.

Figure 11-18.

Brass is Stuck Over and Behind the Bolt Face

This stoppage will prevent the bolt from moving and is caused by the weapon failing to feed or extract properly. To return the weapon to operation:

1. Attempt to place the weapon on safe.
2. Remove the magazine and place the butt stock on the deck.
3. Hold the bolt face to the rear with a sturdy, slender object (e.g., stripper clip, knife, multi-tool). Maintain rearward pressure on the bolt and simultaneously push forward on the charging handle to remove the obstructing round.
4. Check the chamber area to ensure it is clear.
5. Conduct a speed reload.
6. Sight in and attempt to fire, if applicable.

Procedures for Clearing An Audible Pop

An audible pop occurs when only a portion of the propellant is ignited. It is normally identifiable by reduced recoil and is sometimes accompanied by excessive smoke escaping from the chamber area. The only situation where you are responsible for clearing an audible pop is in a combat environment:

1. If an audible pop occurs while in a combat environment, the steps to clear the weapon are:
   a. Take cover.
   b. Place the weapon in Condition 4.
   c. Move the take down pin from left to

right as far as it will go to allow the lower receiver to pivot.
   d. Remove the bolt carrier group.
   e. Inspect the bore for an obstruction from the chamber end.
   f. Insert a cleaning rod into the bore from the muzzle end and clear the obstruction.
   g. Reassemble the rifle.
   h. Conduct a reload.
   i. Sight in and attempt to fire.

Resume engagement

Once the stoppage or malfunction has been cleared, resume the engagement.

Rifle Combat Optics AN/PVQ-31A and B

Nomenclature and Design

The Rifle Combat Optic (RCO) is a compact, dual-source, illuminated telescopic sight. (See Figure 11-19.) The RCO is a 4x32mm optic that does not require battery power. It is calibrated to accommodate bullet drop, thereby eliminating the need for mechanical elevation adjustments. The bullet-drop compensator of the AN/PVQ-31A is matched to the trajectory of the 5.56mm round from a 20" barrel. The AN/PVQ-31B is designed for M4 carbines. The acronym RCO will refer to both.

It is recommended that the tritium lamp be checked prior to deployment of the optic and

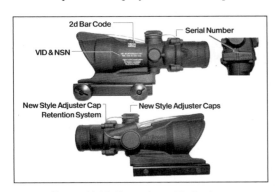

Figure 11-19. Controls and indicators.

every six months or immediately following any incident, which might lead to lamp failure, such as dropping the AN/PVQ-31 onto a hard surface.

To determine that the tritium lamp is functioning in the AN/PVQ-31, enter a dark room and look though the optic. The chevron should be illuminated red. The illumination provided by the tritium lamp is very faint and will be hard to see without a dark-adapted eye. Remain in the dark room for approximately 10 minutes so your eyes can adjust to the dark.

Mounting Methods

The RCO has a flat-top adapter ideally suited for mounting on the M16A4 and M4. To mount the RCO on the service rifle:

Step 1. Loosen the two knobs and place RCO rail assembly mount onto the weapon's mounting rail.

Step 2. Push the RCO forward so that front edge of recoil stop on the flat-top adapter mount is against a recoil groove.

Step 3. Hand tighten the knob on the mount assembly to fix the RCO firmly to mounting rail. Using a coin or flat-blade screwdriver, tighten both thumb screws.

Step 4. Check eye relief. Eye relief for the RCO is 1½". If the RCO needs to be adjusted, loosen the two knobs, lift RCO off mounting rail, move it back or forth and repeat 1 through 3.

Step 5. Tighten the rear knob on the mount assembly then tighten the front knob. (See Figure 11-20.)

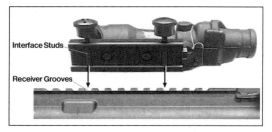

Figure 11-20. Installation rail system.

Note: The flat top rail adapter can be reversed to put the tightening knobs on the right side instead of the left side. This does not interfere with operation of the weapon.

Zeroing the Rifle Combat Optic

Prezero Sight Setting for the Rifle Combat Optic

A zero established at 25 meters is not as accurate as a zero established at 100 meters/yards. Therefore, a prezero sight setting is established at 25 meters and the weapon is zeroed at 100 meters/yards. To establish a prezero sight setting on the weapon:

• Place a universal zeroing target at a range of 25 meters. To be accurate, the target must be placed exactly 25 meters.

• Place a piece of tape over the fiber optic to create a finer aiming point on the reticle. This provides a finer aiming point on the top of the reticle.

• Establish a stable, supported prone firing position (e.g., sandbag, assault pack, bipod).

• Use the 300-meter aim point. (See Figure 11-21.)

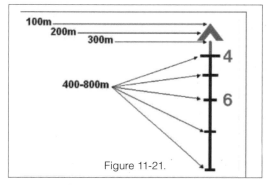

Figure 11-21.

• Fire three rounds to obtain a shot group.

• Triangulate the shot group to find the center.

• Determine the vertical and horizontal distance in inches from the center of the shot group to the center of the target.

a. Adjust the reticle to move the center of the shot group to the desired point of impact (POI).

b. Adjust ~ 10 clicks to move the strike of the round 1" at 25 meters for both windage and elevation.

Note: The RCO may require a shot or two to set the prism into the newly selected adjustment position. It is recommended that the top portion of the RCO be tapped a few times to settle the prism in the newly adjusted position. Do not damage the RCO by striking with brute force. Cycling the weapon three times will also suffice for setting the prism.

- Fire three rounds to obtain a shot group.
- Adjust the reticle to move the center of the shot group to the desired POI.
- Fire four rounds to confirm the prezero sight setting.
- Adjust the reticle as necessary to move the center of the shot group to the desired POI.

Rifle Combat Optic Zeroing

Zeroing the RCO is conducted at 100 meters/yards.

Note: A zero is not established by simply obtaining a prezero sight.

Setting. A zero established at 25 meters is not as accurate as a zero established at 100 meters/yards.

To zero the RCO:

- Place a suitable target with an aiming point that is 4" in diameter and in contrast with the background (e.g., V ring of an a target) at a range of 100 meters/yards and determine an aiming point. (See Figure 11-21 on previous page.) Use the 100-meter aim point on the reticle tip of the chevron center mass on the target.
- Establish a stable, supported prone firing position (e.g., sandbag, assault pack, bipod).
- Fire three rounds to obtain a shot group.
- Triangulate the shot group to find the center.
- Determine the vertical and horizontal distance in inches from the center of the shot group to the center of the target.

- Adjust the reticle to move the center of the shot group to the desired POI. Three clicks moves the strike of the round 1" at 100 meters/yards for both windage and elevation.
- Fire three rounds to obtain a shot group.
- Adjust the reticle to move the center of the shot group to the desired POI.
- Fire four rounds to confirm the zero. The service rifle is considered zeroed when a shot group is inside the 4" aiming area of the target.

Application

Note: Those shooters who are cross-eye dominant, meaning they are using their non-dominate eye behind the optic, will experience a shift in POI when using both eyes open shooting. Encourage these shooters to transition to their dominant side. If not, they must learn to compensate for that shift by aiming in the opposite direction of the shift. For example the shooter, with both eyes open, is hitting a target on the far left side.

The adjusted aiming point would be the far right side. The only other option is to use the optic like a traditional scope and close the non-shooting eye. The disadvantage of this choice is much slower in close-quarters shooting. The degree of shift is based on the indifference between the eyes. Some shooters experience a small shift in POI, and others can be completely off target at 15 yards.

The RCO is a four-power scope. When using it to engage targets at close distances, the magnification can slow down reaction time. Presentation drills at close ranges will aid in learning how to acquire the target using the scope. The AN/PVQ-31 is designed for both eyes open from muzzle to 300 meters for quick target acquisition and engagement. This allows the AN/PVQ-31 to be utilized as a reflexive sight when speed is critical at these distances. To acquire a target, keep both eyes open, focus on the target, bring the weapon/optic up into the line of sight (do not switch focus to the reticle), and engage the target.

Bindon Aiming Concept

With both eyes open, present the weapon. As the weapon is moved, the perceived image is unmagnified, permitting extremely rapid target acquisition. As soon as the weapon movement is stopped, the targeted image "zooms" into magnification, permitting greater shooting accuracy with higher hit ratios. This concept, known as the Bindon Aiming Concept (BAC), is particularly useful for moving targets or for targets in dense cover.

Maintenance

Cleaning and maintenance should be done with the issued lens pen. To clean the AN/PVQ-31, remove all foreign material from the unit with lens pen if fresh water is not available.

Pay special attention to the lenses. All foreign material must be removed before continuing. Next, remove the cap from the opposite end of the lens pen to expose the felt lens cleaner. Ensure there is NO foreign material on the felt surface. Starting in the center of the lens, press the felt surface of the lens cleaner against the lens and in a spiral motion, work from the center to the outside edge of the lens. Repeat if necessary. When finished, depress lens brush slider and retract the brush into the len pen. Replace the cap over the felt lens cleaner.

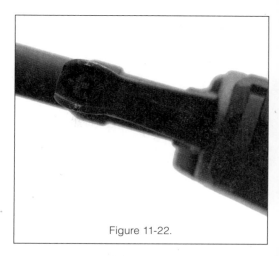

Figure 11-22.

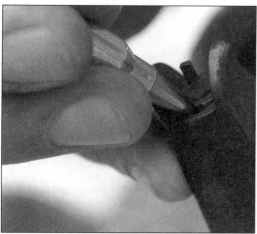

Figure 11-23.

Iron Sight Sighting System

The sighting system of the service rifle consists of a front sight post, two rear sight apertures, an elevation knob, and a windage knob. Scales of the sighting system can be applied accurately to both yard and meter measurements. For example, a rear sight elevation setting of 6/3 can be used for 300 and 600 meters/yards.

Front Sight

The front sight post is used to adjust for elevation. The front sight consists of a square rotating sight post with a four-position spring-loaded detent. (See Figure 11-22.)

To adjust for elevation, use a pointed instrument or the tip of a cartridge to depress the detent and rotate the front sight post. (See Figure 11-23.) To raise the strike of the bullet, rotate the post clockwise (i.e., in the direction of the arrow marked up) or to the right. To lower the strike of the bullet, rotate the post counterclockwise (i.e., in the opposite direction of the arrow) or to the left.

Backup Iron Sight

The backup Iron Sight (BUIS) system consists of a rear sight aperture, a rear sight elevation drum, and a rear sight windage knob.

Backup Iron Rear Sight

The rear sight consists of a single sight aperture that is used for all firing situations. (See Figure 11-24.)

Figure 11-24.

Backup Iron Sight Rear Elevation Drum

The rear sight elevation drum is used to adjust the sight for a specific range to the target. The elevation drum is indexed as shown in Figure 11-24. Each number on the drum represents a distance from the target in 200 meters/yard increments, out to 600 meters/yards. To adjust for range to the target, rotate the elevation drum so that the desired setting is aligned with the index on the left side of the sighting system.

Note: A hasty sight setting is the setting placed on the rear sight.

Hasty sight Settings for ranges of 400 to 600 meters/yards are applied by rotating the rear sight elevation drum to the number that corresponds with the engagement distance of the enemy.

Backup Iron Windage Knob

The windage knob, located on the right side of the sighting system, is used to adjust the strike of the round right or left. The windage knob is marked with an arrow and the letter "R" that shows the direction the strike of the round is being moved. (See Figures 11-24 and 11-25.)

To move the strike of the round to the right, rotate the windage knob clockwise in the direction of the arrow marked "R".

To move the strike of the round to the left, rotate the windage knob counterclockwise.

Figure 11-25.

Backup Iron Sight Zeroing Process

A prezero sight setting is established on the BUIS at 33 meters/36 yards using the same procedures as those for the RCO. Ideally, zeroing of the BUIS should be conducted at the same time the RCO is zeroed. The recommended sequence of events is as follows:

• Mount the BUIS on the last groove of the rail system and flip it up. Set the elevation drum on the BUIS at three.

• Establish a prezero sight setting on the BUIS at 33 meters/36 yards as follows:

a. The front sight post is moved to make elevation adjustments.

b. The BUIS windage knob is moved to make lateral adjustments. Three clicks of the windage adjustment will move the strike of the round on the target approximately ½" at 33 meters/36 yards.

AN/PEQ-15

Specifications. The AN/PEQ-15 advanced target pointer illuminator aiming light is a multifunction laser device that emits visible or infrared (IR) light for precise weapon aiming and target/area illumination as follows:

• The visible aim laser provides the ability for active target acquisition in low light and close quarters combat situations without night vision devices.

• The IR aim and illumination lasers provide the ability for active, covert target acquisition in low light or complete darkness when used in conjunction with night vision devices.

• The AN/PEQ-15 can be used as either a handheld illuminator/pointer or be mounted to weapons equipped with a rail system. (See Figure 11-26.)

Figure 11-26.

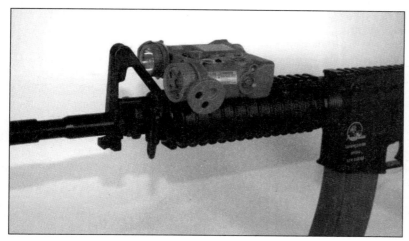

Figure 11-27.

• Leave the elevation drum on three. Flip the BUIS down. Mount the RCO on the rail system just forward of the BUIS.

• Zero the RCO as previously discussed.

Night Aiming Devices

The night aiming devices used within the service are the AN/PEQ-15 and AN/PEQ-16a. Devices have similar capabilities, with the AN/PEQ-16a being equipped with an internal white light illuminator that allows for hands free white light usage. **For details on zeroing and mount refer to corresponding technical manual.**

AN/PEQ-16A

Specifications. The AN/PEQ-16A (mini-integrated pointer illuminator module) is a multifunction laser device that emits visible or IR light for precise weapon aiming and target and/or area illumination. It is equipped with a white light illuminator. It is hand held, weapon mounted, and battery operated (requires two 3-volt batteries). (See Figure 11-27.)

CHAPTER 12

Combat Marksmanship Training

Whenever the situation warrants the application of deadly force, the Marine rifleman must be able to deliver well-aimed shots to eliminate the threat. Sometimes the need for a well-aimed shot may even be heightened by the presence of noncombatants in close proximity to the target. The proficient rifleman handles this challenge without unnecessarily escalating the level of violence or causing unnecessary collateral damage. Well-trained riflemen can deliver accurate fire against the enemy under the most adverse conditions. A well-trained rifleman is not only confidant that he can help his unit accomplish its mission, he is confidant that he can protect his fellow Marines and himself.

The Marine Corps Combat Rifle Program (MCCMRP) utilizes a building block/training continuum approach towards developing Marines into proficient combat marksmen. To accomplish this, the MCCMRP is broken down into different stages of training; Preparatory Training and Tables 1 through 6. Marines will begin by learning the fundamentals of marksmanship (Preparatory Training & Tables 1 & 2) and then incrementally learn new combat shooting skills (Tables 3-6) as they complete each Table of training in sequential order. Marines must master each Table of training prior to advancing to the next Table.

Preparatory Marksmanship Training. Prior to beginning Table 1 training, Preparatory Marksmanship Training is required for all shooters. The unit is responsible for this period of training. The unit Combat Marksmanship Trainer (CMT) is responsible for training Marines through a series of classes and practical application exercises. During Preparatory Marksmanship Training, Marines develop a sound foundation of marksmanship knowledge and practice skills under close supervision of the CMT. This training is critical to correct any shooting problems, before the Marine ever begins live fire training. Preparatory training provides the basis for all follow-on marksmanship training. Correct firing techniques must become second nature. Therefore, it is important to develop and master weapons handling and an understanding of basic marksmanship skills during this stage of training. After completing Preparatory Training, shooters' proficiency is determined by the following:

Table 1: Fundamental Marksmanship Firing. During Table 1 training, the marksmanship skills learned in Preparatory Marksmanship Training are applied on a known distance (KD) range where further development and refinement of those skills achieved during live fire. This table provides the opportunity to apply the fundamental marksmanship skills learned to date. Therefore, it is essential that the Marine practice and employ correct firing techniques and make a continued effort to master weapons handling skills. Immediate feedback is critical to identify areas where the shooter needs improvement.

For completion of Table 1, a shooter must demonstrate proficiency in his ability to engage stationary targets with the service rifle at KDs. In addition, proficiency in zeroing the service rifle/carbine is demonstrated during this table of training in the MCCMP.

Table 2: Basic Combat Marksmanship. Table 2 training consists of class instruction, practical application exercises and live fire exercises. Both the unit and the Rifle Range personnel conduct training within Table 2. The unit is responsible for the preparatory classroom instruction. The Rifle Range is responsible for conducting the practical application and live fire exercises. Rifle Range personnel may conduct the preparatory classroom instruction as long as there is an agreement established between the unit and Range. The Range CMTs are responsible for coaching Marines through dry and live fire exercises. In Table 2 training, Marines take the marksmanship fundamentals taught in Tables 1 and apply them in a variety of field firing conditions. This table also helps the Marine develop increased confidence with his weapon. Where possible, Table 2 training is conducted immediately upon completion of Tables 1. For completing Table 2, shooters must demonstrate proficiency in the following:

- Zeroing and weapons carries.
- Presentation: control pair and failure to stop drill.
- Perform tactical and speed reloads.
- Engaging multiple targets.
- Engaging moving targets.

Table 3-6: Intermediate Combat Marksmanship.

Table 3-6 reinforces and improves basic combat shooting skills and introduces additional techniques and procedures. Upon completion of Table 3-6, the Marine will have demonstrated the required skills for successful completion of the tasks assigned to the Marine rifleman.

Preparatory Marksmanship Training

Preparatory marksmanship training is taught in eight steps. To complete the training, it is essential that the basic steps be taught in the following sequence:

Step 1. Sighting and Aiming.
Step 2. Positions.
Step 3. Trigger Control.
Step 4. Rapid Fire.
Step 5. Sight Adjustments.
Step 6. Effects of Weather.
Step 7. Zeroing.
Step 8. Data Book.

Sight Picture With Rifle Combat Optic

Sight picture is the placement of the optic reticle pattern in relation to the target. The RCO is calibrated to accommodate bullet drop. The reticle pattern of the RCO is a bullet drop compensator with designated aiming points to compensate for the trajectory of the 5.56mm round at ranges of 100 to 800 meters. (See Figure 12-1.) This feature eliminates the need for mechanical elevation adjustments on the service rifle. Sight picture changes are based on the range to the target. To compensate for range to the target, the aiming points seen in Figure 12-2 (on next page) are used with the RCO. The horizontal mil scale

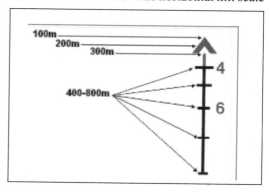

Figure 12-1.

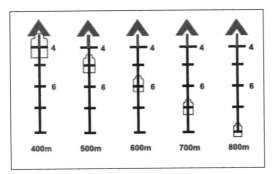

Figure 12-2.

is removed to emphasize the bullet drop compensator by performing the following:

- Hold the tip of the chevron center mass on a target at 100 meters or less.
- Hold the crotch of the chevron center mass on a target at 200 meters.
- Hold the tip of the red post center mass on a target at 300 meters.
- Hold a horizontal stadia line center mass on a target at each of the ranges indicated beyond 300 meters.

Factors Affecting Rifle Combat Optic Sight Picture

Stock Weld

Stock weld is the point of firm contact between the cheek and the stock of the service rifle. (See Figure 12-3.) The Marine's head should be as erect as possible to enable his aiming eye to look straight through the optic. If the position of his head causes him to look across the bridge of his nose or out from under his eyebrow, his eye will be strained.

Note: The eye functions best in its natural forward position. Changing the placement of the cheek either up or down on the stock from shot to shot can affect the zero on the service rifle because of the perception of the reticle pattern in the optic.

A consistent and proper stock weld is critical to the aiming process because it provides consistency in eye relief, which affects the ability to obtain sight picture. Consistent placement of the buttstock in the shoulder will assist in achieving a consistent stock weld.

With the RCO, if the butt of the service rifle is placed in the shoulder correctly and the stock weld is correct, the Marine should be looking through the optic as the service rifle is presented. As the service rifle levels, the Marine should see the chevron and establish a sight picture.

Stock weld changes with the Marine's position. The Marine needs to be aware of the ghost image of the front sight post through the optic and keep it as close to the center of the optic as possible in each position. For example, a right-handed Marine's stock weld will be centered on the service rifle in the prone position and the front sight post will be centered in the lower part of the optic. As the Marine moves to a higher position, the stock weld will move to the left side of the service rifle and the ghost image of the front sight post will move to the right. Keeping the ghost image of the front sight post as centered as possible will provide a consistency in both zero and shot placement.

Eye Relief

Eye relief is the distance between the optic and the aiming eye. (See Figure 12-3.) Optimal eye relief with the RCO is approximately 1½". The distance between the aiming eye and the optic depends on the size of the Marine and the

Figure 12-3.

firing position. While eye relief varies slightly from one position to another, it is important to have the same eye relief for all shots fired from a particular position.

With the RCO, improper eye relief can cause scope shadow, which can result in improper shot placement, because what appears in the center of the optic is offset by the shadow. (See Figures 12-4 and 12-5.) With the RCO, if eye relief is too far, scope shadow may occur and the field of view will be smaller, affecting zero and shot placement.

Eye relief with the RCO is shorter than with iron sights to open the field of view and eliminate scope shadow. However, eye relief that is too short can cause the RCO to hit the Marine above the eye during recoil. To eliminate scope shadow, adjust eye relief. To adjust the RCO for proper eye relief, use the buddy system and perform the following actions:

- assume the standing position.
- have another Marine move the RCO forward and backward on the rail until the Marine finds the optimum position for field of view and no scope shadow. Secure the RCO on the rail.

Wearing of Glasses

Wearing glasses, ballistic protective eyewear, or sun/wind/dust goggles can alter the perception of sight alignment and sight picture.

If wearing glasses, it is critical to look through the optic center of the lens. If wearing eye protection, ensure that the portion being looked through is clear and not scratched.

Rifle Firing Positions

In a combat environment, a Marine must be prepared to engage the enemy under any circumstance. There are four basic firing positions: prone, sitting, kneeling, and standing. These positions provide a stable foundation for effective shooting. Any firing position must provide stability, mobility, and observation of the enemy. During training, a Marine learns positions in a step-by-step process, guided by a series of precise movements until the Marine assumes a correct position. The purpose of this is to ensure that the Marine correctly applies all of the factors that assist him in holding the rifle steady. The Marine will gradually become accustomed to the feel of the positions through practice and eventually will be able to know instinctively whether his position is correct. In combat, it may not be possible to assume a textbook firing position due to terrain, available cover, engagement time, dispersion of targets, and other limiting factors. Modifications to the basic positions may have to be made to adjust to the combat environment. The Marine must strive to assume a position that offers stability for firing, maximum cover, and concealment

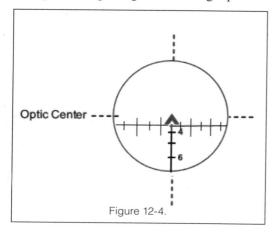

Figure 12-4.

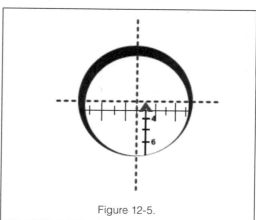

Figure 12-5.

from the enemy, and maximum observation of the target.

Factors Common To All Positions

There are five factors that are common to all shooting positions that affect the ability to hold the rifle steady, maintain sight alignment, and control the trigger. The way these factors are applied differs slightly for each position, but the principles of each factor remain the same.

Forward Hand. In combat, the body's position will be squared to the target rather than angled. Therefore, the rifle will not be angled against the chest and the support-side elbow and triceps will not be inverted against the torso in the standing position. The placement of the forward hand affects how much muscular tension must be applied to hold the weapon up, thereby affecting stability of hold.

Rifle Butt in the Shoulder. Placement of the rifle butt firmly in the shoulder provides resistance to recoil, helps steady the rifle, and prevents the rifle butt from slipping during firing. With body armor donned, it may be difficult to place the rifle butt in the pocket of the shoulder. Instead, while still in the shoulder, the buttstock may be moved inboard slightly. This placement of the buttstock may extend eye relief, making acquiring proper sight picture more difficult. (In addition, the body being more squared to the target will extend eye relief.) The rifle butt should be placed where it will not slip during recoil but still allow acquisition sight picture.

Grip of the Firing Hand. The principles for applying the grip between fundamental marksmanship training and basic combat marksmanship remain the same. However, due to the flak jacket being worn and the placement of the rifle butt in the shoulder, it may require additional rearward pressure from the grip to help keep the rifle butt firmly in the shoulder. Proper placement of the firing hand on the pistol grip allows the trigger to be moved straight to the rear without disturbing sight alignment.

Firing-side Elbow. The placement of the firing-side elbow is the same between fundamental marksmanship training and basic combat marksmanship. Muscular tension is increased in the firing arm to hold the rifle butt in the shoulder due to the rearward pressure from the grip. The placement of the elbow should remain consistent from shot to shot, ensuring the resistance to recoil remains constant.

Stock Weld. The placement of the shooter's cheek against the stock should remain firm and consistent from shot to shot. Stock weld is correct when the cheekbone rests on the stock. Consistency of stock weld is achieved in combat through consistent presentation. Presentation to the target stops at stock weld with a firm contact between the cheek and stock. Sight picture should be acquired the instant stock weld is achieved. In combat, firing positions are more squared to the target. This can cause eye relief to extend, making sight acquisition more difficult. To achieve proper eye relief, the head may be rolled forward to reduce the distance between the aiming eye and the rear sight. Hold your head as erect as possible to allow the aiming eye to see directly through the sights.

Prone Position

The prone position provides a very steady foundation for shooting and presents a low profile for maximum concealment. However, the prone position is the least mobile of the shooting positions and may restrict a Marine's field of view for observation. In this position, the Marine's weight is evenly distributed on the elbows, providing maximum support and good stability for the rifle.

Sitting Position

There are three variations of the sitting position: crossed ankle, crossed leg, and open leg. Experiment with all the variations and select the position that provides the most stability for firing. Although the sitting position provides an extremely stable base, it limits lateral movement and maneuver ability. It has several variations that can be adapted to the individual Marine. The sitting position provides greater elevation than the prone position while still having a fairly low profile.

Kneeling Position

The kneeling position is quick to assume and easy to maneuver from. It is usually assumed after initial engagement has been made from a standing position. It can easily be adapted to available cover. The support-side foot, firing-side foot, and firing-side knee form a tripod when the Marine assumes the position, providing a stable foundation for shooting. The kneeling position also presents a higher profile to facilitate a better field of view as compared to the prone and sitting positions.

Standing Position

The standing position is the quickest position to assume and the easiest to maneuver from. It allows greater mobility than other positions. The standing position is often used for immediate combat engagement. The standing position is supported by the shooter's legs and feet and provides a small area of contact with the ground. In addition, the body's center of gravity is high above the ground. Therefore, maintaining balance is critical in this position.

Three-Point Tactical Sling

Application

The three-point tactical sling can provide stability during firing as well as a wide range of mobility while moving. The three-point sling is designed mainly for a combat application and can be used in the prone, sitting, kneeling, and standing positions with minimal adjustments.

Attaching the Sling System

- Take the permanently attached front keeper with 1" webbing and buckle and feed it through the front, side, or bottom sling mount, and then through the buckle.
- Remove the rear stock strap from the sling system and disassemble it by sliding the short end of the rear stock strap off the long end. You should have an L shape afterwards.

- Remove the rear keeper from the tri-glide. Set the rear keeper with 1" webbing aside. It won't be needed. Place the weapon with the ejection port cover down keeping the pistol grip toward you.
- Flip the sling over and lay it flat across the weapon with the buckles facing down. Slide the middle tri-glide to where it sits on the buttstock approximately 1½" from the edge of the buttstock. The side of the tri-glide with one bar should be facing you.
- Place the rear stock strap on the buttstock where the long side is up and the short side is to the right. Feed the short end through the middle tri-glide. Pull it to the right until the stitching prevents it from going any further.

Note: Left-handed shooters will maintain the same orientation of the rear stock strap. The only difference will be that the sling will be pulled tight on the left side of the buttstock where the short strap attaches to the long rear stock strap.

- Flip the sling over so the quick release buckles are facing up. Wrap the short end around the back of the buttstock. Feed the long end of the stock strap through the slot in the short end.
- Feed the coarse end of the Velcro through the slot closest to the material of the stock strap, then through the other slot on the buckle. Fasten it tightly ensuring the triangular grommet is facing down.
- Pull the sling hard to ensure it is secure.

Donning the Three-Point Tactical Sling

- While grasping the pistol grip in the firing hand, place the toe of the rifle buttstock in the shoulder.
- Using the support hand, separate the sling with the thumb to create a triangle. (See Figure 12-6 on next page.)
- Insert your head and support hand and arm into the triangle while maintaining

control of the weapon. (See Figure 12-6.)
• Adjust the tri-glide so you can easily bring the weapon into action while keeping the sling tight.

Figure 12-6.

Sling Adjustments

Once a sling adjustment is found that provides maximum control of the weapon, the same sling adjustment must be used every time a particular firing position is assumed. Varying the sling tension on the rifle will affect the strike of the bullet. Using the same sling adjustment will maintain the zero and ensure the accuracy of the rounds on target. Position the sling keeper near the feed end of the sling and secure.

Trigger Control

Trigger control is the skillful manipulation of the trigger that causes the rifle to fire without disturbing sight alignment or sight picture. Controlling the trigger is a mental process, while pulling the trigger is a physical process.

Grip

A firm grip is essential for effective trigger control. The grip is established before starting the application of trigger control and it is maintained through the duration of the shot. To establish a firm grip on the rifle, position the "V" formed between the thumb and index finger on the pistol grip behind the trigger. The fingers and the thumb are placed around the pistol grip

in a location that allows the trigger finger to be placed naturally on the trigger and the thumb in a position to operate the safety. Once established, the grip should be firm enough to allow manipulation of the trigger straight to the rear without disturbing the sights.

Trigger Finger Placement

Correct trigger finger placement allows the trigger to be pulled straight to the rear without disturbing sight alignment. The trigger finger should contact the trigger naturally. The trigger finger should not contact the rifle receiver or trigger guard.

Types of Trigger Control

There are two techniques of trigger control: uninterrupted and interrupted.

Uninterrupted Trigger Control. The preferred method of trigger control in a combat environment is uninterrupted trigger control. After obtaining sight picture, the Marine applies smooth, continuous pressure rearward on the trigger until the shot is fired.

Interrupted Trigger Control. Interrupted trigger control is used at any time the sight alignment is interrupted or the target is temporarily obscured. An example of this is extremely windy conditions when the weapon will not settle, forcing the Marine to pause until the sights return to his aiming point. To perform interrupted trigger control:
• Move the trigger to the rear until an error is detected in the aiming process.
• When this occurs, stop the rearward motion on the trigger, but maintain the pressure on the trigger, until sight picture is achieved.
• When the sight picture settles, continue the rearward motion on the trigger until the shot is fired.

Follow-through

Follow-through is the continued application of the fundamentals until the round has exited the barrel. In combat, follow-through is important to avoid altering the impact of the round by keeping the rifle as still as possible until the round exits the barrel.

Recovery

It is important to get the rifle sights back on the target for another shot. This is known as recovery. Shot recovery starts immediately after the round leaves the barrel. To recover quickly, apply a consistent amount of muscular tension within the position throughout the shot process to allow recovery of the sights back on target as quickly as possible. During recovery, release the pressure on the trigger slightly to reset the trigger after the first shot is delivered (indicated by an audible click). Do not remove the finger from the trigger. This places the trigger in position to fire the next shot without having to reestablish trigger finger placement.

Reloading

The first priority when performing a reload is to get the rifle reloaded and back into action. The second priority when performing a reload is to retain the magazine so when you move, the magazine moves with you. When time permits, retain magazines securely on your person (e.g., empty mags will not be retained in a magazine pouch, flak jacket, cargo pocket, load-bearing vest). The combat situation may dictate dropping the magazine to the deck when performing a speed reload. This is acceptable as long as it is picked up before moving to another location if the tactical situation permits.

Note: However, that a dirty or damaged magazine can cause a stoppage.

Tactical Reload

A tactical reload is an administrative function and is performed when the weapon is in Condition 1 by replacing the magazine before it runs out of ammunition when there is a lull in the action. To perform a tactical reload, perform the following steps:

- Withdraw a magazine from the initial load pouch or the next furthest away magazine pouch. Grasp the filled magazine with an extremely low beer can grip. Grasp the magazine to be replaced high on the magazine with the thumb and fingers, controlling both magazines with the same hand.
- Depress the magazine release button to remove the magazine. Right-handed shooters, press the magazine release with the index finger of the firing hand and remove the magazine with the support hand. Left-handed shooters, bring the support hand to the slip ring and wrap the hand around the magazine well. Press the magazine release button with the thumb of the support hand and remove the magazine with the firing hand.
- Observe the magazine to ensure it is filled.
- Fully insert the magazine into the magazine well until the magazine catch engages the magazine. The magazine catch will "click" as it engages, which can be felt or heard by the shooter. Without releasing the magazine, tug downward on the magazine to ensure it is seated.
- Empty or half empty mags should never be stored in magazine pouches.

Speed Reload

A speed reload is required when the magazine in the weapon has been emptied and the bolt has locked to the rear. A speed reload is conducted as quickly as possible. To perform a speed reload:

- Seek cover or take a knee to lower the shooter target profile. If bolt lock is obtained while on the move it is imperative the shooter continues to move while reloading on the move. If the shooter is inside a building (in a doorway or hallway) and he drops to a knee to reload or clear a malfunction he will cause all movement behind him to cease making the rest of his team an easy target for the enemy.
- With the trigger finger straight, press the magazine release button and remove the empty magazine. Right-handed shooters,

press the magazine release with the index finger of the firing hand. Left-handed shooters, press the magazine release with the thumb of the non-firing hand.

• Insert a filled magazine into the magazine well and tug downward on the magazine to ensure it is properly seated.

• Depress the bolt catch to allow the bolt carrier to move forward and observe the round being chambered. Right-handed shooters, strike the upper portion of the bolt catch with the palm of the support hand. Left-handed shooters, strike the upper portion of the bolt catch with the palm of the firing hand. This places the rifle in Condition 1.

Effects of Weather

The weather condition that presents the greatest problem to shooting is the wind. Wind affects a bullet's trajectory. The effect of wind on the bullet as it travels down range is referred to as deflection. The wind deflects the bullet laterally in its flight to the target.

The bullet's exposure time to the wind determines the amount the bullet is deflected from its original trajectory. Deflection increases as the distance to the target increases. There are three factors that affect the amount of deflection of the bullet:

• **Velocity of the wind.** The greater the velocity of the wind, the more the bullet will be deflected.

• **Range to the target.** As the distance to the target increases, the speed of the bullet slows allowing the wind to have a greater effect on shot placement.

• **Velocity of the bullet.** A bullet with a high muzzle velocity will not be affected by the wind as much as a bullet with a low muzzle velocity.

Determining Windage Adjustments to Offset Wind Effects

The velocity and direction of the wind in relationship to the bullet must be determined to offset the wind's effects. If Marines can classify wind values and determine velocity within five mph, they can effectively engage targets in windy conditions.

Wind Direction

Determine wind direction by observing direction vegetation is moving, by feeling the wind blow against the body, or by observing direction of a flag (in training).

Wind Value Classifications

Winds are classified according to the direction from which they are blowing in relation to the direction of fire. The clock system indicates wind direction and value. (See Figure 12-7.) Winds can be classified as half value, full value, or no value. The target is always located at 12 o'clock.

WIND CLASSIFICATION
THE CLOCK SYSTEM

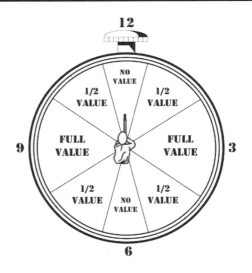

Figure 12-7.

Wind Velocity

There are two methods used to determine wind velocity: observation and flag. The flag method is used as a training tool on the KD range to learn the observation method. This method teaches Marines to relate the effect a given wind condition has on the natural surroundings in order to develop the base of knowledge used during the observation method. The observation method is the primary method used to estimate wind velocity and direction in a tactical situation. The following are guidelines used during the observation method:

- Under 3 miles per hour (mph) the wind can hardly be felt on the face. The presence of a slight wind can be detected by drifting smoke.
- 3 to 5 mph winds can be felt lightly on the face.
- 5 to 8 mph winds keep tree leaves in a constant motion.
- 8 to 12 mph winds raise dust and loose paper.
- 12 to 15 mph winds cause small trees to sway.
- 16 to 25 mph winds cause large trees to sway.

Flag Method

The flag method is primary method used on the KD range. To estimate wind velocity in mph:

- Estimate the angle created between the flagpole and the flag in degrees.
- Divide the angle by four to estimate wind velocity in mph. (See Figure 12-8)

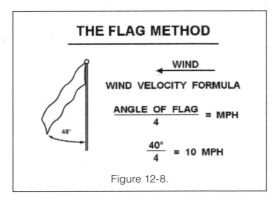

THE FLAG METHOD

WIND VELOCITY FORMULA

$$\frac{\text{ANGLE OF FLAG}}{4} = \text{MPH}$$

$$\frac{40°}{4} = 10 \text{ MPH}$$

Figure 12-8.

Information given is based on a dry flag. A wet flag is heavier and gives a false reading.

Windage Adjustments for the Rifle Combat Optic

Offset Aiming

Unlike the adjustable iron sights on the service rifle, the RCO should not be adjusted for a wind change. The windage turrets on the RCO should only be adjusted during zeroing. For wind corrections during firing, offset aiming is employed so that a hold into the direction of the wind will produce the desired result.

Guidelines for Applying Offset Aiming

The following general guidelines apply when using offset aiming to compensate for a full value wind:

- For distances of 200 meters/yards, with light to medium winds (e.g., 5–15 mph), the aiming point is center mass. A hold is not required.
- For distances of 300 meters/yards, with light winds (e.g., 5 mph), the aiming point is center mass. A hold is not required.
- For distances of 200 meters/yards, with heavy winds (e.g., 20 mph), hold half a body width (i.e., on the edge of the target) into the wind.
- For distances of 300 meters/yards, with 10 mph winds, hold half a body width (i.e., on the edge of the target) into the wind.
- For distances of 200 meters/yards, with strong winds (e.g., 25 mph), hold one body width into the wind.
- For distances 300 meters/yards and medium to heavy winds (e.g., 15–20 mph), hold one body width into the wind.
- For distances 300 meters/yards and strong winds (e.g., 25 mph), hold one and a half body widths into the wind.

- For distances of 400 meters/yards, with light winds (e.g., 5 mph), hold half a body width on the edge of the target into the wind.
- For distances of 400 meters/yards, with winds (e.g., 10 mph), hold one body width into the wind.
- For distances of 500 meters/yards, with light winds (e.g., 5 mph), hold one body width into the wind.

Note: Details on offset windage holds will be found within your databook that will be issued during prepatory combat marksmanship training.

Reading a Mirage for Wind Direction

When observing an area through the RCO, a mirage can be read to determine wind direction.

Mirage refers to the heat waves or the reflection of light through the layers of air of different temperature and density as seen by the human eye on a warm, bright day. A mirage:

- Can be seen best on bright sunny days over unbroken terrain.
- Can be seen with an RCO (i.e., optic) on all but the coldest days, with varying degrees of clarity depending on light and temperature.
- Can generally be seen off of surfaces that generate heat in warm conditions, such as streets and roofs in an urban environment.

A mirage is particularly valuable when reading no value winds, where the mirage gives the appearance of moving straight up with no lateral movement. This is called either a boiling mirage or just a boil. If the mirage is boiling, the effective wind velocity is zero.

The general appearance of the mirage waves can aid in determining wind direction. A lateral moving mirage is indicated by the heat wave becoming horizontal instead of vertical, as in a boiling mirage. For example, the waves will move from left to right if the wind is blowing left to right. The stronger the wind, the more flattened the mirage becomes. When aimed in on the target, the mirage is indicating the wind at the target, which has the least effect on the bullet's trajectory. If time permits, focus on a mirage halfway or three-quarters the distance to your target to get a true sense of the wind direction because the wind at this distance will have the greatest effect on the bullet.

Zeroing

To be combat effective, it is essential for the Marine to know how to zero his rifle. Zeroing is adjusting the sights on the weapon to cause the shots to impact where the Marine aims. This must be done while compensating for the effects of weather and the range to the target. It is critical that Marines can zero their rifles and makes the sight adjustments required to engage targets accurately.

Note: Procedures for zeroing the service rifle and carbine, using the RCO or iron sights, are discussed in Chapter 11 of the publication.

Types of Zero

Zero

A zero is the elevation and windage settings required to place a single shot, or the center of a shot group, in a pre-designated location on a target at a specific range, from a specific firing position, under specific weather conditions. The RCO will be zeroed at 100 meters allowing the bullet drop compensator to be used for more distant target engagements.

Battlesight Zero

A battlesight zero (BZO) is the elevation and windage settings required to place a single shot, or the center of a shot group, in a pre-designated location on a target at 300 yards/meters, under ideal weather conditions (i.e., no wind). A BZO is the sight settings placed on your rifle for combat. In combat, your rifle's BZO setting will enable engagement of point targets from 0–300 yards/meters in a no-wind condition. A BZO will be applied to your BUIS.

True Zero

A true zero is the elevation and windage settings required to place a single shot, or the center of a shot group, in a pre-designated location on a target at a specific range other than 300 yards/meters, from a specific firing position, under ideal weather conditions (i.e., no wind)..

Data Book

Of all the tools that assist the Marine in firing accurately and consistently, the data book, if properly used, is the most valuable asset. It contains a complete record of every shot fired and the weather conditions and their effects on shooting. Maintaining possession of your databook will aid you in being a more effective marksman during training and combat.

CHAPTER 13

Marine Corps Martial Arts Program

*The Marine Corps is a martial culture, meaning combative or warrior like. The legacy of our
Corps is built upon the close combat on ships, the storming of Belleau Wood, the holding
of "Bloody Ridge" on Guadalcanal, and the seizure of Fallujah among other feats of arms.
The mental, character, and physical disciplines of the "ethical" warrior are the foundation
of the Marine Corps Martial Arts Program (MCMAP). The mental discipline consists of
warrior studies, martial culture studies, combative behavior studies, and other
professional military education (PME). The character discipline is built around
the Marine Corps' core values: honor, courage, and commitment. The character discipline
stresses the role of the "ethical" warrior on and off the battlefield.
The physical discipline consists of the techniques taught at each belt level.
Through the successful synergy of these disciplines at each belt level,
a Marine will enhance his own warrior spirit.*

*The MCMAP techniques, complemented with continuous sustainment and subsequent training
to more advanced levels, provide every Marine with the ability and confidence to fight
in hand-to-hand combat using any weapon available, hence the motto
"One Mind, Any Weapon." The training also provides every Marine the self-discipline
to understand the responsible use of force, both on and off the battlefield.*

Precursors

Beginning with the Continental Marines, who were renowned as sharpshooters, Marines have continued to develop and hone their martial skills into the 20th century. During World War I, the skill of the bayonet was supplemented with the first training in unarmed techniques to meet the challenges of trench warfare. This training continued to evolve prior to, and during, World War II. During these early years, the leadership and core values training that are our hallmark today developed in concert with the martial skills.

In World War II, individuals and units followed specialized training based upon the experiences of Marines from the interwar years. These experiences included exposure of Marines to Far Eastern martial arts systems, such as judo and karate. Marines employed these various systems, such as combat hitting skills, the O'Neil System and those of the Marine Raiders during the early island-hopping campaigns in the Pacific.

This trend continued after World War II through the post-Vietnam War period. Marines tested and refined new techniques. During the 1970s and 1980s, in response to changes in society after Vietnam, focus remained on PME and structured leadership training. The 1980s saw the development of the linear infighting neural override engagement (LINE) system. The LINE system, developed in response to a perceived need for a standardized close combat system, was an important step in the evolution of a Marine Corps-specific martial arts program. The LINE system and its descendants continued to grow and develop over the next 20 years. In 1996, a review of the LINE system, combat hitting skills, pugil stick training, and lessons learned from past programs were combined with martial arts disciplines to develop the Marine Corps Close Combat Program. This program combined all aspects of close combat into one program. This paralleled a similar process in 1996, which began to formalize the development of the core values training program.

In 1999, the MCMAP began to morph from the Close Combat Program into its present-day form by combining the best combat tested martial arts skills, time-honored close combat training techniques, with proven Marine Corps core values and leadership training. The MCMAP is—like Marines themselves—unique.

Structure

The Belt Levels of MCMAP

The MCMAP consists of a belt ranking system with five basic levels: Tan, Gray, Green, Brown, and Black Belt. The colored belt levels are identified as "user" levels. The user's responsibilities include participating in all technique classes, tie-ins,* warrior studies, and sustaining techniques. They must also participate in the appropriate belt-level drills and free sparring.

Tan Belt is conducted at entry-level training at both recruit depots and at The Basic School as part of the transformation process and requires 80 percent proficiency in basic techniques and basic understanding of Marine Corps leadership

---

*Tie-ins are briefings conducted at the end of a physical event that bridge the physical and character disciplines of the Martial Arts Program and incorporate core values, leadership, and troop information.

---

and core values concepts. It is a requirement for graduation from recruit training.

Gray Belt is conducted after entry-level training and builds on the basics with introduction to intermediate techniques and requires 90 percent mastery of Tan Belt techniques and 80 percent proficiency of Gray Belt techniques along with continued mental and character discipline training. After receipt of this belt level, a Marine in the grade of corporal and above may qualify to attend the three-week instructor course and become a martial arts instructor (MAI) holding the secondary MOS 0916.

Green Belt is continued development of intermediate-level training and requires 90 percent mastery of previously attained belt levels, and 80 percent proficiency of Green Belt techniques. Leadership, core values development training, and education requirements are needed to qualify for the Green Belt. Marines in grade of sergeant and above, and also MAI qualified (0916), may attend the instructor trainer course and become a martial arts instructor-trainer (MAIT) holding secondary MOS 0917 upon completion of the seven-week program of instruction.

Brown Belt is continued intermediate-level training as well as introduction to advance techniques and requires 90 percent mastery of previously attained belt levels, and 80 percent proficiency of Brown Belt techniques. The Marine continues to expand on his previous belt levels and develops the ability to teach leadership and core values training at all levels to this point in the program.

Black Belt (1st Degree) continues with advanced level skills training and requires 90 percent mastery previously attained belt levels, and 80 percent proficiency in Black Belt techniques that reflect a proven leader and mentor.

2d Degree through 6th Degree Black Belt. The continued development and mastery of all components of the various disciplines, reflecting a proven leader, teacher, and mentor.

Testing. Advancement in the belt ranking system includes meeting mental, physical, and character discipline requirements, and all the prerequisites for each belt level. In addition, each Marine will be required to show that he has maintained proficiency in the disciplines of the current belt as well as the disciplines of the next belt level.

The belt system. The belt system is based upon utility belts in the specific qualification colors to be worn with the MARPAT utility uniform. Instructors are designated by a ½" tan stripe worn on the buckle side of the belt. (See Figure 13-1.) Instructor trainers are designated by a series of ½" red stripes worn on the buckle side of the belt. (See Figure 13-2.)

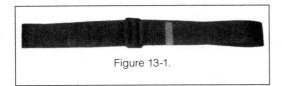

Figure 13-1.

Figure 13-2.

Examples of MCMAP Skills

For the Tan Belt, the required physical disciplines consist of the following:

1. Fundamentals	10. Counters to Strikes
2. Punches	11. Counters to Chokes and Holds
3. Falls	
4. Bayonet Techniques	12. Unarmed Restraints and Joint Manipulations
5. Pugil Sticks	
6. Upper Body Strikes	13. Armed Manipulations
7. Lower Body Strikes	14. Knife Techniques
8. Chokes	15. Mental
9. Throws	16. Character

Throws. The leg sweep takes the opponent to the deck while you remain standing. A leg sweep is particularly effective if the opponent is already off-balanced and moving backward or pulling on you.

Stand facing opponent in the basic warrior stance. (See Figure 13-3.)

Figure 13-3.

With your left hand, grasp the opponent's right wrist. Grab the opponent's clothing or gear if you cannot grab his wrist.

Step forward with your left foot on the outside of the opponent's right foot. At the same time, with your right hand, grasp your opponent's upper left torso area either on gear or flesh. Your foot should be at least in line or behind the opponent's foot. (See Figure 13-4 on next page.) Your foot should be placed outside of the opponent's foot, far enough to provide room to bring the other leg through to execute the sweep.

Begin to off-balance the opponent by pulling his wrist downward close to your body and pushing his shoulder backward.

When pulling the opponent's hand, be sure to bring it down and close to the trouser pocket.

Raise your right knee (no higher than waist high) and bring your foot behind the opponent's right leg and stop. The leg should be bent at the knee. This action takes less movement than straightening the leg prior to the sweep. When your leg is raised, you should be balanced and in a position to easily off-balance the opponent. (See Figure 13-5 on next page.)

Figure 13-4.

Figure 13-5.

Sweep through the opponent's leg, making contact with your calf on the opponent's calf. At the same time, continue off-balancing by pulling the wrist and driving your opponent back with your right side or shoulder. (See Figure 13-6.)

In a combative engagement contact will be made with the cutting edge of the heel on the opponent's Achilles' tendon or calf.

Bending at the waist, continue to drive through the opponent's leg as you force him down to the deck. You have to release your grip on the opponent's shoulder in order to maintain your balance. (See Figure 13-7 on next page.)

Rapidly return to the basic warrior stance. (See Figure 13-8 on next page.)

Chokes. The rear choke is a blood choke performed when you are behind the opponent, the opponent is on the ground or when you are taking the opponent to the ground. Example, from a kneeling position:

Begin with the opponent kneeling on the deck and you standing behind him. (See Figure 13-9 on next page.)

With your right arm, reach over the opponent's right shoulder and hook the bend of your arm around his neck. Ensure that the opponent's

Figure 13-6.

windpipe is positioned within the bend of your arm but that pressure is not being exerted on his windpipe. (See Figure 13-10 on page 183.)

Your chest should be against your opponent's back.

With your left hand, clasp both hands

Figure 13-7.

Figure 13-8.

Figure 13-9.

Ensure the opponent's windpipe is positioned within the bend of your arm but pressure is not being exerted on his windpipe.

While maintaining pressure with your biceps and forearm on both sides of the neck, draw the opponent closer to you by drawing your right arm in.

To increase the effectiveness of the choke, apply forward pressure to the back of the opponent's head with your head by bending your neck forward.

Knife Techniques. The vertical slash is used to close with an enemy. Slashing techniques distract the opponent or cause enough damage to close with him. Target areas are the face, neck, torso, and groin.

Stand facing your opponent. (See Figure 13-12 on next page.)

Thrust your right hand out and bring the weapon straight down on the opponent. (See Figure 13-13 on next page.)

Continue dragging the knife down through the opponent's body. Maintain contact on the opponent's body with the blade of the knife. The slashing motion follows a vertical line straight down through the target. (See Figures 13-14 and 13-15 on page 184.)

together, palm-on-palm, with your right palm facing the deck. (See Figure 13-11 on next page.)

Exert pressure with your biceps and forearm on both sides of the opponent's neck on his carotid arteries. Pressure should be exerted with the forearm along the radial bone, and the knuckles of the right hand should be facing straight up.

Figure 13-10.

Figure 13-12.

Figure 13-11.

Figure 13-13.

Resume the modified basic warrior stance. (See Figure 13-16 on page 184.)

Bayonet Techniques: The Marine Bayonet

History. The use of the bayonet by Marines dates back to the Continental Marines of the American War of Independence. The bayonet evolved through a variety of forms to the 16-inch bladed, M1905 Springfield bayonet with which Marines earned much fame in their storming of Belleau Wood. This long bayonet was carried into World War II, and in 1943, it became the 10-inch bladed Model M1 bayonet for the Garand M1 rifle, which served Marines through the Korean War. After the Korean War it was recognized that by making the bayonet both a bayonet and a combat knife, its double use would lighten the equipment load of Marines. The U.S. arse-

Figure 13-14.

Figure 13-16.

nals designed knife-bayonets for the M1 Garand (the M5 and M5A1 bayonet), the M14 rifle (the M6 bayonet), and the Vietnam War M16 rifle (the M7 bayonet used through Operation Desert Storm in 1991). All of these bayonets were adequate, but none were excellent, and none were designed by Marines for Marines.

Today. In 2003, a long development program finally introduced the first ever made-for-Marines-by-Marines bayonet/combat knife. This new weapon is the Ontario Knife Company's OKC3S bayonet (see Figure 13-17) and OKC3T bayonet trainer. (See Figure 13-18.) A superb weapon and tool, it was developed in coordination with the Marine Corps Martial Arts Center of Excellence.

Figure 13-15.

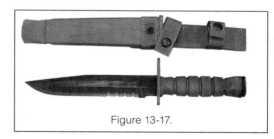

Figure 13-17.

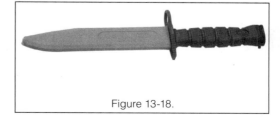

Figure 13-18.

GUIDEBOOK FOR MARINES

This unique Marine weapon is designed to serve as a bayonet, a combat knife, and a utility knife, and every Marine will keep it clean and sharpened at all times. In MCMAP and MCMAP training, the combined rifle and bayonet is the initial close combat weapon (think spear) of the martial arts Marine. This instruction is followed by the bayonet's employment as a combat knife, then leading to unarmed ground fighting.

Bayonet Techniques. The slash. The slash is used to cut through the aggressor's defenses or to kill him. It is best to follow up the slash with a thrust to maximize the damage and trauma to the aggressor. The primary target areas of the body are the aggressor's throat, groin, or face. The torso can be another target area if it is not protected by body armor. The slash is executed with the primary cutting edge of the blade.

From the modified basic warrior stance, retract the left hand slightly toward the left shoulder. (See Figure 13-19.)

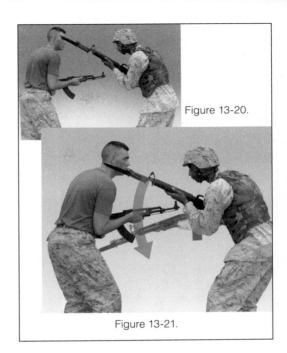

Figure 13-20.

Figure 13-21.

Figure 13-19.

Bring the left hand down and to the right (diagonally) cutting through the target with the blade. (See Figures 13-20 and 13-21.) To generate more power, take a small step with your left foot when you slash, rapidly bringing your right foot back up to the modified basic warrior stance.

The Instructional Levels of MCMAP

In addition to the belt levels of MCMAP there are two instructional levels as well, each with clearly delineated responsibilities. (See Figure 13-22.)

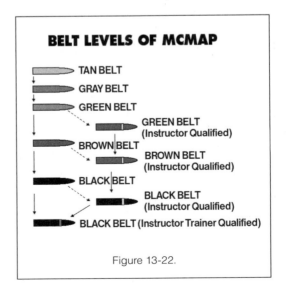

BELT LEVELS OF MCMAP

TAN BELT
GRAY BELT
GREEN BELT
GREEN BELT (Instructor Qualified)
BROWN BELT
BROWN BELT (Instructor Qualified)
BLACK BELT
BLACK BELT (Instructor Qualified)
BLACK BELT (Instructor Trainer Qualified)

Figure 13-22.

The MAI. Here the individual transforms into someone who gives back to the Corps and MCMAP. MAIs are the unit's means of developing the mental, moral, and physical strength of Marines through the use of MCMAP training. They train Marines in Martial Arts techniques in order to give Marines the ability to defend themselves. MAI's educate Marines in leadership, moral truthfulness, and warrior cultures, which arms Marines with tools they need to prepare, survive, and thrive in chaos.

The instructor course consists of three-weeks of intense training designed to enhance overall knowledge of the program and the ability to instruct Marines. The minimum requirement for attending the course is to be a Gray Belt with the appropriate level of PME, in grade of corporal or above, with commander's consent, scoring first class on the PFT and CFT, and medically screened. The instructor courses can be found all around the Marine Corps under the leadership of MAIT with the current MOS 0917.

The MAIT. The MAIT prepares the instructors within his unit and develops a unit-level training plan coordinating the resources and abilities of the instructors within the unit. The MAIT convenes (MAI) instructor courses at the unit level, producing Marines qualified to Black Belt instructor. MAIT's are responsible to the commander for the quality of all MCMAP instruction in their unit.

The MAIT course consists of a seven-week course producing MOS 0917 Marines, convened only at the Martial Arts Center of Excellence at Marine Corps Base (MCB) Quantico, VA. The minimum requirements for attending the course include Green Belt instructor or higher, in grade of sergeant or above, with appropriate level education, commander's consent, a first class PFT and CFT, current MAI qualification, and medically screened in a full duty status.

Why "MARTIAL"?

When one uses the words "martial art," it often conjures images of individuals dressed in white kimonos throwing and kicking each other around the "dojo" or training hall. A more appropriate concept treats the term martial as suggestive of war, connected with the armed forces or the profession of arms. Everything in MCMAP prepares Marines for combat-related duties. This means that everything we do is martial in nature, and as we study it and grow in our capabilities, we approach it as an art.

The Disciplines of MCMAP

The MCMAP consists of three components: mental discipline, character discipline, and physical discipline. Each discipline is divided into blocks and presented systematically to Marines at each belt level. Those disciplines taught at lower belt levels are then reviewed and reinforced during follow-on training and at the next belt level. Many skills specific to one discipline reinforce the strengths of the other disciplines. This creates a synergistic effect whereby the program proves stronger than its individual parts. (See Figure 13-23.) For example, martial culture studies strengthen the mental character of Marines through the historical study of war,

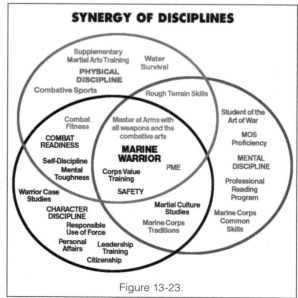

Figure 13-23.

at the same time reinforcing the importance of character to an "ethical" warrior and a martial society.

Mental discipline has two main components, warfighting doctrine and PME. This encompasses the study of the art of war, the professional reading program, Marine Corps common skills training, decision-making training, the historical study of war, the tactics and techniques of maneuver warfare, force protection, and the study of Marine Corps history, customs, courtesies, and traditions. The mental discipline creates a smarter Marine, capable of understanding and handling the complexity of modern warfare, a Marine who is tactically and technically proficient and one who is capable of decision making under any condition from combat to liberty. This training, which begins with the transformation of recruit training, serves as the foundation of the "strategic corporal" and the future leadership of our Corps. Mental discipline is also taught through warrior case studies, martial cultures studies, and tie-ins.

Character discipline encompasses troop information training as well as the study of the human dimensions of combat. Designed to instill the Marine Corps ethos into every Marine, character discipline is the spiritual aspect of each Marine and the collective spirit of the Corps. The components of character discipline instill in every Marine the warrior spirit and emphasizes the best of our traditions for developing esprit de corps, camaraderie, and an "ethical" warrior mindset. By building the character of a Marine, we develop the Marine as a defender-protector, one who embodies our core values and one who is self-disciplined, confident, and capable of making the right decision under any condition from combat to liberty. The character discipline is also taught through warrior studies, martial culture, studies, and tie-ins interrelated by all MAI and MAITs around the Corps.

Physical discipline consists of two main components: martial arts and physical fitness. MCMAP is a weapons-based system beginning at assault fire and moving to the *four elements of the fighting component: rifle and bayonet,* *edged weapons, weapons of opportunity, and unarmed combat,* with unarmed combat having a role across the entire spectrum of combat. The various armed and unarmed combat techniques are combined as part of the MCPFP.

It is the sinew of what every Marine must be prepared to execute—to seek out, close with and destroy the enemy by fire and movement or repel his assault by fire and close combat. This is how we win our Nation's battles, fight the three-block war and ensure success during the final 300 meters of combat. It is battlefield oriented, combat equipment based, and develops in the Marine the ability to overcome physical hardship and physical obstacles (water survival, assault climber, cold weather training) under any climatic condition. It is designed on the philosophy that there are no time limits, level playing fields, or second chances in combat. It develops a physical toughness in every Marine that will translate into mental toughness. It produces a Marine who possesses great physical prowess and the ability to handle any situation that confronts him.

What makes this a complete program is the synergy of all three disciplines. All three components are inextricably linked to each other and to the advancement process within the belt ranking system. A commander is required to certify that the Marine meets annual training requirements, meets the prerequisites of each specific belt level, and possesses the maturity, judgment, and moral character required by his recommendation. This ensures that as a Marine develops the physical skills to make him a lethal warrior, he also develops a commensurate level of maturity and self-discipline. These characteristics function as a three-legged stool. Each leg works with the other two to support the concept. Concentrating on one discipline without training to the other two collapses the "stool."

Summary

While borrowing specific techniques from various established martial arts, the MCMAP is unique. It is a weapons-based system rooted in the credo that every Marine is a rifleman and will engage the enemy from 500 meters to 500 millimeters. In addition to the physical disciplines associated with other martial arts, this program places an equal emphasis on training in the mental and character disciplines. The MCMAP fuses together the physical disciplines of combat with the leadership and core values training that are the hallmark of our Corps. This synergy of training will create an "ethical" warrior who will embody all that is best of country and Corps, a United States Marine.

CHAPTER 14

Grenades and Accessories

Hand Grenades

History

There are several types of hand grenades. Each has different characteristics, and each provides the Marine with a variety of capabilities. Hand grenades kill enemy soldiers, destroy enemy equipment, give signals, and control riots. Historically, the most important hand grenade is the fragmentation grenade. It is the Marine's personal, indirect-fire weapon system.

It was not until the Revolutionary War that we have the first account of hand grenades being used. Continental Marines, under cover of accurate musket fire, threw hand grenades from the riggings onto the decks of British ships, setting them afire, and exploding their powder magazines.

During the Civil War, the Union Army used the first grenade that consisted of a fixed-powder train delay fuse. The Confederate Army modified DUD artillery and mortar shells to make rampart grenades.

During WWII, the United States fielded the Mark 2 fragmentation hand grenade, popularly known as the "pineapple." During the Korean and Vietnam conflicts, the United States' new standard offensive/defensive hand grenade became the M26. The standard hand grenade now in use is the M67 with the M213 fuse.

Common Characteristics

All hand grenades share three characteristics: range, effective casualty radius (ECR), and time-delay fuse.

Range. The range of any hand grenade depends entirely on the throwing ability of the individual Marine.

Effective Casualty Radius. ECR is defined as the radius of a circular area around the point of detonation within which at least 50 percent of the exposed personnel will become casualties. The ECR of a grenade is relatively small when compared to that of other bursting weapons. However, casualties may occur at distances much greater than the ECR.

Time-Delay Fuse. All standard grenades have a time-delay element in the fuse:

- The time-delay element permits the safe throwing of the hand grenade.
- All casualty-producing hand grenades (fragmentation and white phosphorus [WP]) have a 4 to 5-second time delay.
- Burning chemical hand grenades have a 2-second time delay fuse.
- One burning chemical grenade has a 1.4–3-second time delay fuse (M25A2 riot control hand grenade).

Main Parts

Although hand grenades vary, they all have three main parts: body, filler, and fuse assembly.

Body. The body is the container which holds the filler. It usually is made of metal, and it may provide fragments. Grenade bodies are hollow (to contain a filler), and they have an opening into which the fuse is inserted. The body is colored and marked to identify the type of grenade. Basic body colors are:

- High Explosive–Olive drab with yellow markings.
- Chemical–Gray with markings indicating the filler type (old). Green with black markings indicating filler (new).
- Practice–Blue with white markings (old). Blue with white markings and brown band (new).
- Dummy (inert/training)–Black with white markings.

Filler. The filler is the substance with which the grenade body is filled. This filler may be any of the following:

- TNT.
- Composition B.
- Various chemical compounds.

Fuse Assembly. The fuse assembly is a mechanical and chemical device that causes the filler to detonate or burn. It is classified as either a detonating or an igniting type fuse. Most of our grenades now are provided with a silent, sparkless, smokeless fuse. The fuse assembly consists of:

- Safety lever.
- Safety-pin pull ring.
- Safety pin.
- Safety clip.
- Striker.
- Striker spring.
- Primer.
- Delay element.
- Detonator or igniter.

Functions of the Fuse Parts

Fuse Body. Holds the other parts of the fuse. It is screwed into the body of the grenade.

Safety Lever. Holds down the striker arm after the safety pin is removed. One end of the safety lever is under the T-lug on the fuse body.

Safety Pin. Holds the safety lever to the fuse body. When the pin is withdrawn, the grenade is armed. At this time, only the pressure of the thumb on the safety lever holds the safety lever and prevents the fuse from functioning.

Striker. Acts like a firing pin. When the safety lever is released, the striker spring forces the striker to pivot in an arc, throwing off the safety lever and continuing until it strikes the primer.

If the grip is loosened on the safety lever, the striker may be released and strike the primer without the lever flying off. It is important that a firm grip be kept on the safety lever at all times after the safety pin has been removed.

Primer. Contains a sensitive chemical that burns when the striker strikes it. The primer ignites the delay element.

Delay Element. A train of powder enclosed in a small tube. It burns at a controlled rate and prevents the filler from exploding or burning immediately after the striker hits the primer. When the delay element has completed burning, it sets off the igniter or detonator.

Detonator. Similar to a small blasting cap and detonates high explosive or WP-type fillers. An igniter is used in place of a detonator in a grenade with chemical filler.

Steps in Functioning

When the safety pin is pulled, the safety lever is held down firmly by the thrower's thumb. When the safety lever is released, it is thrown free from the grenade, allowing the striker to hit the primer. The primer sets off the delay element, which burns into the detonator or igniter. The bursting or burning of the filler in the grenade body ends this chain reaction. The entire action requires only a few seconds.

Types of Hand Grenades

There are four types of combat hand grenades and one type of practice hand grenade. The four combat types are: fragmentation, chemical smoke, riot control, and special purpose. This section will look at each type of grenade in detail.

Practice Hand Grenade

The M69 practice hand grenade (Figure 14-1 on next page) simulates the M67-series of fragmentation hand grenades for training purposes. The grenade provides realistic training and familiarizes the Marine with the functioning

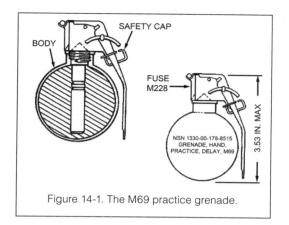

Figure 14-1. The M69 practice grenade.

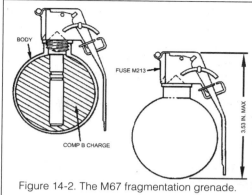

Figure 14-2. The M67 fragmentation grenade.

and characteristics of the fragmentation hand grenade.

General information on the practice grenade includes:

- Body—Steel.
- Fuse—M228, inserted into grenade body.
- Weight—14 ounces.
- Safety clip—Yes.
- Capabilities—Can be thrown 35 meters by an average Marine. The M69 grenade emits a small puff of white smoke after a delay of 4 to 5 seconds and makes a loud popping noise. The grenade body can be used repeatedly by replacing the fuse assembly.
- Color/markings—Light blue with white markings. The safety lever of the fuse is light blue with black markings and a brown tip.

Warning: Fuse fragments may exit the hole in the base of the grenade body causing injuries.

Fragmentation Hand Grenades

a. **M67.** (See Figure 14-2.)
- Body—Steel sphere.
- Filler—6.5 ounces of Composition B.
- Fuse—M213.
- Weight—14 ounces.
- Safety Clip—Yes.
- Capabilities—Can be thrown 35 meters by an average Marine. The effective casualty-producing radius is 15 meters.

- Color/markings—Olive drab body with a single yellow band at the top. Nomenclature and or lot number markings are in yellow.

Warning: Although the killing radius is 5 meters and the casualty-producing radius of this grenade is 15 meters, fragments can disperse as far away as 230 meters.

Chemical Smoke Hand Grenades

a. **TA/M83.** (See Figure 14-3.) This grenade is used to produce dense clouds of white smoke for signaling and screening.
- Body—Sheet steel cylinder.
- Filler—19 ounces of Type C, HC smoke mixture.
- Fuse—M201A1.
- Weight—24 ounces.
- Safety clip—No.

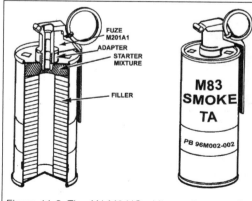

Figure 14-3. The AN-M8 HC white smoke grenade.

• Capabilities—Can be thrown 35 meters by an average Marine. The grenade emits a dense cloud of white smoke for 105 to 150 seconds.

• Color/Markings—Light green body with black markings and a white top.

Warning: Any damaged TA/M83 grenades that expose the filler are hazardous. Exposure of the filler to moisture and air could result in a chemical reaction that will ignite the grenade.

Warning: The TA/M83 hand grenade produces harmful hydrochloric fumes that irritate the eyes, throat and lungs. It should not be used in closed-in areas unless Marines are wearing protective masks.

b. **M18 Colored Smoke (CS).** (See Figure 14-4.) This grenade is used as a ground-to-ground or ground-to-air signaling device, a target or landing zone marking device, or a screening device for unit movements.

• Body—Sheet steel cylinder with four emission holes at the top and one at the bottom to allow smoke release when the grenade is ignited.

• Filler—11.5 ounces of CS mixture (red, green, yellow, and violet).

• Fuse—M201A1.

• Weight—19 ounces.

• Safety clip—No.

• Capabilities—Can be thrown 35 meters by an average Marine. The grenade produces a cloud of CS for 50 to 90 seconds.

• Color/markings—Olive drab body with the top indicating the smoke color

• Field expedient—When employing the M18 or TA/M83 hand grenade, it may be desirable to use one of these grenades without the fuse. To do this, the following procedure should be used in combat only:

- Remove the tape from grenade bottom to expose the filler.

- Remove the fuse by unscrewing it from the grenade.

- Ignite starter mixture with open flame.

- Immediately throw the grenade to avoid burn injury.

Warning: With both the AN-M8 and M18, there is danger of starting a fire if used in a dry area.

Riot Control Hand Grenades

a. **ABC-M7A2 and ABC-M7A3 CS.** (See Figure 14-5.) The ABC-M7A2 and the ABC-M7A3 riot control hand grenades contain only CS as a filler. They differ only in the amount of filler and the form of the CS they contain.

• Body—The bodies of both grenades are sheet metal with four emission holes at the top and one at the bottom.

• Filler—5.5 ounces of burning mixture and 3.5 ounces of CS in gelatin capsules in the ABC-M7A2 grenade, and 7.5 ounces of burning mixture and

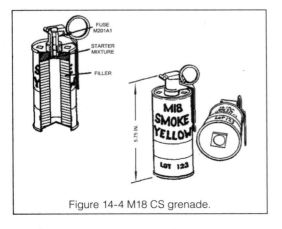

Figure 14-4 M18 CS grenade.

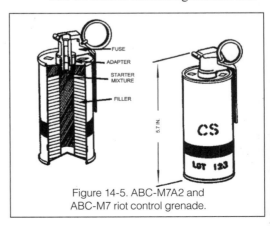

Figure 14-5. ABC-M7A2 and ABC-M7 riot control grenade.

4.5 ounces of pellet CS agent in the ABC-M7A3 grenade.
- Fuse—M201A1.
- Weight—Approximately 15.5 ounces.
- Safety clip—No.
- Capabilities—Can be thrown 35 meters by an average Marine. Both grenades produce a cloud of irritant agent for 15 to 35 seconds.
- Color/markings—Gray body with a red band and red markings.

Warning: Friendly forces should put on protective masks before throwing these grenades.

b. **ABC-M25A2.** (See Figure 14-6.) The ABC-M25A2 riot control hand grenade is a bursting munition with an integral fuse. The M25A2 grenade is an improved version of the M25A1 grenade. The two grenades differ primarily in body construction.
- Body—Compressed fiber or plastic.
- Filler—CS1 varies in weight and composition according to the type of agent contained in the grenade. All fillers are mixed with silica aerogel for increased dissemination efficiency.
- Fuse—Integral.
- Weight—8 ounces.
- Safety clip—No.
- Capabilities—Can be thrown 35 meters by an average Marine. The

radius of burst (visible cloud agent) is about 5 meters, but grenade fragments may project as far as 25 meters.
- Color/markings—Gray body with a red band and red markings.

Warning: Friendly forces should put on protective masks before throwing these grenades.

Special-Purpose Hand Grenades

a. **Incendiary.** (See Figure 14-7) The AN-M14 TH3 incendiary hand grenade is used to destroy equipment. It can damage, immobilize, or destroy vehicles, weapons systems, shelters, or munitions. The grenade also may be used to start fires in areas containing flammable materials.
- Body—Sheet metal.
- Filler—26.5 ounces of thermate (TH3) mixture.
- Fuse—M201A1.
- Weight—32 ounces.
- Safety clip—No.
- Capabilities—Can be thrown 35 meters by an average Marine. A portion of the TH3 mixture is converted to molten iron, which burns at 4,000 degrees Fahrenheit. It will fuse together the metallic parts of any object that it contacts. TH3 is an improved version of thermite, the incendiary agent used in hand grenades during World War II.

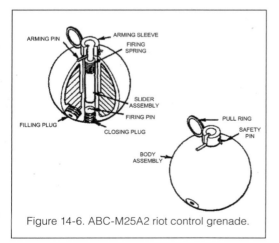

Figure 14-6. ABC-M25A2 riot control grenade.

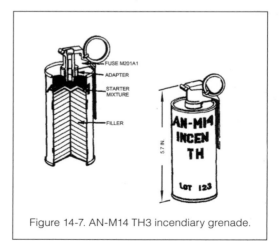

Figure 14-7. AN-M14 TH3 incendiary grenade.

The TH3 filler of the AN-M14 grenade burns for 40 seconds and can burn through a ½" homogenous steel plate. It produces its own oxygen and will burn under water.

• Color/markings—Gray with purple markings and a single purple band (current grenades). Under the standard color-coding system, incendiary grenades are light red with black markings.

Warning: Avoid looking directly at the incendiary grenade as it burns; the intensity of the light is potentially hazardous to the retina.

Grenade Throwing

Holding the Grenade

As shown in Figure 14-8, grip the grenade firmly in the fingers of the throwing hand. Left-handed throwers need to ensure the top of the fuse points downward. Hold the safety lever firmly under the thumb. Next, place the fore-

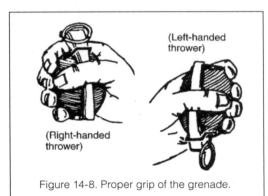

Figure 14-8. Proper grip of the grenade.

finger of the throwing hand near the top of the grenade body. Remove the thumb safety clip, still firmly grasping the grenade. Hook the forefinger of the other hand through the safety ring attached to the end of the safety pin. From there, throw the grenade, using one of the appropriate techniques mentioned in the next section.

Throwing Techniques

The grenade should be thrown like a baseball, using the throwing motion most natural to the individual. The grenade is given a spin in flight by allowing it to roll off the tips of the fingers and releasing it with a snap of the wrist. The individual Marine should not radically alter throwing style, although minor corrections may be necessary to improve throwing skill.

Throwing Positions

Standing. Half face the target with the weight of the body balanced evenly on both feet (See Figure 14-9(a-c), b and c on next page.) Hold the grenade in front of the body, chest high, and remove the safety pin with a pulling, twisting motion. As the grenade leaves the

Figure 14-9(a). Pull pin firmly.

Figure 14-9(b). Cock arm.

quickly, pushing upward and to the rear. Do not rest the weight of your body on the grenade. The left knee (if throwing right handed) remains on the ground. The right leg is slightly bent so that the body can twist, getting more power while preparing to throw. As the grenade leaves your hand, follow through and fall to the ground, breaking the fall with your arms. Watch the strike.

Prone. This position is an extremely awkward one and limits both range and accuracy. It is used when pinned down with little or no cover and the grenade cannot be thrown from any other position. Throwing from this position varies among individuals, so no set manner for it is prescribed. (See Figure 14-11(a-d) on pages 197 and 198.) Lie on your back, hold the grenade across the chest and pull the pin. When throwing, hold onto any substantial object with the

hand, take an additional step forward and follow through, falling forward face down onto the ground. When possible, keep your eyes on the target to observe the strike of the grenade as you fall to the prone position. Errors can be detected, and necessary corrections can be made on the next throw.

Kneeling. Half face the target and kneel on the knee nearest to the target. When the grenade leaves the hand, continue the throwing motion so you will fall forward, breaking the fall with your arms. Watch the strike so as to make corrections, if necessary, in the next throw.

Kneeling from Prone. Being in the prone position, hold the grenade in front of your body and pull the pin. (See Figure 14-10(a-d), on next page.) Move your hands along both sides to the shoulders and raise your body

Figure 14-9(c). Follow through.

Figure 14-10. Left to right (a) pull pin (b) and rise to knee.

Figure 14-10. Left to right (c) follow through (d) and fall to ground.

free hand in order to improve both range and accuracy. As the grenade is released, roll on the stomach to complete the follow-through.

Underhand. This throw is used in built-up areas, woods, or jungle where a high degree of accuracy is necessary. It will give good control of aim for short throws under low-hanging tree limbs or into pillbox embrasures and other openings close to the ground. When releasing the grenade, let it roll off your finger-tips in the same manner as when pitching a softball. The underhand throw may be employed from the standing or kneeling position.

Figure 14-11(a). Pull pin while lying on back.

Figure 14-11(b). Brace back leg and grab a solid object with free hand.

Figure 14-11(c). Push off, roll, and throw.

Figure 14-11(d). End up face down and prone.

GUIDEBOOK FOR MARINES

CHAPTER 15

Explosives, Demolitions, and Protective Measures

This chapter describes various techniques by which all Marines must understand attack and defense using explosive devices. The procedures used to avoid such attacks and to enhance individual and team protection in the field. Demolitions remain weapons of the specialist only. However, all Marines must recognize and understand how explosives and demolitions are used in war and how to avoid falling victim to mines, booby traps, and other devices. Finally, the protective measures used against these and all other types of attack provide a common requirement.

Countermeasures to Explosive Hazards

Foreign Land Mines

A foreign mine is any mine used in combat not employed by U.S. personnel. During Operation Desert Storm, we discovered that Iraq was using some U.S.-made mines in their minefields. Though these mines are familiar to us, we still must treat them as foreign mines.

Anti-tank Mines are designed to disable or destroy armored vehicles. Older anti-tank mines are usually metal. More modern anti-tank mines may use a plastic body to make detection difficult or impossible.

Metal. Normally an older type mine, the body is made completely of metal and will have one or two secondary fuse wells. These types of mines are easily detectable with metallic mine detectors. An example of this type is the TM 46 antitank mine. (See Figure 15-1.)

Plastic. These types of mines were designed to make it difficult to detect them with metallic

mine detectors. Several plastic mines contain small amounts of metal (normally the firing pin) and may still, though difficult, be detected with

Origin: Russia
Type: Blast
Initiating action: Pressure/Tilt rod
Main charge: TNT
Casing: Sheet metal

Figure 15-1. TM 46/TMN 46 (has secondary fuze well).

metallic mine detectors.

Anti-Personnel mines are designed to kill or wound personnel. There are three types: blast, bounding, and fixed directional. New international laws have prohibited their use. However not all countries have signed the conventions, and terrorists and illegal combatants could employ them against U.S. forces.

Blast Type. Designed to cripple the foot or leg of the person who steps on it. It can also burst the tires of a wheeled vehicle that passes over it. (See Figure 15-2.)

Origin: **Russia**
Type: **Blast**
Initiating action: **Pressure**
Main charge: **TNT**
Casing: **Plastic, Rubber, and Metal**

Figure 15-2. PMN.

Fragmentation. Bounding fragmentation mines when activated by pressure or trip wire throw a canister into the air which bursts and scatters shrapnel throughout the immediate area. The Valamara 69 is a bounding fragmentation type anti-personnel mine. (See Figure 15-3.)

Fixed Directional. When activated, throws shrapnel towards personnel. Normally command detonated but may be booby-trapped with trip wire. Claymore type mines. The MON 100 is a Claymore-type Mine. (See Figure 15-4.)

Anti-Personnel Mine Fuzes. Fuzes for anti-personnel mines are normally pressure activated or from a pull on a trip wire. Anti-personnel mines with their fuzes are very sensitive and require small amounts of pressure or pull

Origin: **Italian**
Type: **Bounding fragmentation**
Initiating action: **Pressure, Pull**
Main charge: **Composition B with 1200 steel cubes**
Casing: **Plastic, Valamara 59 has Metal casing**

Figure 15-3. Valamara 69.

Origin: **Russia**
Type: **Fixed directional**
Initiating action: **Trip wire, break wire, and command detonation**
Main charge: **TNT has 400 steel fragments**
Casing: **Metal**

Figure 15-4. MON 100.

Origin: **Former Yugoslavia**
Type: **Bounding fragmentation**
Initiating action: **Pressure, Pull**
Main charge: **TNT**
Casing: **Steel**

Figure 15-5. PROM-1.

(normally under 20 pounds) to activate. Most anti-personnel mines are easily defeated by mine clearing devices like the line charge, mine plows, and mine rollers. (See Figure 15-5.)

Booby Traps

Booby traps are cunning devices, usually explosive in nature, which actuate when an unsuspecting person disturbs an apparently harmless object or performs a presumably safe act. They may be designed to kill or incapacitate. The aim of using booby traps is to cause unexpected and random casualties and damage in order to create an attitude of uncertainty and suspicion in the enemy's mind, thereby lowering morale and inducing a degree of caution that will restrict or slow his movement.

Indications of Booby Traps:

• Disturbances of the surface of the ground and scattered loose soil.
• Wrappers, seals, loose caps from shells, safety pins, nails, and pieces of wire or cord.
• Improvised methods of marking traps, such as piles of stones and marks on walls and trees.
• Evidence of camouflage, such as withered vegetation or signs of cutting.

• Breaks in the continuity of dust, paintwork, and vegetation.
• Trampled earth or vegetation and footprints.
• Lumps and bulges under carpet and in furniture.

Safety Procedures:

• Always treat with suspicion any object that appears to be out of place or artificial in its surroundings. Remember that what you see may well be what the enemy wants you to see.
• Before approaching mines and booby traps, examine them from all angles and check for alternative means of firing.
• It takes only one man to check on a booby trap.
• Never use force. If force is necessary, stop.
• Never touch a trip wire until both ends have been investigated and all devices found have been disarmed or neutralized.
• When tracing trip wires, check for further traps located along and beneath them.
• Treat all parts of a trap with suspicion, as each part may be set to actuate the trap.
• Mark all traps until they are cleared.
• Expect constant change in enemy techniques.

Never attempt hand clearance when pulling or destruction in place is possible and acceptable. All handling of booby traps and disarming must be left to trained combat engineers or explosive ordnance disposal personnel.

Improvised Explosive Devices

Threat. Improvised Explosive Devices (IEDs) are dangerous weapons that are constructed or placed in an improvised manner and are designed to cause death or injury by using explosives alone or in combination with other materials. IEDs can be produced in varying sizes and can have different types of containers, functioning, and delivery methods. They may be built using commercial or military explosives, homemade explosives, or military ordnance and ordnance components. Although primarily constructed using conventional high-explosive charges, chemicals, biological agents, or radiological material, may be included to add to the destructive power and increase the psychological effect of the device. Every IED is unique because the IED builder improvises and constructs each device using materials at hand. Additionally, every IED is designed to defeat a specific target, or type of target, and they generally become more difficult to detect and protect against as they become more sophisticated. The degree of sophistication depends on the ingenuity of the designer and the tools and materials available. IEDs may range in size from a cigarette pack to a large vehicle and can be used as a simple distraction or for destruction of hardened buildings.

IED Components. IEDs can vary widely in shape and form. However, they tend to share a common set of components that consist of the main charge, initiating system, and casing.

Main Charge. The explosive component of IEDs, designed to have a destructive, catastrophic, or psychological impact on the intended target. Military munitions are the most commonly used main charge. Usually, 122mm or greater mortar, tank, and/or artillery rounds are utilized since these items are the easiest to use, provided a ready-made fragmentation effect, and they allow for relatively easy "daisy chaining," which is linking multiple main charges together over long or short distances for simultaneous detonation. Other IEDs have used military and commercial explosives such as PE-4, TNT, and ammonium nitrate (fertilizer) mixed with fuel oil (ANFO). As military stores and caches are depleted, the IED makers may resort to homemade explosives (HME).

Initiating System. The initiation system causes the main charge to function and is typically categorized as one of three types: time, command, or victim operated. The complexity of the systems range from a simple hard wire for command detonation to cellular telephones and remote controls for radio-controlled IEDs. The

initiating system almost always includes a blasting cap and batteries, as a power source for the detonator. Batteries may be as small as 9-volts and AA or as large as car and truck batteries. IEDs may even be wired into the local power supply of a home or office. The initiating system may be a stand-alone type, as named above, or may consist of any combination of time, command, or victim-operated initiators.

Casing. The casing contains the main charge and can be made from numerous materials ranging in size and composition. The container is used to help hide the IED and to possibly provide fragmentation. Aside from military munitions, a myriad of other types of containers have been used as casings, including pipes, soda cans, vehicles, animal carcasses, plastic bags, propane tanks, and vests or satchels for suicide bombers. (See Figure 15-6 on next page.)

Initiation Methods

Time. Time-initiated IEDs are designed to function after a preset delay, allowing the enemy to make his escape or to target military forces that have created an operational pattern. Timers used typically include igniferous (fire producing), chemical, mechanical, and electronic types. Examples are analog clocks and watches, washing machine timers, digital clocks, digital electronic timing circuits, cannon fuses, powder trails, and acid delay. (See Figures 15-7 and 15-8 on next page.)

Command. Command-initiated IEDs are a common method of employment and allow the enemy to choose the optimum moment of initiation. They are normally used against targets that are in transit or where a routine pattern has been established. The most common types of command-initiated methods are command wire or radio-controlled devices that utilize long-range cordless telephones (LRCTs), cellular phones, and remote car openers and alarms. (See Figures 15-9 through 15-11 on next page.)

Victim. A victim-operated IED is initiated by the actions of its victim(s) and is a means of attacking an individual or group of individuals. There are various types of initiation devices, including pull or trip, pressure, pressure release,

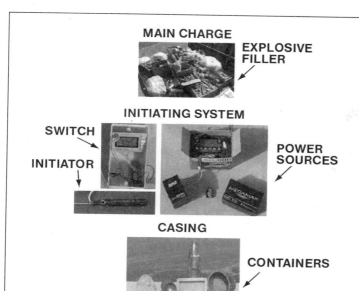

MAIN CHARGE

EXPLOSIVE FILLER

INITIATING SYSTEM

SWITCH

INITIATOR

POWER SOURCES

CASING

CONTAINERS

Figure 15-6. Basic IED Components.

Figure 15-7. Digital Watch.

Figure 15-8. Washing Machine Timer.

Figure 15-9. Command wire.

Figure 15-10. Radio controlled.

Figure 15-11. Radio-controlled initiators.

Figure 15-12. Pressure plate.

Figure 15-13. Trip wire.

Figure 15-14. Movement sensitive/passive IR.

Figure 15-15. Typical EFP detonation and projectile formation.

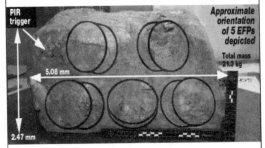

Figure 15-16. EFP array encased in foam and camouflaged.

movement-sensitive, light-sensitive, proximity, and electronic switches. Victim-operated initiators can be tailored to exploit a specific procedure, pattern or action of an individual. (See Figure 15-12 through 15-15.)

Explosively Formed Projectile

An explosively formed projectile (EFP) is a particularly devastating type of IED. EFPs are constructed such that a large portion of the casing is fired at high velocity at the intended target. The shape of the projectile combined with the velocity is traveling enabling it to penetrate armored vehicles. EFPs are typically found assembled in multiple EFP arrays and encased in foam to increase lethality and aid in camouflaging the device. The initiation system usually consists of command wire or radio-controlled arming circuit combined with a movement or heat-sensitive initiator. (See Figure 15-16.)

IED Employment Techniques:

• Disguised static IEDs can be concealed with just about anything (trash, boxes, tires, etc.) and can be placed in, on, or under a target or in/under unsecured vehicles.

• Disguised movable IEDs consist of vehicle-borne IEDs (VBIEDs), suicide vehicle-borne IEDs (SVBIEDs), and person-borne IEDs (PBIEDs) (also known as suicide bombers).

• Thrown, projected, or dropped IEDs (can be improvised grenades or mortars) are used mostly from rooftops and roadway overpasses.

• Hoax IEDs are objects that resemble an actual IED but have no main charge or a fully functioning initiator. They can be employed to learn friendly TTPs, entrap forces for an ambush, delay missions, provide a nonexplosive obstacle, or foster a sense of complacency that may increase the effectiveness of future IED attacks.

• IEDs emplaced as secondary or tertiary devices to attack first responders or explosive ordnance disposal personnel. These devices are usually concealed near the primary device or in likely cordon positions in order to exploit known friendly TTPs.

The Fundamentals of IED Defeat

Predict. These activities are used to identify and understand enemy personnel, equipment, infrastructure, TTPs, support mechanisms, or other actions to forecast specific enemy IED operations directed against U.S. interests. This is driven largely by success in analysis of established enemy patterns, technology, and vulnerabilities.

Detect. These activities contribute to the identification and location of enemy personnel, explosive devices and their component parts, equipment, logistics operations, and infrastructure in order to provide accurate and timely information. These actions assist in the efforts to identify enemy IED activities.

Prevent. These activities disrupt and defeat the IED operational chain of events. The actions focus on the enemy, to interdict or destroy key enemy personnel (bomb makers, leaders, and financiers), their infrastructure/logistics capabilities (suppliers and bomb factories), and surveillance/targeting efforts (reconnaissance and overwatch operations) before emplacement of the device. They also include actions to deter public support for the use of IEDs by the enemy.

Avoid. These activities keep friendly forces from IEDs when prevention activities are not possible or have failed. Avoid activities include increasing situational understanding of the area of operations, continually refining the common operational picture, altering routes and routines to avoid patterns, marking suspect IEDs, and the timely and accurate dissemination of related information.

Neutralize. These activities may be proactive or reactive in nature and contribute to the destruction or reduction of enemy personnel, explosive devices, or supplies in order to provide unrestricted movement of friendly forces. Neutralize activities are generally not the preferred course of action because they destroy forensic evidence.

Protect. Survivability and other protective measures that are implemented to prevent the enemy from inflicting damage as friendly forces maneuver. These activities improve survivability of IED targets through hardening, awareness training, and other techniques.

IED Protective and Detection Techniques

Five- and 25-meter checks. Utilized as a method of detection and prevention of IED attacks. Upon halting, members of the patrolling or maneuvering element will conduct visual and physical checks of their immediate area, approximately 5-meter radius, searching for IED indicators (disturbed earth, suspicious objects, or anything out of the ordinary). After searching the immediate area, the search will then be expanded out to a 25-meter radius.

"Five Cs". Utilized upon detection or detonation of an IED in order to ensure that the situation is handled quickly and safely.

1. **Confirm.** The presence of the suspected IED should be confirmed from a safe distance using hard cover and optics where available. Once confirmed, the explosive hazards spot report (SPOTREP) must be sent to higher HQs.

2. **Clear.** All personnel should be cleared from the area to a tactically safe position where 5- and 25-meter checks are performed at each position.

3. **Cordon.** The area around the IED is cordoned off out to a safe distance in order to prevent unauthorized personnel and vehicles from entering the site. Cordoning a site preserves it for explosive ordnance disposal personnel and provides protection and security against command-initiated IEDs.

4. **Check.** The immediate area around the site and each cordoned position is checked for secondary devices, IED indicators, and suspicious personnel. Five- and 25-meter checks as well as detailed search methods and optics are utilized.

5. **Control.** Control the area inside the cordon to ensure that only authorized personnel have access. Only emergency services (medical, firefighting, or EOD) should be allowed to enter the cordon through the

initial control point (ICP) or entry control point (ECP).

Other Protective Measures

There is a Marine Corps rule for fighting that says, "Unit leaders are responsible for the all around security of their own unit." This does not mean that just the officer or the NCO in charge of your group is the one to see that you and your outfit are protected. It is also your responsibility to take quick measures to protect yourself when your unit may be stopped in a forward movement in battle and at other times when protection is needed. When your outfit cannot advance farther, you usually need protection quickly against the fire of enemy small arms, mortars and artillery. This protection should be simple, available almost at once, and should be capable of further improvement as long as you remain in that position.

Entrenchments

Entrenchments are located to cover a selected area with fire and, at the same time, provide concealment from aerial and ground observation and protection from enemy fire. The three most commonly used entrenchments are briefly explained in this section.

The Fighting Position. Fighting positions are entrenchments normally dug for individual protection when contact with the enemy is imminent or in progress. They provide protection against small arms fire, artillery shell fragments, airplane fire or bombing, and the crushing action of tanks. The one- and two-man fighting positions are basic types, the choice of type resting with the squad leader if not prescribed by higher authority. The two-man fighting hole consists essentially of two joined one-man fighting holes. It is used when Marines must work in pairs or when, for psychological reasons, battlefield comradeship is desirable. Keep the hole small. The smaller the hole, the less likely it is that rounds, grenades, or airburst fragments will get into it. It should be large

enough for you and your buddy in full combat gear and deep enough to reach the armpits when standing inside. It should extend beyond the edges of the frontal cover enough to let you and your buddy observe and fire to the front. The hole is usually dug straight, but it may be curved around the frontal cover. (See Figure 15-17.)

Figure 15-17. Two-man fighting position.

The Hasty Fighting Position. When there is little time for preparation, build a hasty fighting position. It should take advantage of whatever natural cover can be found. It should give frontal cover from enemy direct fire but allow firing to the front and the oblique.

There are three types of hasty fighting positions: (1) prone position, (2) skirmisher's trench, and (3) crater position. If there is a natural hole or ditch available, use it. If not, dig a prone shelter that will give some protection. The hole should be about ½ meter (18 to 20") deep. Use the dirt from the hole to build cover around the edge of the position. (See Figure 15-18 on next page.)

Connecting Trenches. Connecting trenches are conspicuous to aerial observers and on aerial photographs and thus reveal the defensive dispositions. Continuous connecting trenches are not dug as a normal procedure. When two forces are in contact and dispositions have been revealed beyond any question, a few short

Figure 15-18. Crawl trench.

Figure 15-19. Connecting trenches.

trenches may be dug in inconspicuous places to permit necessary daylight movement across exposed areas. Necessary connecting trenches also may be dug in close country, such as jungle, where the position probably will not be disclosed. Further, they may be dug whenever the improved protection, control, communications, and supply outweigh the sacrifice of concealment. The depth of the trenches depends on the time and type of help and equipment available to dig them. Without engineer help, crawl trenches about 1 meter deep and 2/3 of a meter wide are probably all that can be dug. Dig the trenches zig-zagged so that the enemy will not be able to fire down a long section if he gets into the trench, and so that shrapnel from shell bursts will lose some of its effectiveness. (See Figure 15-19.)

Survivability Positions

Survivability positions are purpose- built structures providing protection in semi-permanent sites that require continuous occupation. For example, airfield perimeters, vital facilities, and forward operating bases require guard posts and observation posts, at a minimum, that will protect their occupants but also allow free use of individual and crew-served weapons. Depending upon the threat, engineers or other services will construct these positions to resist the types of weapons systems the enemy may use against them, potentially small arms, mortars, or rocket launchers.

Camouflage

Camouflage has been defined as the science of military deception. It affords protective concealment for your position so that you can see without being seen. This permits you to strike first, fatally, and at no cost to yourself.

Hide, Blend, Deceive. There are three general ways in which you can camouflage yourself. You can hide, you can blend yourself with your surroundings, or you can deceive the enemy.

• To hide yourself, use the advantages offered by nature in the terrain. If nature has given you enough camouflage for you and your supplies, let nature do the work unaided.

• Blend with your surroundings so that you match surrounding terrain features and are not conspicuous.

• You can deceive the enemy by using such tricks as making a dummy position with poor camouflage. This may lead the enemy to the dummy position and your range of fire.

Rules of Camouflage. In addition, to these general means of camouflaging yourself, there are a number of rules that you need to learn well if you are going to protect yourself successfully.

• Pick out a position that uses as much as possible of the tactical and concealment values of the terrain.

• Practice camouflage discipline by keeping your position free of tell-tale signs of occupancy, such as paths, dead leaves on camouflage materials and so on.

• Select your camouflage materials to match the color and texture of the local terrain. If you use natural materials, such as grass or trees, keep them fresh in appearance.

• Avoid over-camouflaging your position. This is just as obvious as no camouflage. Use common sense in covering regular outlines and tell-tale shadows.

• Don't look up from your position. Your face is smooth and reflects a great deal of light. Never look up when a plane is overhead, or if you do, break off a branch or bush and look carefully. Never throw down a cigarette. Pinch out the fire, split the paper, and roll it into a small ball. Scatter the shreds of tobacco around so no clues will be left.

• Some objects shine like mirrors in the sunlight and can be seen for miles. Watch your mess gear and weapons. Keep them under cover or in the shade.

• Tape your dog tags so that they do not clink. Put them together and bind them with a piece of friction tape or adhesive tape.

• Follow the paths laid out for you. The paths may be wired, they may be taped or they may just be blazed. But they were laid out for a purpose. Don't try to take short cuts away from them, you will make new tracks.

• Don't cut the brush or limbs you plan to use for camouflage from a bush next to your position. Go some distance for them and don't take them all from the same place.

• Bury all waste material. Fill the dirt back very carefully and cover the spot with leaves or dry grass. Go as far as to sod the spot if you find it necessary.

• Stay off the horizon. It is important that you know where the horizon is. If the enemy is downhill from you, you usually are on the horizon and present the enemy with a good target.

• Stay in the shadows and also be sure you have a blending background. You can be seen in silhouette if you are in shadow with a lighted background beyond you.

• Smoke billowing up in a straight column is always bad. Build your fires under trees or put a screen over the fire.

Obstacles

Classifications. All obstacles are classified in two broad categories, existing and reinforcing.

• Existing obstacles are natural, such as lakes, rivers, and mountains, or cultural, towns, railroad embankments, etc. Reinforcing obstacles are placed on the battlefield to strengthen existing obstacles.

• Reinforcing obstacles include, but are not limited to, minefields, road craters, and log and wire obstacles.

When employing obstacles there are some principles to be considered:

• Keep under friendly observation and covered by fire.

• Tied in with other natural or man-made obstacles.

• Of no advantage to the enemy.

• Concealed from enemy observation by incorporating terrain features, such as reverse slopes, hedges, woods, and fence lines.

Obstacle Intent/Effect

An obstacle is any obstruction that fixes, disrupts, turns, or blocks movement or maneuver.

• A fixing obstacle is one that slows the enemy within an engagement area. It will allow time for friendly units to engage with direct and indirect fires.

• A turning obstacle is one that manipulates the enemy's direction of movement by presenting open bypass routes. These bypass routes should be designed to lead the enemy into friendly engagement areas. A turning obstacle should be easier to bypass than to breach.

• A blocking obstacle "blocks" an avenue of approach. It prevents movement through an engagement area. Enemy advancement through a blocking obstacle can only be done at an extremely high cost.

• A disrupting obstacle breaks up formations and unit tempo. It is designed to interrupt a unit's timetable. Disrupting obstacles are designed to cause a premature breach and cause a piecemeal attack.

Wire Obstacles

Entanglements are classified according to their use and their depth and whether fixed or portable.

Types:
- Triple standard concertina.
- Double apron fence.
- Four-strand cattle fence.
- Tangle foot.
- Concertina roadblock.

Entanglements are classified by use as tactical, protective, or supplementary. The employment of these types in a defensive area is shown in FM 5-34.

Tactical. Tactical wire entanglements are sited parallel to and along the friendly side of the final protective line. They are used to break up enemy attack formations and to hold the enemy in areas covered by the most intense defensive fire. Tactical entanglements extend across the entire front of a position but are not necessarily continuous.

Protective. Protective wire entanglements are located to prevent surprise assaults from points close to the defense area. As in the case of all anti-personnel obstacles, they are close enough to the defense area for day and night observation and far enough away to prevent the enemy from using effectively from points just beyond the obstacle, normally 40 to 100 meters.

Protective wire surrounds the individual units of a command, usually the platoons, to enclose entire defensive positions. Protective entanglements are erected around rear area installations in the same manner and to serve the same purpose as protective wire around defensive positions in forward areas. Protective wire also includes the entanglements, which should be installed over the tops of installations provided with overhead cover.

Supplementary. Supplementary wire entanglements in front of the forward edge of the battle area are used to conceal the exact line of the tactical wire. To the rear of the Forward Edge Battle Area (FEBA), supplementary wire is used to enclose the entire defensive position by connecting the protective wire entanglements. Supplementary wire entanglements used to break up the line of tactical wire should be identical to the tactical wire entanglements and constructed simultaneously with them whenever possible.

Entanglements are classified by depth as belts, bands, or zones.

Belt. A belt is an entanglement one fence in depth.

Band. A band consists of two or more belts in depth, with no interval between them. The belts may be fences of the same type, or the band may be composed of two or more fences of different types.

Zone. A zone consists of two or more bands or belts in depth, with intervals between them.

CHAPTER 16

Basic Communications

*Throughout the Marine Corps, at all echelons, there is a constant need to exchange information.
We often refer to this exchange as "passing the word." Every Marine should know the
basic facts concerning the means of communication and communication equipment
found in the Marines. Electronic Communication takes the form of radio or
data signals, delivered by various systems utilizing multiple waveforms.*

Radio

Radios are widely used at all echelons of the Marine Corps. Radio communications are flexible. The equipment can go anywhere a Marine can go, and it provides one of the fastest means of communication available. Since an enemy can monitor ordinary radio communications, cryptographic devices must be used with tactical radios to achieve security. The length of each transmission should, of course, be made as short as possible since the enemy is able to determine the location of an active radio, whether it is used with a cryptographic device or not. The following rules apply to radio transmissions:

Rule 1. Always listen before starting to talk so as not to create interference. Know what you are going to say before transmitting.

Rule 2. Press the push-to-talk button on the handset. Do not start talking until the crypto keying tone ceases.

Rule 3. Speak distinctly and in a normal tone.

Rule 4. Release the push-to-talk button immediately after speaking.

Rule 5. In an extreme emergency, the cryptographic device may be switched to the plain (or clear) mode if the radio will otherwise not function.

Rule 6. Avoid contact with the antenna while transmitting. Do not allow the antenna to contact power lines while the radio is being transported.

Figure 16-1.

SINGLE CHANNEL	Single channel (SC) frequency modulation (FM) operation in very high frequency (VHF) band. Narrowband (30-512 MHz) 10 watts output power. Wideband (225-2000 MHz) 5 watts peak output power. SATCOM (243-318 MHz) 20 watts output power (frequency range is limited on the 117F 30-512Mhz). Power Amplified (PA) 50 watts peak output power in vehicular or rack mounted.
FREQUENCY HOPPING	Frequency hopping (FH) mode for electronic counter measure (ECCM) operation. SINCGARS ECCM, Havequick I/II ECCM.
ADAPTIVE NETWORKING WIDEBAND WAVEFORM (ANW2)	10 Mbps. Range - 30Km. Voice, VOIP, DATA. Self Healing network.
OTHER WAVEFORMS	Soldier Radio Waveform (SRW). Integrated Waveform (IW). High Performance Waveform (HPW) and HPW-IP. VHF/UHF/Line-Of-Sight (VULOS), Beacon.
SATCOM	Dedicated UHF SATCOM. DAMA UHF SATCOM.
DIGITAL TUNING	Quick, silent, precise, digital tuning.
VISUAL DISPLAY	Electronic visual displays provide for quick checks and prompts.
PRESET CHANNELS	Preset channels: eight for SC mode and six for FH mode, each of which may be loaded with COMSEC and used in CT or PT mode.
VOICE DATA	Voice or digital data communication. Provide data rates of 600, 1200, 2400 and 16,000 bits per second (BPS); also provides analog data interface.
FREQUENCIES	More than 2000 SC frequencies.
COMSEC	Secure voice and data communications, High-Assurance IP Encryption (HAIPE), VINSON, ANDVT/KYV-5, KG84C encryption.
WEIGHT	8.2 lbs. (3.7 kg) without battery. 12 lbs (5.44 kg) with battery and box.

Figure 16-2. RT capabilities.

MODULATION	POWER	RATED RANGE	VOICE	PA	10 KM to 35 KM
VOICE	LOW	200 M to 400 M	DATA (600-4800 BPS)	HIGH	3 KM to 5 KM
VOICE	MEDIUM	400 M to 5 KM	DATA (16,000 BPS)	HIGH	1 KM to 3 KM
VOICE	HIGH	5 KM to 10 KM			

Figure 16-3. Manpack radio performance data.

Above data applies equally to dismount radios and RCUs.

Ranges shown are for planning purposes only. They are based upon line of sight and are average for normal conditions. Ranges depend upon location, sighting, weather and surrounding noise level among other factors. Use of the OE-254 or COM-201B antenna will increase ranges for both voice and data transmissions. Enemy jamming and mutual interference conditions will degrade ranges. In data transmissions, use of lower band rate increases the range.

The Marine Corps' primary tactical radio is the AN/PRC-152. (See Figure 16-1 on page 210 and Figures 16-2 and 16-3 on page 211.)

Wire

Wire is the most reliable means of communications, and everyone has had experience in using a telephone. Wire has the inherent characteristics of speed and reliability. Unless appropriate speech security devices are available to the users, however, it should not be assumed that telephone systems can be used to pass classified information. Wire is the primary means of communication in a semi-permanent location or when a unit assumes a defensive position. Learn to recognize the appearance of communication wire because the movement of our own armored vehicles often cuts it. When driving a vehicle, try to avoid running over field wire if at all possible. In the event you discover a break in a wire line, report the location of the break to the nearest HQs. Profanity is prohibited on both radio and telephone sets, and from time to time, transmissions are monitored by higher echelon.

Visual and Sound Communications

In addition to the arm and hand signals depicted in Chapter 18, other visual communications within your platoon or squad are widely used. Some examples are flags, flashing lights, pyrotechnics, and aircraft panels. Additionally, sound communications, such as sirens to warn of enemy aircraft or armor, are used.

Messengers

At any time in the field a Marine may be called upon to deliver a message—the most secure means available at the squad and platoon levels. A messenger receiving an oral message

repeats it to the sender so that there will be no misunderstanding. Messengers then repeat the message to themselves until they have committed it to memory.

Messengers must know their principal and alternate routes prior to departure. Cover, concealment, length, and conditions of the various routes available must be taken into account. At all times, additional protection for messengers, in the form of another Marine or a fire team, will have to be provided, dependent on the local combat situation and the time of day the message must be delivered. Sometimes, messengers may follow wire lines to maintain their direction during the night or in difficult terrain. When delivering messages to a battalion or larger unit, a messenger normally delivers the message to the message center. While at the message center, he checks for message traffic for his unit. Messengers should know the names of unit commanders, be able to read a map, and know how to use a field message book.

The Phonetic Alphabet

When talking over the radio, certain words in the conversation may be misunderstood because of similarity in sound to other words. In order to eliminate any misunderstanding by

PHONETIC ALPHABET			
LETTER	EQUIVALENT PHONETIC	LETTER	EQUIVALENT PHONETIC
A	Alfa	N	November
B	Bravo	O	Oscar
C	Charlie	P	Papa
D	Delta	Q	Quebec
E	Echo	R	Romeo
F	Foxtrot	S	Sierra
G	Golf	T	Tango
H	Hotel	U	Uniform
I	India	V	Victor
J	Juliet	W	Whiskey
K	Kilo	X	X-ray
L	Lima	Y	Yankee
M	Mike	Z	Zulu

Figure 16-4. Phonetic Alphabet.

the receiving party, the sender uses the phonetic alphabet to spell out words that might be misunderstood. (See Figure 16-4 on previous page.)

Numeral Pronunciation

Numbers are important in military messages and should be spoken clearly in telephone and radio conversations. The sending party should exaggerate the pronunciation of numerals to avoid misunderstanding. Each digit of large numbers is pronounced separately except in the case of even "hundreds" and "thousands." (See Figure 16-5.)

NUMERAL PRONUNCIATION	
1 – wun	6 – six
2 – too	7 – seven
3 – tree	8 – ait
4 – fo-wer	9 – nine
5 – fife	0 – zero

EXAMPLES		
70	–	seven zero
84	–	ait fo-wer
131	–	wun tree wun
500	–	fife hun-dred
1,468	–	wun fo-wer six ait
7,000	–	seven thou-sand

Figure 16-5. Numeral Pronunciation.

Message Pad

Messages are relayed using the standard forms contained in the message pad, which contains chemically treated paper allowing copies and printed instructions for the user. These are used by radio operators to send and receive messages but may also be used by telephone and foot messengers. They are simple and formatted with the essential handling information, with lined space for the brief message. (See Figure 16-6 on next page.)

Characteristics of the AN/PRC-152 Field Radio

Description. The AN/PRC-152 is an advanced multi-band tactical handheld radio. This enables a wide variety of applications for the user, including ground-to-ground, ground-to-air, and tactical satellite communications. Over these links, the type of communication traffic includes voice and data for command and control application. Since much of this information is highly sensitive, encryption is critical.

Frequency and Range. The frequency range of the AN/PRC-152 is 30.0000 MHz to 511.9999 MHz with 1 Hz spacing per channel. The range planning factor of the AN/PRC-152 is up to 5 miles depending on varying factors such as atmospheric conditions, terrain considerations, and environmental build up:

1. VHF Low Band: 30.0000 MHz to 89.9999 MHz.
2. VHF High Band: 90.0000 MHz to 224.9999MHz.
3. UHF Band: 225.0000 MHz to 511.9999 MHz.

AN/PRC-152 Radio Assembly. This part of the radio has the connectors, switches, and buttons for programming the radio. It is the receiver-transmitter unit (RTU). (See Figure 16-7 on next page.)

Rechargeable Li-Ion Battery. The lithium-ion battery has a quick twist mount for easy connect and disconnect. Do not expose the battery to temperatures above 160 degrees as the battery can explode if it becomes too hot. Lithium-ion batteries should not be exposed to acid because this will contaminate the battery and damage it making it inoperable. (See Figure 16-8 on next page.)

VHF/UHF or VHF Blade Antenna. All antennas attach to the radio via the threaded N-connector (TNC) antenna connector. The VHF/UHF blade antenna is 45" in length and operational over VHF/UHF 30 MHz to 512 MHz frequency range. The VHF blade antenna is also 45" in length and operational over VHF 30 MHz to 108 MHz frequency range. (See Figure 16-9 on next page.)

PREC.	DTG		FM	
TO:			INFO	
BT	CLASS			
BT				
X SEND SECURE VOICE	☐ SEND CLEAR		RELEASING OFFICER'S SIGNATURE	
TOR			TOD	

Figure 16-6.

Figure 16-7.   Figure 16-8.

Figure 16-9.

VHF/UHF/HB Hand Held Antenna. This antenna attaches to the radio via the threaded N-connector (TNC) antenna connector. The VHF/UHF/HB hand held antenna is 138" in length and is operational over the 30 MHz to 870 MHz frequency range. (See Figure 16-10 on next page.)

Accessory Carrying Bag. The accessory carrying bag is utilized to store accessories. Modular straps are sewn to the back to allow attachment to a pack, flak jacket, or SAPI plate carrier. (See Figure 16-11 on next page.)

Radio Functions and Controls.

1. **Volume Control**. Use the "up" arrow to increase the volume. Use the "down" arrow to decrease the volume. This button is not lockable.

2. **Push To Talk (PTT) Button**. This button is used to key a voice transmission for the radio. If the current waveform is configured for voice, the radio will continuously transmit RF over the air while the button is pressed. This button is still functional even

Figure 16-10.

Figure 16-11.

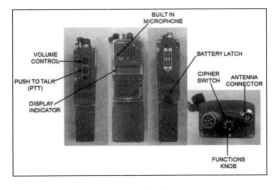

Figure 16-12.

if a handset is connected to the radio. (See Figure 16-12.)

3. Display Indicator. The AN/PRC-152 display shows operational and programming screens.

4. Microphone. The AN/PRC-152 has a built in microphone located next to the speaker.

5. Battery Latch. The battery latch slides up to unlock battery for removal from RT.

6. Antenna Connector. The antenna connector provides 50-ohm antenna port.

7. Cipher Switch. The cipher switch has three options: PT, LD, and CT:

a. **Plain Text (PT).** This places the radio in plain text, non-encrypted mode.

b. **Load (LD)**. This places the radio off-line, ready to load COMSEC and Transmission Security (TRANSEC) variables from an external Type-1 fill device.

c. **Cipher Text (CT).** This places the radio in the cipher text encryption mode.

8. Functions Knob. The functions knob has nine selections on it; they are OFF, 1, 2, 3, 4, 5, S, F, and Z:

a. [OFF] turns the radio off.

b. [1, 2, 3, 4, 5] selects system presets 1 through 5.

c. [S] places the Radio in Scan Operation.

d. [F] places the radio in Front Panel Mode, permitting access to all system presets and keypad functions.

e. [Z] zeroizes all programmed variables, including encryption variables.

Installation Procedures

Lithium-Ion Battery. The lithium-ion battery has a quick twist mount for easy connect and disconnect. Attach a charged battery to the transceiver by seating the battery on the base of the radio at an angle to the base, and then twist the battery into position in a clockwise direction as viewed from the bottom of the battery. The battery latch on the side of the radio snaps into the lock position when the battery is properly positioned on the radio.

Antenna. Screw either the whip or blade antenna to the TNC antenna connector. If operating in Satellite Communications mode (SATCOM), connect the optional SATCOM antenna cable to the AN/PRC-152 TNC antenna connector, and deploy the SATCOM antenna according to the separate instructions provided with the antenna.

Cipher Switch. Rotate the Cipher Switch to [PT] or [CT] position.

Function Knob. Turn the function knob to [1] to [5] or [F] position. This initializes the AN/PRC-152 software and performs a power-on self-test.

Power-On Self-Test (POST). When the radio is first turned on, the "HARRIS" logo screen is displayed, followed by the "FALCON III" screen. The initializing screen is displayed next and shows the radio's operating software version. This screen stays on till the radio finishes powering up. The next screen will be either POST FAILED or POST PASSED. If POST FAILED an audible warning will sound and user will be instructed to run a Self-Test operation on the entire radio to determine more details about the component that caused the POST Failure.

Self-Test. This runs the Built-In Test for all hardware modules. (See Figure 16-13.) Press the (7) Key to go into the Test Options Menu, then do the following:

1. Navigate to "TEST OPTIONS," press "Enter."

2. Select "SELF TEST," press "Enter."

3. Select "YES" for "RUN SELF TEST," press "ENTER."

4. Once the test starts, you will see a screen that says "TEST IN PROGRESS." The test may take up to one minute.

5. You will see either a "TEST PASSED" (then you will press "ENT" or "CLR" to return to Main Menu) or a "TEST FAILED" screen indicating a specific module along with a fault code that can be referred to for trouble shooting.

Programming menus allow for SINCGARS configuration to be performed from the radio front panel "F." When in Program Mode, the radio is offline and cannot send or receive communication. Make sure that your Cipher Switch is on Plain Text (PT). SINCGARS programming involves two menu structures:

1. Set the Cipher Switch to PT.

2. Obtain an authorized frequency.

3. Set the Function Switch to [1-5] to power on the RT.

4. Allow the RT to run through the BIT process.

5. Press the 0 (NEXT) button to change to the VULOS Channel main screen.

6. Press the RIGHT [>] Arrow to highlight the RX frequency.

7. Enter the assigned frequency and press enter.

8. Confirm the TX frequency is the same as the RX frequency and press [ENT] to confirm.

9. Press the CLEAR [CLR] button to return to the VULOS main screen.

10. Enter the name for the system preset (up to 11 characters) and press [ENT].

11. Transmit a formatted message using procedural words, phonetic alphabet, and numerals.

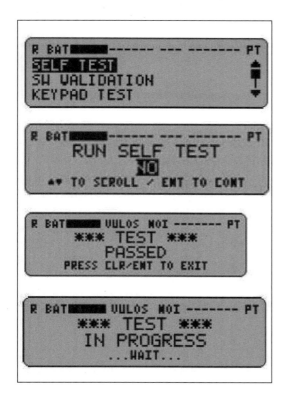

Figure 16-13.

12. Receive acknowledgement of the message from the distant site.

Radio Check. This alerts the receiver that the sender requests a response indicating the strength and readability of his transmission. Conducting radio checks is necessary before any operation and should be conducted throughout the operation to ensure that both sender and receiver can communicate clearly to one another:

    1. To conduct a radio check, the sender will begin by calling the receiver and saying "Radio check, over."

    2. A response of "ROGER" indicates the transmission is loud and clear.

      a. A response of "WEAK BUT READABLE" indicates that the transmission is weak but can be understood.

      b. A response of "WEAK AND GARBLED" indicates that the transmission is weak and unreadable.

      c. A response of "STRONG BUT GARBLED" indicates that the transmission is strong signal but unreadable.

      d. The sender will then end the transmission by saying "Roger, out."

Reports that Marines may have to call for when seeing the enemy are the SALUTE report, SITREP, SPOTREP, and POSREP.

SALUTE Report. The acronym SALUTE provides a simple method for remembering how and what to report about the enemy.

    Line 1. Size.
    Line 2. Activity.
    Line 3. Location.
    Line 4. Unit.
    Line 5. Time.
    Line 6. Equipment.

An example of such report is "Seven enemy soldiers, traveling SW, crossed road junction on black ridge on 211300 August. They were wearing green uniforms and carrying one machinegun and one rocket launcher."

Situation Report (SITREP). A Situation Report is the report that is giving a situation in an area of a reporting unit or formation.

    Line 1. Date Time Group (DTG).
    Line 2. Friendly position.

Line 3. Activities conducted since last report.
Line 4. Actions planned next 12 hours.
Line 5. Logistical requirements.
Line 6. Personnel casualties since last report.
Line 7. Remarks.

Spot Report. A Spot Report is a concise narrative report of essential information covering events or conditions that may have immediate and significant effect on current planning and operations that is afforded the most expeditious means of transmission consistent with the requisite security. Usually reported after a significant event such as enemy contact.

    Line 1. Event.
    Line 2. Time and date of event.
    Line 3. Location of friendly.
    Line 4. Action taken.
    Line 5. Friendly casualties.
    Line 6. Enemy casualties.
    Line 7. Detainees.
    Line 8. Weapons/equipment captured.

POSITION Report. A Position Report (PosRep) is the report that is giving a unit or individual position in an area of operation.

    Line 1. Unit.
    Line 2. Location.
    Line 3. Direction of movement/speed of movement.
    Line 4. Remarks (status, activity, etc.).

Procedural words. Words or phrases for radio procedure used to communicate information in a condensed standard verbal format.

    1. "THIS IS... ." Alerts the receiver as to who is sending the transmission.

    2. "OVER." Alerts the receiver that the sender has ended his transmission and is awaiting a response from the receiver.

    3. "OUT." Alerts the receiver that the sender has ended his transmission and requires or expects no response/answer.

      a. OVER and OUT have different meanings. These two procedural words are never used together.

    4. "ROGER." Indicates to the sender that the receiver hears and understands the message or question.

5. "SAY AGAIN... ." Indicates to the sender that the receiver did not receive or understand that last transmission and requests the transmission be repeated.

6. "I SAY AGAIN... ." This alerts the receiver that the sender is resending the transmission or the portion requested.

CHAPTER 17

Land Navigation

*Marines must be able to determine their position on the battlefield at all times.
Squad leaders and team leaders normally perform this function, but combat shows no particular
favors, and therefore, every Marine must be able to navigate using a map and compass.*

*A map is a picture, a picture of the land and the things people have built on the land.
A map is flat, and when we look at a map, we are looking at a picture of the ground from a spot high
in the air. That view is different from the one we have looked at all of our lives, from one point
on the ground to another point on the ground. That is the first thing to remember about maps.
Maps are views of things from directly above. They give a view as though you were hovering
over a football stadium in a helicopter. In map reading, we are looking from overhead at
something with many more details than a football game, and at an area much larger
and not so near to us, the land itself really looks strange.*

What Is on a Map?

A map is a picture, but it is not a photographic picture. It is a drawing on paper, and a big difference between a map and a photograph is that the map has signs and symbols instead of photographs of objects. These signs and symbols represent various things on the ground.

To read a map, then, we have to learn what these various signs mean. Map signs and symbols usually look something like the actual things for which they stand. The signs are simple to draw and are easily recognized. In order to better understand the use of signs, look at Figures 17-1 through 17-24 (on next page).

For example, Figure 17-1 shows a pick crossed with a sledge hammer, the sign for a mine. These two tools are used in mining. Figure 17-2 shows the sign for a schoolhouse, a black block with a flag flying from it. Most schools have a flag on a flagpole, and so the sign gives you the idea of a school.

Let us put these signs on a map and see what they look like. Figure 17-25(a) (on page 221) shows you the mapping signs for the things you see in the photograph of the land in Figure 17-25(b) (on page 221). Identify the signs shown.

The map, however, is still incomplete. So far, we just have our objects on a flat, blank piece of land, but land is not like that. It has much more on it than these signs alone can show us.

On a football field, we see the players not on a blank area, but against a background marked off with lines.

These lines mean something to us, and we can tell where the players are by watching how far they are from these lines—the goal lines, the yard lines, and the side lines. The lines form a pattern that connects the different objects on the

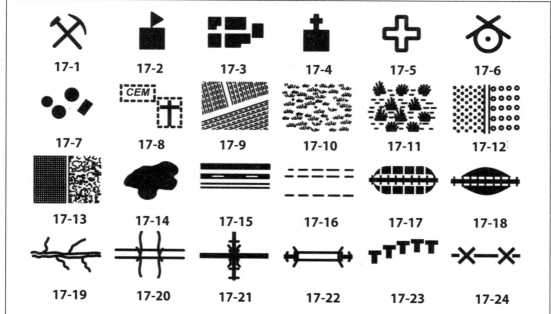

Figures 17-1 through 17-24. 1-Mine, 2-School, 3-Buildings, 4-Church, 5-Hospital, 6-Windmill, 7-Oil Tanks, 8-Cemetery, 9-Cultivated Fields, 10-Grassland, 11-Swamp, 12-Orchard, 13-Woods, 14-Lakes or Ponds, 15-Primary or First Class Highway, 16-Dirt Road or Trail, 17-Cut, 18-Fill, 19-Stream, 20-Bridge, 21-Railroad Underpass, 22-Tunnel, 23-Telegraph, Telephone Wires, 24-Barbed Wire Strand Fence.

field. On the map on which our signs are placed, there are already certain main lines that make a general pattern. These main lines are also shown by signs, and they stand for such important landmarks as streams, roads, railroads, and fences.

We try to make these lines look different from one another, so that we don't get them confused. At the same time, we try to make them resemble the objects they are supposed to represent. Figures 17-15 through 17-24 are examples of these main lines and the signs used to show them on a map.

The heavy line in Figure 17-15 is a primary or first class highway; the second line is a secondary highway; these are sometimes red on your map. The solid parallel lines mean other surfaced roads. The two dashed parallel lines in Figure 17-16 mean dirt road, while the single dashed line means a trail or footpath.

Telegraph or telephone wires are often on tall T-shaped poles across the country. The map sign is also T-shaped in Figure 17-23.

In Figure 17-24, the sign is given for a barbed-wire strand fence, not the kind that is a military entanglement. The sign for a smooth wire fence is a series of small o's connected by dashes. (For example, o-o-o-o-o-o.)

This covers the signs that are most used in mapping. It is important to remember the colors used with these signs. All water, such as swamps, rivers, and lakes, is in blue. Woods and other heavy vegetation are in green. Cuts, fills, some cultivated fields, and some roads may be in reddish brown.

Other roads, railroads, buildings, bridges, and most man-made objects are printed in black.

If we put all of these signs and colors on a map and give them names, we find ourselves with the land picture you see in Figure 17-26 (on next page). This is more like it! Now we have a pattern of ground on which our signs begin to make sense. This is a simple map, but it tells us much more about the area it represents.

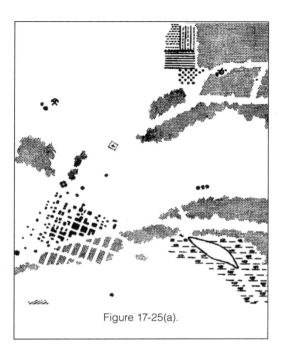

Figure 17-25(a).

Figure 17-25(b).

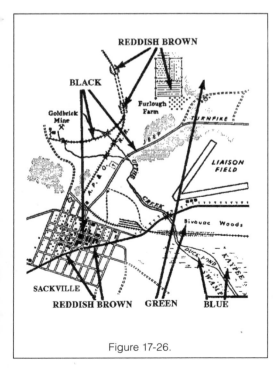

Figure 17-26.

Elevation and Contour

So far, everything on our map is flat. We must now find a way to learn something about the different ground levels. It means something to us to know that a hill is in a certain place, but we would further like to know how high it is. A picture of a hill taken from above will not show this, but there is a way for the map to give you this information.

A hill is broader at its base than it is at its top. Let us take an object which is like a hill, a cone, for example, and see what we can do to a picture of it from above to let us know how high it is.

To Judge Height

First, suppose there are two boulders on the side of the cone, as in Figure 17-27, Example 1 (on next page). When we look at this from above (Examples 2 and 3), we can still tell that there are two boulders there. We would not know which boulder was higher and how high up the cone either boulder was if we had not already seen the cone from the side.

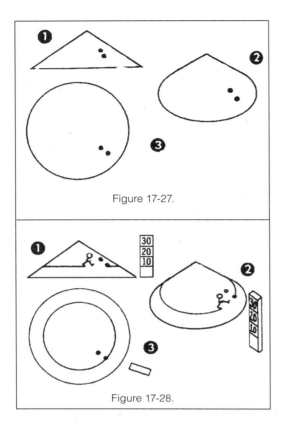

Figure 17-27.

Figure 17-28.

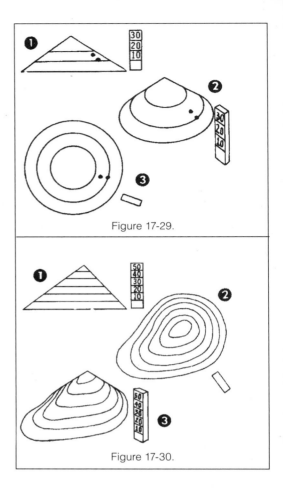

Figure 17-29.

Figure 17-30.

Next, let us suppose that we walk up this cone until we are 10 feet higher than the base (Figure 17-28). Now let us walk around the cone, staying 10 feet high all the way around. Finally, we will come back to the place we started from. If we had a leaky flour bag with us as we walked, we would have left a mark on the hill that would look like Example 1. From above, this line would look like it does in Examples 2 and 3.

Now what do we know about this mark as we look at it from above? We know that anything on it is 10 feet higher than the base of the cone. Notice that one of the boulders is right on this line; therefore, its elevation, or height, is 10 feet. We know that anything between the line and the base of the cone is lower than 10 feet.

Let's move up the cone until we are 10 feet higher and do the same thing again. The result is another flour line (Figure 17-29). What do we know about this line? We know that everything on it is at an elevation of 20 feet, and that the elevation of everything between it and the first

line is somewhere between 10 and 20 feet. Now the second boulder is about halfway between the two lines, so we can judge that its elevation is about 15 feet.

To Judge Shapes

These lines tell us still more—the shape of objects. They tell us that the cone is round, for example. If the object is not round, an object other than a cone, these lines can tell us that also. Suppose we stretch one side of the cone so that it looks like Figure 17-30, Example 1. If we do our flour bag stunt again, from above the lines look like Examples 2 and 3. We can tell which side it bulges on.

We find, then, that these lines can tell us two things, elevation and shape. Maps have many such lines, and if you understand what they

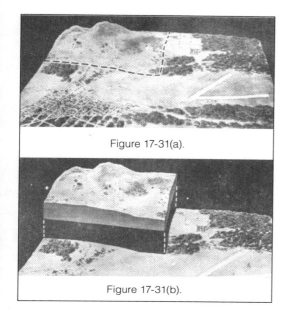

Figure 17-31(a).

Figure 17-31(b).

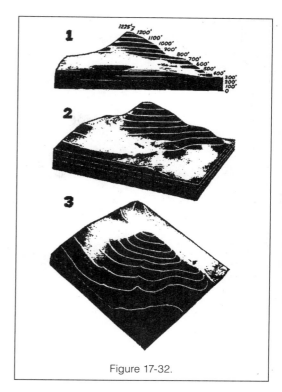

Figure 17-32.

mean, they are easy to read and very helpful. On maps, these lines are called contours or contour lines.

Let us see what happens when we place contour lines on a map. The dashed line in Figure 17-31(a) encloses the hill that overlooks the town of Sackville. In Figure 17-31(b), we have lifted the hill right off the map so we can examine it more closely.

First, let us make flour marks on the hill, just the way we did on the cone. From the side, it looks like Figure 17-32, Example 1. As we rise into the air, we can see more of these lines, as Examples 2 and 3.

Finally, we have a view from directly above, and we can see that the shape of the hill is shown in Figure 17-33(a) (on next page) just as the shape of cone was shown in Figure 17-30. If we take these lines out of the photograph and put them on a map, as in Figure 17-33(b) (on next page), we can tell which parts are high and which low.

It would clutter up the map too much to have the number showing the elevation of each contour line, so only a few of them are numbered. To make it easy to count these lines, every fifth line is heavier than the others. The distance between contour lines on each map is shown by means of a note at the bottom of the map. This note may read, for example, Contour interval: 10 feet.

This means that the distance between any two neighboring contour lines on that map is 10 feet in a vertical direction. The contour interval is noted on maps just below the graphic scales. On our map of Sackville, the contour interval is 100 feet.

Since the highest point on the hill in Figure 17-33(b) (on next page) does not fall exactly on a contour line, this point is labeled with the exact elevation. On maps, such elevation numbers are found often. Some objects take their names from these numbers. If there are a number of road junctions on a part of a map, and we wish to name one of them in a particular way, we may call it RJ 124 (that is, the road junction which is marked as being at an elevation of 124 feet).

Begin at Sea Level

It may be seen, also, that the elevation of the base of a hill in Figure 17-32, Example 1 is 300 feet rather than 0 feet. The reason for this is that elevation is figured from sea level. In other

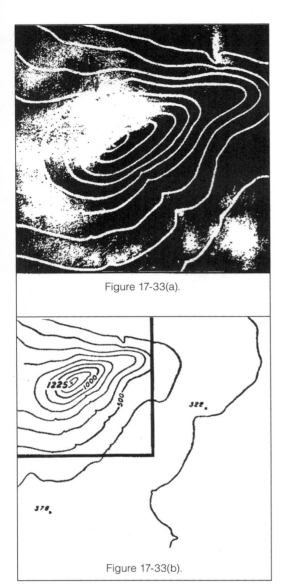

Figure 17-33(a).

Figure 17-33(b).

1225'ABOVE SEA LEVEL
300' ABOVE SEA LEVEL
OCEAN
SEA LEVEL

Figure 17-34.

words, we compare the elevation of all land anywhere to the average sea level.

In Figure 17-34, although the hill is far from sea, the base of the hill on the land is 300 feet above sea level. Sea level is zero for all elevation measurements.

Other Contour Information

It is clear that these contour lines are very helpful things to have, and they can help us in other ways. Suppose we have a high spot of ground that breaks off suddenly and becomes a cliff. From the ground, as in Figure 17-35(a), it is easy to tell this is a cliff. It is also easy to tell this by examining the contour lines of the map. When a hill or cliff is steep, the contour lines appear close together as in Figure 17-35(b). This arrangement of contour lines on a map always shows a sharp rise in the ground. If however, the lines are spaced evenly and fairly apart, it means that the hill rises gradually.

If there are two hills with a saddle between them, as in Figure 17-36(a), the contour lines, as in Figure 17-36(b), tell us exactly what they look like.

A special kind of valley is formed by a stream, as in Figure 17-37(a), and contour lines in the area are usually regularly spaced as in Figure 17-37(b). They form "Vs" where they cross the stream. It is important to remember that these Vs all point uphill or upstream.

Contours, then, can tell us several things about streams. They can tell us the location of a

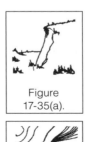

Figure 17-35(a).

Figure 17-36(a).

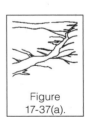

Figure 17-37(a).

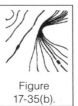

Figure 17-35(b).

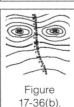

Figure 17-36(b).

Figure 17-37(b).

GUIDEBOOK FOR MARINES

streamor valley; they can tell us which way the stream is flowing, which shows the slope of the ground; and by the spaces between the contour lines, they can tell us how steep the valley is. Remember, V-shaped contours show valleys or streams.

Figure 17-38 shows the map of Sackville and vicinity with contour lines on it. The map is becoming more complete. The contour lines show the shape of the ground. We can tell now that the land has a hill, with the ground sloping very gradually from its base toward the town and toward the airfield.

Measuring Distance

We have now put a map together and looked at many of its parts, so that at this point we can learn a good deal about a region by reading a map of that same region.

Distances on a map can be measured. The reason for this is that a map is a true picture of the land. Figure 17-39 is a picture of a bayonet, and we want to find out how long the blade is. If we know how much smaller the picture is than the real bayonet blade, we can find out how large the blade is. By measuring the blade on the picture in Figure 17-39, we find that it is 2½" long in the picture.

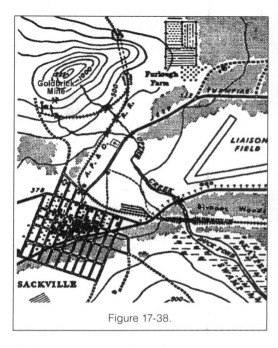
Figure 17-38.

Now suppose someone tells us that the picture is just one-quarter the size of the real bayonet. We can now figure out how long the blade is. If the picture is one-quarter the size of the real bayonet, the real bayonet is four times as large as the picture.

Let us put these figures to work. The picture of the blade is 2½" long. The real blade is four times as long; so the real blade is four times 2½" or 10" long.

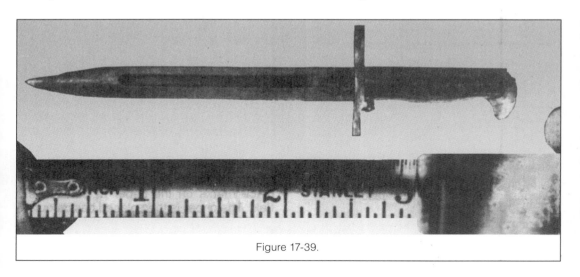
Figure 17-39.

$4 \times 2\frac{1}{2}" = 10"$

In the same way, a map always tells you how much smaller it is than the real land. A map can tell you this in two ways.

By Scale

One way is the same as we have just used on the picture of the bayonet.

A distance is measured on the map. The map tells you how much smaller this distance is than the actual ground by means of a number found in the bottom margin about in the center. (See Figure 17-40.) This number is called the scale.

The scale number may be shown in two ways, both meaning the same thing. It may be written as a fraction, 1/25,000, or it may be written 1:25,000. In either case, it is the same as saying that one inch on the map is equal to 25,000" on the ground, just as in our picture of the bayonet, where 1" on the picture was equal to 4" on the real bayonet. The scale of that picture of the bayonet would have been 1/4 or 1:4.

Let us try this out on our map. We want to find out how long the right-hand runway of Liaison Field is. First, place an ordinary ruler along the runway, as in Figure 17-41.

It reads 1". Now our scale reference says 1:25,000, or 1" on the map equals 25,000" on the field. So for each inch, we have measured on the runway, we must substitute 25,000." That means 1 times 25,000, or 25,000."

Distances on the ground are not usually given in inches. By the equivalents listed below, we can change inches into other units of measure.

Linear Measure:
1 foot (') = 12 inches (").
1 yard = 3 feet = 36 inches.
1 statute mile = 1,760 yards = 5,280 feet = 63,360 inches.
1 meter = 39.37 inches = 1.094 yards.
1 kilometer = 1,000 meters = 1,094 yards = .62 miles.
1 mile = 1.61 kilometers.

For example, let us divide 25,000" by 12, 36 and 39.37 and find out the number of feet, yards, and meters in the runway.

25,000 divided by 12 equals 2,083 feet.
25,000 divided by 36 equals 694 yards.
25,000 divided by 39.37 equals 635 meters.

By Graphic Scale

Another method for finding distances is by use of the graphic scale. This method is even easier to use than the one we have just discussed. Just below the notation of scale, 1:25,000; are located several objects that look like rulers. (See Figure 17-42). They are special kinds of rulers made just for that particular map. These rulers have already done your arithmetic for you.

Let's look at our bayonet picture again with such a ruler and see how it works. The ruler is a special one made just for this particular picture. All we have to do is place this ruler on the picture of the bayonet with the zero at the tip of the blade, as in Figure 17-43 (on next page). We can see at a glance that the real bayonet blade is 10" long. The special ruler has shown us the real length of the bayonet.

This special ruler is called a graphic scale, and it is used with a map in the following manner:

A straight strip of paper is placed on the map alongside the airfield. (See Figure 17-44(a) on next page.) We then place marks on the paper at

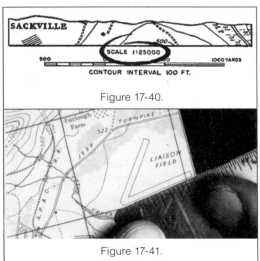

Figure 17-40.

Figure 17-41.

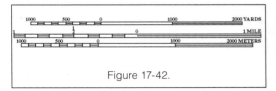

Figure 17-42.

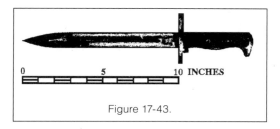

0   5   10 INCHES

Figure 17-43.

both ends of the field. The paper is then placed beside our graphic scale on the map, which shows how long the field really is. (See Figure 17-44(b).)

There is another thing to notice about this scale. It has two parts. (See Figure 17-45.) From the zero mark to the right it reads in large numbers, 500 yards apart. (See Part A of Figure 17-45.) From the zero mark to the left it breaks down this large distance into smaller distances (Part B of Figure 17-45) 100 yards apart, so that we can measure more accurately.

For example, in Figure 17-44(b), the marks on our strip of paper are farther apart than the distance between the zero and the 500-yard mark on the graphic scale. If we place the right-hand mark at the 500-yard point on the graphic scale, the left-hand mark overlaps into the "B" part of the graphic scale. We see that it is about at the second mark to the left of the zero, or at the 200-yard mark. By adding 200 yards to the first 500 yards, we can say that the runway is about 700 yards long.

For purposes of allowing different units of measure to be used, three graphic scales are usually found on a map. These scales are usually measured in miles, yards, and meters. Refer again to Figure 17-44(b), imagining this time that it measures meters instead of yards. You would follow exactly the same procedure to determine the length of the field in meters that you followed to find its length in yards. The paper strip would be placed along the meter scale, with the right-hand mark at the 500-meter point. The left-hand mark would again overlap into the "B" area. Add "B" to "A" and you have the total length of the field in meters.

In order to measure a curved or irregular line, for example, a section of the Burma Road (Figure 17-46(a) on next page), we divide the

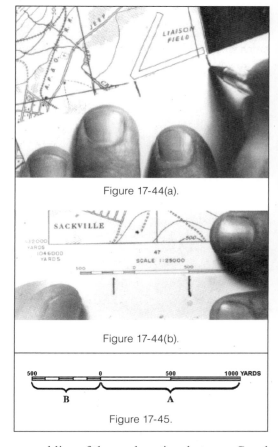

Figure 17-44(a).

Figure 17-44(b).

Figure 17-45.

curved line of the road section, between C and D, into small straight sections. (See Figure 17-46(b) on next page.) Then we lay the edge of a strip of paper on the tick marks, one after the other, adding each section to what we already have marked. We finish with a straight piece of paper with the total length of the curved road on it. We measure this with the graphic scale, in the same way as we measured the runway.

Watch the Fraction

It is important to know which is the larger scale, a 1:25,000 map or a 1:50,000 map. The 1:25,000 map is the larger scale. The numbers are fractions and 1:25,000 of something is bigger than 1:50,000, just as 1/2 is larger than 1/4. It is clear enough to us, but these numbers are a little tricky, and it is easy to make mistakes and forget that the larger the number in the lower part of the fraction, the smaller the scale of the

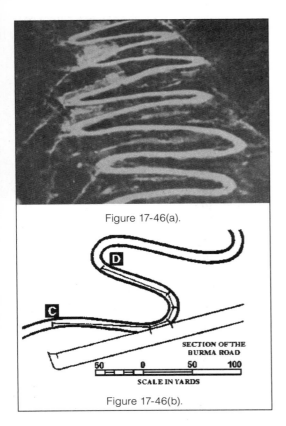

Figure 17-46(a).

SECTION OF THE
BURMA ROAD

50   0   50   100

SCALE IN YARDS

Figure 17-46(b).

map. It may be easier to remember that a large-scale map covers a small area and a small-scale map covers a large area.

Determining Location

In a town or city, it is easy for us to tell someone that the church is at the corner of 6th Avenue and 3rd Street. If you made a date with someone to meet you at the church, you could be pretty sure that both you and your date would be able to find the place.

In the Marine Corps, however, we are faced with a different problem. We must be able to give to someone else the location of a lone tree in the middle of a large field, or a machine gun or sniper in the woods, or a guard along a stream. There are no streets in those places, but our maps have a system of letting us tell someone else where these points are.

The Grid System

This is done by placing on the face of the map a network of lines in the form of squares. These squares are somewhat like the blocks formed by the street system in a city. Any point on the map can be located in relation to these lines or "streets." The method of describing a location is practically the same as we use in town with real streets. The only differences are in the way we name our "streets" and in the way we "spell-out" the description.

Such a method is called a grid reference system, and the pattern formed by the lines is called a grid. There are several types of grids used on our maps. The most common is the Universal Transverse Mercator Grid. You will also find maps bearing British Grids. But don't get confused by this—as far as grid referencing is concerned, all grids look alike in that they are made up of lines forming squares. Figure 17-47(a) (on next page) shows our map with a military grid on it.

The "streets" in a grid all have very simple names. The names are all numbers. When we use these numbers to locate a point on the map, we say we are giving a street address in a town. Before we can use these numbers, however, we must learn a few simple facts and rules.

Every tenth line is made heavier in weight. This is to help you find the line you are looking for. Each grid line on the map has its own number. This number appears in the margin of the map at both ends of the line. It also appears within the map on the line itself.

On some maps, two large figures are used to identify a line; on others, only one figure is used; in a few rare cases, three figures are used. The number of large figures depends upon the scale of the map, and the grid used on the map. Don't be confused by all this, regardless of what scale map you have in your hands, use only the large figures to identify a grid line for referencing purposes, whether the number consists of one, two, or three large figures. By following this simple rule, you can never make a mistake.

Locating a point by the grid reference system is a simple matter. For example, let us work out, step-by step, the grid reference for the letter "R"

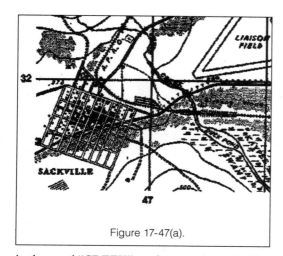

Figure 17-47(a).

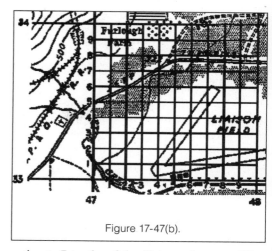

Figure 17-47(b).

in the word "CREEK" on the map shown in Figure 17-47(a). Four steps are required. First, read the large figures labeling the first vertical grid line to the left of the point (47). Second, mentally divide the distance between "line 47" and "line 48" into 10 parts. (See Figure 17-47(b).) Estimate how many tenths (to the nearest tenth) there are between "line 47" and the letter "R," the point being referenced. The estimated tenths is one. Third, read the large figures labeling the first horizontal grid line below the point (33). Fourth, mentally divide the distance between "line 33" and "line 34" into 10 parts. Estimate the nearest number of tenths between "line 33" and the point being referenced. In this case, the point falls almost on "line 33." The estimated tenths is zero.

The grid reference is written as a continuous number, 471330. Notice that the grid reference always has an even number of digits in it. If there is an uneven number of digits, someone has made an error in copying the grid reference number.

In working this sample grid reference, we were following a simple rule of map reading. The rule is "READ RIGHT UP" and helps us to remember which number to read first in giving a grid reference or in following out a grid reference.

Suppose your platoon leader tells you to meet a patrol at a point that is referred as 477336. Mentally break the number down to read 47-7-33-6. You look at the map (Figure 17-47(b)) and read right until you come to the vertical grid line that is numbered 47. Still going to the right

estimate 7 tenths of the distance between "line 47" and the next vertical line to the right, which, of course, is "line 48." Then from this point read up until you come to the horizontal line that is numbered 33. Still going up estimate 6 tenths of the distance between "line 33" and the next horizontal line above, which, of course, is "line 34." If you've followed these steps correctly, you will find the patrol sitting around waiting for you at the north end of the upper runway of Liaison Field.

If you understand everything that has been explained, you know how to give and you know how to follow a reference given on a map at the scales of 1:50,000, 1:25,000, or larger. Sometimes you can use our street system just to locate quickly a big, easily identified object. Just as you might tell a friend to meet you at the downtown library rather than give an exact address, you can identify a particular thing on a map by a general location. You just use the two streets that form the lower left hand corner of the grid square containing the thing you describe. For example, in Figure 17-47(a), if you say the duck pond (4732), the particular pond you are describing is known. Our READ RIGHT UP rule still applies, for you have moved right to line 47, which is part of the square around the pond, and up to line 32.

On some maps, you will find some letters printed on the face of the map at the intersections of heavy grid lines, like in Figure 17-48 (on next page).

These maps are at the scale of 1:100,000 or 1:250,000. The grid lines on such maps are usually labeled with only one large number. (See Figure 17-48.) If you have studied these instructions carefully, you will remember that a reference for a point taken from such a map is made up of four numbers, like 4733. But the reference is not complete until you add, in front of the number, the two letters that label the corners of the heavy lined square in which the point of reference falls. Thus, the grid reference for the point marked "X" in Figure 17-48 would be KR4733.

There are a few more things we should know about this map street system.

The grid lines are sometimes called easting lines or northing.

Instead of saying that the grid lines are up and down lines or vertical lines; we simply say they are easting grid lines; and instead of saying they are side to side lines or horizontal lines, we simply say they are northing grid lines. The numbers that make up a grid reference are sometimes called coordinates. You will also hear them referred to as grid coordinates. A coordinate is made up of an easting ordinate (read first) and a northing ordinate. The easting ordinate is the part of the number of the grid reference (we worked out above) made by reading right. It consists of the number in large type labeling the first vertical (easting) grid line to the left of the point and the estimated tenths from that line to the point. The northing ordinate is the part of the reference (the last part) that you made by reading up. It consists of the number in large type labeling the first horizontal (northing) grid line below the point of reference and the estimated tenths from that line to the point. In the reference 471330, which we figured out to be the identification of the letter "R" of the word "CREEK" on the map shown in Figure 17-47(a) on page 229, the easting ordinate is 471 and the northing ordinate is 330. Another point is that the unit of measure and the distance between lines of the grid will not be the same on all military maps. The unit of measure may be either meters or yards, depending upon the grid appearing on the map.

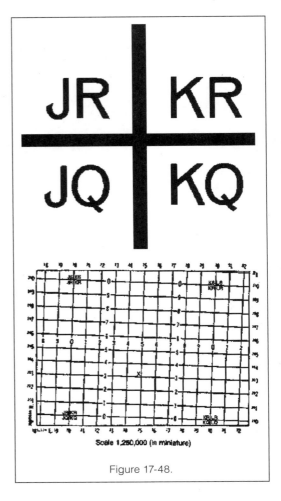

Figure 17-48.

The distance between grid lines, which we call the grid interval, may be either 1,000 units or 10,000 units, depending upon the scale of the map. Maps of the scales of 1:25,000 and 1:50,000 use a grid interval of 1,000 units. Maps at the scales of 1:100,000 and 1:250,000 use a grid interval of 10,000 units. A note appearing in the margin of each map will tell what unit of measure and what interval is used for the grid on the map. Read this note before you use the grid.

For example, Figure 17-47(a) (on page 229) has the 1,000-meter grid on it. We can tell from the map that the circle in town is about 1,000 meters from the first building alongside the airfield runway because it is about the same distance as that between the two grid lines. This is another way to tell distances on a map, and you can use it instead of the graphic scale.

Use of the Compass

On the ground and on the map, the Marine Corps has an easy way to point out the direction of things. It is easy because the same idea is used wherever we are.

The idea is simply this: we suppose that wherever we happen to be at any given moment, we are in the center of a circle that has "avenues" running off in all directions, as in Figure 17-49.

What Is an Azimuth?

The circle is marked off into 360 avenues. (See Figure 17-50.) Each of the 360 spaces is called a degree, and each avenue has a name called an azimuth. This azimuth is just a name for a direction line; each of these direction lines has a number, depending upon which of the 360 avenues it is.

We can march off on one of these avenues, or azimuths, starting at the center of the circle. The avenues all start where you are, whether you are in a jungle, on a hill or on highway, just as with the man in Figure 17-51. The man has been told to go along the avenue marked "azimuth 60 degrees" (written as 60°), and he is pointing his finger at it. You can think of him in the center of the circle with 360 avenues or azimuths running out from him like the spokes from the hub of a wheel. To make it easier to locate an avenue, every tenth avenue is numbered.

There are two important things to remember about this circle of avenues.

1. The zero – 0 – avenue must always point north.

2. The avenues are numbered clockwise. That means we number them in the direction that we number hours on a clock. Figure 17-52 (on next page) shows what we mean by clockwise direction.

With this knowledge, let's put this circle to work for us. You are told that there is a sniper in a tree in the orchard at Furlough Farm and, if you crawl up the creek to where the railroad

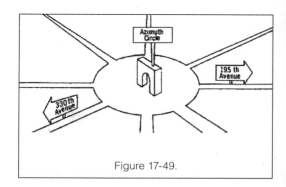

Figure 17-49.

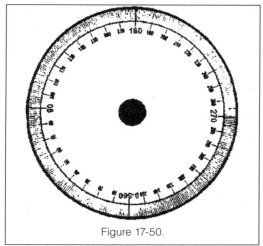

Figure 17-50.

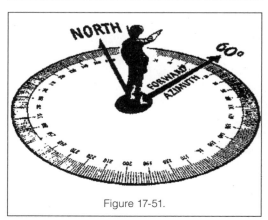

Figure 17-51.

crosses it at the foot of the hill, you can see the sniper's tree on an azimuth of exactly 60 degrees (60°). Figure 17-53 (on next page) shows the situation.

From the map, you find where the railroad crosses the creek and go there. You remember

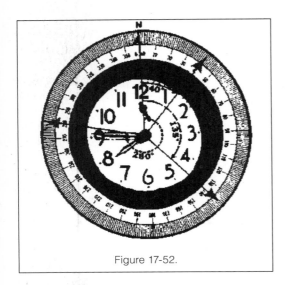

Figure 17-52.

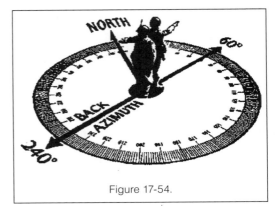

Figure 17-54.

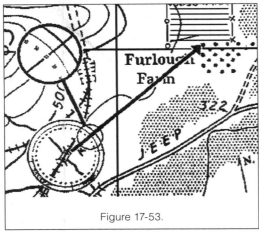

Figure 17-53.

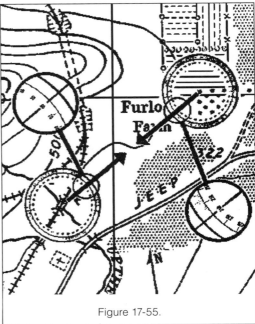

Figure 17-55.

that the center of the circle of azimuths is right where you are. The first thing to do is to point the zero mark on the circle at the north. (You will learn later how to do this with your compass). Now it is easy to see which tree is on the avenue or azimuth marked 60° on the circle, using the azimuth system of direction.

You take a bead on the sniper and knock him from the tree with your first shot. You move cautiously up to the tree, examine the sniper carefully and find that he is dead. You walk back to the railroad where it crosses the creek. Now what azimuth did you walk back on? Was it 60°? No, it wasn't. Look at Figure 17-54. It shows you that if you face in one direction you have

a forward azimuth; if you face in the opposite direction, you have a back azimuth. The back azimuth is a straight line back through the center of the circle from the forward azimuth. Figure 17-55 shows you that at the railroad, with the zero of the circle pointing north, the azimuth on the circle reads 60° from there to the tree, and that at the tree, with the zero of the circle still pointing north, the azimuth on the circle reads 240° from the tree to where the railroad crosses the creek.

The back azimuth of a line is its forward azimuth plus 180°, or if this sum is greater than

360°, the back azimuth is the forward azimuth minus 180°. For example, if the forward azimuth of a line is 60°, the back azimuth is 60° + 180° = 240°. If the forward azimuth of a line is 310° the back azimuth is 310° - 180° = 130°.

The back azimuth is an important thing to know about because if you know how to use it, it will take you back to your starting point. For example, if you are sent on a mission at night to a point in a strange country, your back azimuth will show you the direction in which you return.

The Lensatic Compass

We come now to the compass, that useful instrument that finds north for us and finds our azimuth for us. The compass has on it the circle of numbered avenues or azimuths, which we have been talking about in the last few pages. In other words, the compass is our direction-finding tool, and it has everything on it to help us find our way.

There are several types of compasses, but the one that we shall use here is called the lensatic compass. There are other types of compasses, but they all work on the same principle. If you understand how to use the lensatic compass, you will find it easy to learn to use the others.

Let us refer now to Figure 17-56 for a good look at the lensatic compass. The most important thing about the compass is that no matter how you turn it, as long as you hold it level, the arrow always points in the direction of magnetic

north. It won't let you down if you remember one thing—never use it near any metal object if you can help it.

To ensure the proper functioning of your compass, keep a safe distance from the following metal objects:

High-tension power lines .... 55 meters
Field gun, truck or tank .... 10 meters
Telegraph or telephone
   wires and barbed wire .... 10 meters
Machine gun .... 2 meters
Rifle .... 1/2 meter
Steel rim glasses .... 1/3 meter

Besides the compass needle that points north, there is another important part of the compass. That is the numbered circle of avenues or azimuths right on the face of the dial. Everything on the compass is designed to help you line up your compass with things on the ground and on your map and to help you read the azimuth numbers.

Compass Reading

Hold the compass correctly. Remember to point the compass in the general direction you want to go before you try to use it, and hold it level. Figure 17-57 shows the compass ready to be used in daytime sighting. Figure 17-58 shows how to hold the compass so that it is steady.

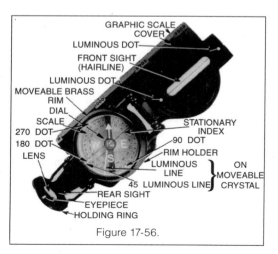

Figure 17-56.

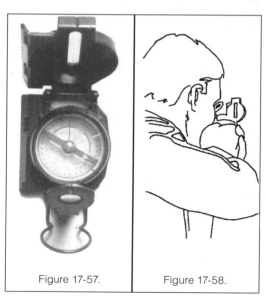

Figure 17-57.

Figure 17-58.

Notice that it is held with the eyepiece close to the eye. Figure 17-59 shows how to line up a tree. You look at the tree through the slit in the eyepiece and through the slit in the cover with the hairline, the front sight. The glass eyepiece is used only to read the azimuth numbers on the dial. It is there only so you will be able to glance down and read these numbers at the same time you line up an object with the compass. The view you get when you use the compass correctly is shown in Figure 17-60. The Marine here has lined up the tree in the compass sights and found that the tree is on an azimuth of 60 degrees.

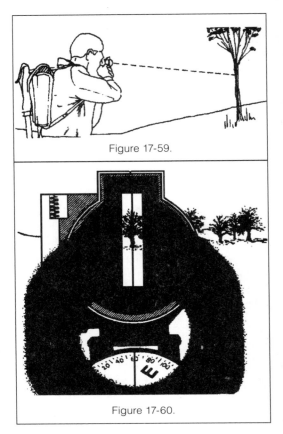

Figure 17-59.

Figure 17-60.

Finding the Back Azimuth

With a compass, you can see how easy it is to find a back azimuth. You can do it two ways. First, read your back azimuth right off the dial by taking the number that is opposite the forward azimuth on a straight line through the center of the dial.

The second way is to sight from the point you have reached, back to the point you started from. The main difference between these two methods is that in the first, you do not have to be able to see your starting point in order to get the back azimuth.

Aligning the Map With the Ground

Before the compass and the map are ready to be used together, the map must be placed in a position so that the directions on the map are lined up with the directions on the ground. There are two ways to do this, one of them without the aid of a compass and the other with the help of a compass or of some other way of finding north. This act is called orienting the map.

By Inspection

The first method of lining up your map is called "terrain association," which simply means "looking at the ground with the map in front of you." This can be done when you have found objects on the ground that you recognize on your map and that you can see.

For example, in Figure 17-61(a) (on next page) you hold your map so that the crossroads on it line up with the crossroads on the ground in front of you. Your map is then oriented.

If the objects on the ground are not as simple as crossroads, such as in Figure 17-61(b) (on next page), you can still line up your map by inspection.

You must know your approximate position on the map, and then turn your map in front of you until the distant object (the tower) on the ground lines up with the same object on the map and with your position on the map. The dashed line in Figure 17-61(b) (on next page) illustrates this lining-up process. Your map is then oriented.

By Compass

Another way to line up your map is by using the compass. The compass needle points to

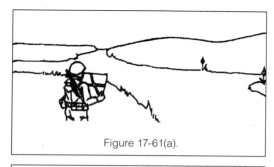

Figure 17-61(a).

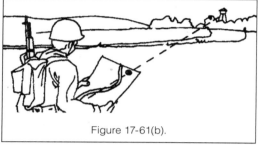

Figure 17-61(b).

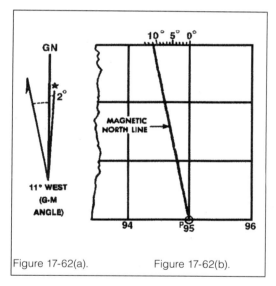

Figure 17-62(a).   Figure 17-62(b).

diagram represents true north and is marked with a star. The three lines are not always in the same position shown in Figure 17-62(a). The position of these three lines, in relation to each other, will vary on maps in different parts of the world.

The angle between grid north and magnetic north is called the G-M (grid-magnetic) angle. The numerical value of this angle is printed with the declination diagram, as in Figure 17-62(a).

There are two ways to use this angle and a compass to orient your map with the ground.

To use the first method, you must draw the magnetic north line on your map. This is easily done with most new maps where you find at the top margin a scale marked off in degrees and at the bottom a circle marked "P" called the pivot point as in Figure 17-62(b). Read the number of degrees of the G-M angle on the declination diagram. Then draw a line from the pivot point to that number of degrees on the scale.

In Figure 17-62(b), the magnetic north line is drawn to the 11° mark, the amount of the G-M angle on the declination diagram shown in Figure 17-62(a). Do not try to draw the magnetic north line by extending the magnetic north prong on the declination diagram. The diagram may be exaggerated, especially if the angles are very small. Some maps have the following caution printed beside the declination diagram: Use only to obtain numerical values.

With the magnetic north line drawn in, lay your map on a flat surface with the top pointing to the general direction of north. Open your compass and place it on the map so the edge of the meter scale lines up with the magnetic north line. (See Figure 17-63 on next page). Turn the map until the compass needle lies under the stationary index. The map is then oriented.

If your map does not have a pivot point and scale, or if it is folded so as to cover the magnetic north line, you can use the compass another way to orient the map with the ground. Lay your map on a flat surface as in the first method. Place the open compass so that the edge of the meter scale lies on top of a vertical grid line. (See Figure 17-64 on next page.) Read the G-M angle on the declination diagram and note

magnetic north. The difference between magnetic north, grid north, and true north is shown on your map by a declination diagram. (See Figure 17-62(a).)

The line with the half arrowhead represents magnetic north. The "GN" is grid north, parallel to the vertical grid lines. (You have probably already noticed that maps such as we have been studying are printed with north toward the top of the sheet.) The third line on the declination whether magnetic north is right or left of grid north. Turn the map until the compass needle points to the right or left of the stationary index by the amount of the G-M angle. If the declination diagram shows magnetic north right of grid north, then the map should be turned until the

compass needle points right of the vertical grid line. In Figure 17-64, the declination diagram shows an 11° G-M angle, with magnetic north left of grid north. The map in the illustration is oriented because the compass needle points 11° to the left of the grid line.

Without a Compass

Even without a compass, however, you can orient your map with a north line. There are ways to find north without a compass.

• During daylight hours, you can determine direction without the aid of a compass by the Shadow Tip Method. Find a fairly straight stick about three feet long and push it into the ground, as shown in Figure 17-65(a) (on next page). Mark the tip of the shadow with a small rock. (See Figure 17-65(b) (on next page). Then wait 10 to 15 minutes. The shadow will have moved during this time, so you place another rock at the tip of the second shadow as shown in Figure 17-65(c) (on next page). You then draw a line from the first rock to and beyond the second rock. (See Figure 17-65(d) (on next page).) Now stand with the toe of your left foot at the first rock and the toe of your right foot at the second rock as shown in Figure 17-65(e) (on next page). You are now facing north.

• At night, in the Northern Hemisphere, we find north without a compass by means of the stars. In the Northern Hemisphere, one way to use the stars is to find the Big Dipper. The Big Dipper is made up of seven fairly bright stars in the shape of a dipper with a long curved handle, as in Figure 17-66(a) (on next page). If you can see the Big Dipper, use as pointers the two stars that form the side of the cup farthest from the handle. These point in the direction toward which you would pour from the dipper. These pointers aim at a bright star that is about five times the distance between the two stars of the Dipper cup. This bright star is the North Star and is directly over the North Pole. If you hold a finger away from your eyes so it just fits between the two

Figure 17-63.

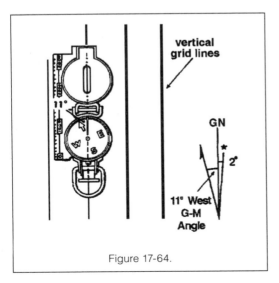

Figure 17-64.

GUIDEBOOK FOR MARINES

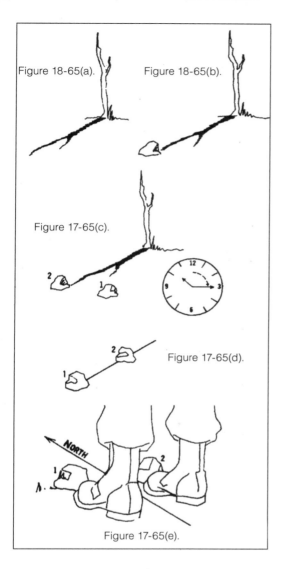

Figure 18-65(a). Figure 18-65(b).

Figure 17-65(c).

Figure 17-65(d).

Figure 17-65(e).

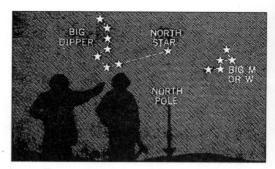

Figure 17-66(a).

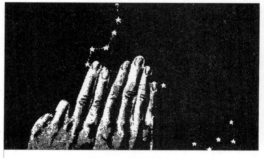

Figure 17-66(b).

pointers, and then, keeping your hand the same distance from your eyes, measure five finger-widths from the end pointer, your farthest finger will just touch the North Star. (See Figure 17-66(b). Sometimes, however, you cannot see the Big Dipper, although you may be able to see other stars. In that case, we use a star pattern called the Big "W" or the big "M." Look at it in Figure 17-66(a). Notice that it is on the other side of and about the same distance from the North Star as the Big Dipper. The top of the "W" is open in the direction of the North Star.

On a clear night you will always be able to see, in the Northern Hemisphere, either the Big Dipper or the Big "W." Sometimes you will be able to see both. In either case, you can find the North Star. The Big Dipper and the Big "W" appear to rotate around the North Star during the night. Only occasionally are they in just the positions shown in Figures 17-66(a) and (b). Their position in relation to the North Star and to each other does not change.

• In the Southern Hemisphere you can find true south by relation to the Southern Cross. Two bright pointer stars in the vicinity of the Southern Cross serve as locators to help pick up the right group of stars. (See Figure 17-67 on next page.) There are five stars in the Southern Cross. The outer four are fairly bright and form a cross. Imagine this cross as the frame of a kite. Put a straight tail on the kite 4½ times as long as the length of the kite itself. Using

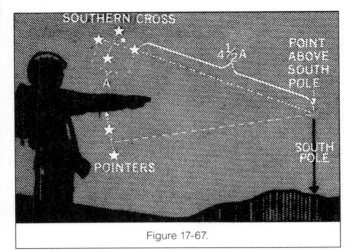

Figure 17-67.

Azimuth on the Map

We have learned how to find the azimuth of an objective on the ground by sighting with the compass. Now we come to the problem of learning to find the azimuth of something on a map.

For example, how do you find what the azimuth is from the house (point A) to the bridge (point B) in Figure 17-68(a)? First, you draw a line lightly on your map between the house and the bridge. Next, you orient your map using the magnetic line and your compass as explained earlier in the chapter. Then lay your compass on the map so that the edge of the graphic scale and the pencil line coincide. You read the azimuth 84° on the compass (Figure 17-68(b)), and you have your answer.

Suppose that you wanted to show on the map that a machine gun was on the path at an azimuth of 105° from the bridge. To find the correct point on the map, you would proceed as follows: first, orient your map; then lay your compass so that the "0" indicator on the graphic scale

fingerwidths for a measuring stick, as with the Big Dipper in Figure 17-66(b) (on previous page), the end of this tail will be close to a position directly over the South Pole. (See Figure 17-67.) Usually you won't be able to see a star in that immediate vicinity because there is no bright star that can be seen directly above the South Pole.

• Another way to find the approximate location of the South Pole without measuring the 4½ finger-width distance along the kite tail of the Southern Cross is to imagine a straight line perpendicular to the center of a line between the pointers. This perpendicular line intersects the extension of the Southern Cross kite tail. The point of intersection is approximately above the South Pole. This method is shown in Figure 17-67. The Southern Cross and pointers appear to rotate around the South Pole during the night, just as the Big Dipper and the Big "W" do in the northern sky.

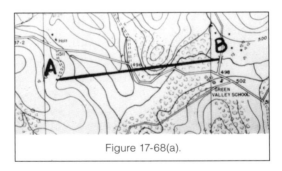

Figure 17-68(a).

The Map and Compass at Work

We know enough now about the compass and the map to start to use them together in a practical way.

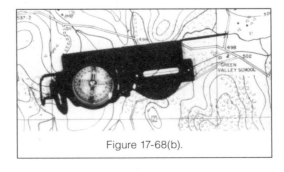

Figure 17-68(b).

is directly over the bridge. (See Figure 17-69.) Pivot the compass, keeping the "0" indicator at the bridge until the stationary index lines up with the 105° on the dial. Draw a line along the edge of the graphic scale from the bridge until it crosses the path. The machine gun is located where the line crosses the path ("X" in Figure 17-69).

Finding Your Location (Resection)

Many times you will need to know accurately your location on a map. If your location is somewhere between the airfield and the creek on the Sackville map, to find your exact location:

- Orient your map with a compass.
- Find two things on the ground in front of you that you can also find on your map.
- With your compass, take an azimuth on a point, for example, the building at the mine. Sight through the compass, line up the building with the hairline in the compass (Figure 17-70(a), and read the azimuth through the glass eyepiece (305°)).
- Find the back azimuth by subtracting 180° from 305° (305° - 180° = 125°).
- Lay your compass on your map with the "0" indicator on the graphic scale directly over the building at the mine. (See Figure 17-71(a). Then pivot the compass slowly until 125° on the dial lines up with the stationary index. Draw a line along the edge of the graphic scale.
- You are somewhere along this line on your map, but you still need to know exactly where. Repeat the procedure with a second point, for example, the tip of the

left-hand runway of the airfield. (See Figure 17-70(b)). A forward azimuth reading shows it to be 67°. Lay the "0" indicator of the graphic scale directly over the tip of the runway on your oriented map and line up the stationary index with 247° (67° + 180° = 247°).

- Draw your line along the graphic scale until it crosses the first line you drew. The two lines cross at your exact location. (See Figure 17-71(b).)

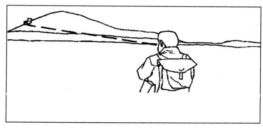

Figure 17-70(a).

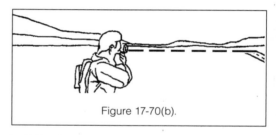

Figure 17-70(b).

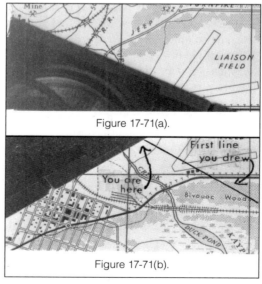

Figure 17-71(a).

Figure 17-71(b).

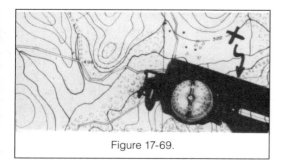

Figure 17-69.

Finding an Objective

Suppose you are somewhere southeast of Sackville and your platoon leader tells you to go to a certain bridge, points out the bridge on the map, and draws a line on the map from your position to the bridge. By laying your compass on the oriented map, you find that the bridge is on an azimuth of 51° from where you are. (See Figure 17-72.) Your job is to get to the bridge. That means that you must march along the azimuth.

First you take your compass, sight on an azimuth of 51° and discover that you cannot see the bridge at all from where you are. You know, however, that it is somewhere up ahead, along that line on which you are sighting. You can see the edge of the woods (Figure 17-73(a)) on your line of sight. So you head for the edge of the woods (Figure 17-73(b)), and when you get there, you find a bridge in front of you. (See Figure 17-73(c).) If it so happened that you could not see the bridge from the edge of the woods, you would do the same thing again, picking out a tree, fence, or other object along your line of march, until you finally reached a point where you could see the bridge.

We cannot always march in a straight line, because we may encounter obstacles, such as the pond in Figure 17-74(a) on next page. The method for detouring around an obstacle is shown in Figure 17-74(b) on next page. A very important rule to remember is that when you make a right turn, you add the number of degrees in the turn to your azimuth.

When you make a left turn, you subtract the number of degrees in the turn from your azimuth.

You begin your march on an azimuth of 70°. After making a 90° right turn, you are marching on an azimuth of 160° (70° + 90° = 160°).

As you march along line "A" in Figure 17-74(b), you must march the same distance on line "B" to arrive back on your original line of march. When you have gone far enough along line "A" to clear the pond, you make a 90° left turn and you are again marching on an azimuth of 70° (160° - 90° = 70°). When you have gone far enough to clear the south end of the pond,

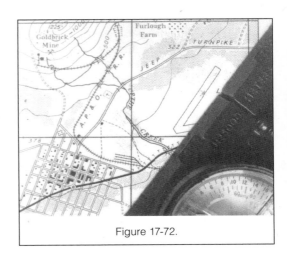

Figure 17-72.

Figure 17-73(a).

Figure 17-73(b).

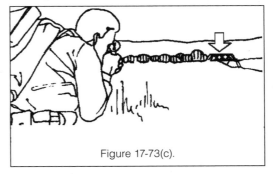

Figure 17-73(c).

you make another 90° left turn and you are marching on an azimuth of 340° (70° - 90° = -20°). We do not use negative azimuths in the Marine Corps, so you must subtract your negative azimuth from the total degrees in a circle to obtain the correct azimuth (360° - 20° = 340°).

You now march on line "B" the same number of paces you marched on line "A," and when you make a 90° right turn, you are on your original line of march on an azimuth of 70° (340° + 90° = 430°). We do not use azimuths larger than 360°

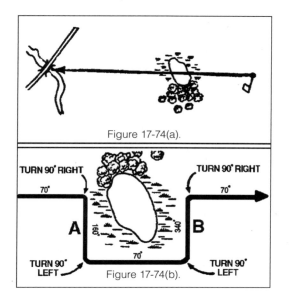

Figure 17-74(a).

Figure 17-74(b).

in the Marine Corps, so to obtain the correct azimuth, you must subtract the total degrees in a circle from 430° (430° - 360° = 70°).

The Compass at Night

The lensatic compass has two glass faces, one under the other. The top glass face rotates; the under one does not. The top glass rotates with a clicking sound; each click means it has turned 3°. On the top glass are two lines visible at night. One line is about three times as long as the other. These lines are 45° apart.

On the under, or stationary, glass face are three luminous dots and a black line (stationary index). Each of these marks is 90° from the other, or one-quarter of the way around the face of the dial. On the compass dial itself, the letters E, S, W, and the arrow for North are luminous. On the inside cover, lined up with the hairline sight, are two more luminous dots. Beneath the dial on the inside of the case is a fixed luminous sector that permits reading azimuths at night.

To follow an azimuth accurately at night, we must be able to pick up aiming points ahead of us, just as we do in the daytime. At night, this is not easy to do. You cannot see very far ahead,

therefore, your aiming points will be very near you. If it is so dark that you cannot find an aiming point, send another Marine out a little ahead of you. Direct him to move either to the right or left, until he is in your line of sight. Be sure he does not move until you have reached him. Then do the same thing over again until you find some aiming point in the area ahead or you reach your objective.

Usually, it is not necessary to follow a given azimuth exactly. In combat, the need to move quickly will not always allow the use of this time-consuming method. If it is impractical to use the sights on your compass, we have an easy way to follow an approximate azimuth:

- Turn the movable glass until the long luminous line is directly over the black line (stationary index) on the lower fixed glass, as in Figure 17-75(a) (on next page).
- Turn the movable glass 17 clicks to the left (counterclockwise). This is a total of 51° (3° per click).
- Rotate the whole compass until the North arrow is directly under the long luminous line on the movable glass, as in Figure 17-75(b) (on next page). Your compass is now set on an azimuth of 51°.

Now all you have to do to march on this azimuth in the darkness is to keep the North arrow under the long luminous line and follow the line formed by the stationary index on the lower fixed glass and the two luminous dots on the cover.

Notice the way the compass is held in Figure 17-76. You do not aim through the eyepiece as before. You simply point the compass in the direction you are going by lining up the long luminous line on the upper glass and the North arrow. Then line yourself up with the two luminous dots on the cover and the stationary index and pick out an aiming point that falls on an extension of that line. You walk to your aiming point and repeat the process until you reach your objective.

Figure 17-76.

Figure 17-75(a).

Figure 17-75(b).

Because all metal objects exert a magnetic pull on the needle of your compass (causing it to move), carry only essential metallic objects with you on a compass march. Keep all metallic objects far enough from the compass so that they will not cause the needle to move from magnetic North.

Use Your Map and Compass

When you are sent out on a reconnaissance or scouting assignment, you will find information that must be sent back to your commander. That is your mission. It is necessary, then, to know how to send back this information.

Name Things Exactly

First, you must know the names of things on the land. It is not necessary to know what names things are called by, until you have to tell someone else about them. Then it is very important that you know exactly what the names of land forms are. Figure 17-77 (on next page) is a sketch showing the names of various land forms. Learn these names. It is important that you are able to describe things accurately and in the right words, so that the Marines you work with can understand what you mean.

The Overlay

An overlay is used to send back information obtained by reconnaissance. An overlay is simply a tracing, on a plain piece of transparent paper, of a section of a map. To make an overlay, lay a piece of transparent paper over the section of the map you are interested in and draw on it the corners of the grid squares, as in Figure 17-78 (on page 244). These crosses are called register marks, and they are put on the overlay to show whoever uses it just where to place it on his map. The register marks should be numbered with the numbers of the grid lines, so that whoever uses the overly will know exactly where to place it.

Once the register marks are on the overlay, you need only to indicate on it the objects you are concerned with. Write your message right on the overlay with the usual information that is commonly put on ordinary written messages.

The person who gets the overlay places it on his map so that the register marks line up on the grid lines, and the message can be read.

On the Road

It is very easy to get lost when you drive along a highway, even in the United States where there are all kinds of signs and directions for the use of the motorist. It is even easier to lose your way in a strange country and in wartime. Maps and compasses are important instruments to keep you on the right road.

You must keep your map oriented, preferably by inspection, if you are to find the right roads on your map. (See Figure 17-79 on page 245.)

The odometer is especially important in a case like Figure 17-80 (on page 245). Here the driver finds two left intersections on the road, a mile apart. The map is out of date and shows just one road. Which one should the driver take? By measuring the distance from the starting point to the junction on the map, the driver can find

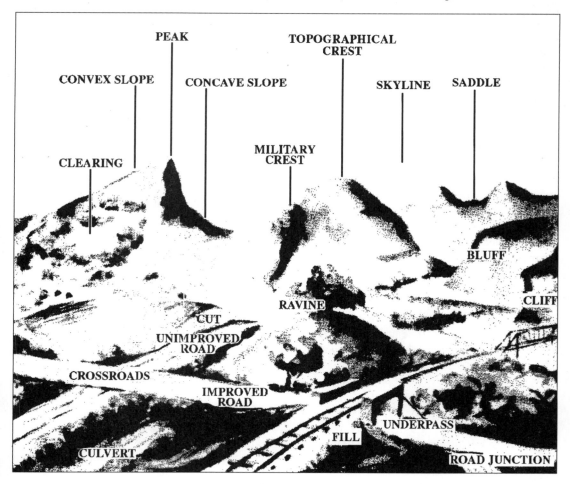

Figure 17-77.

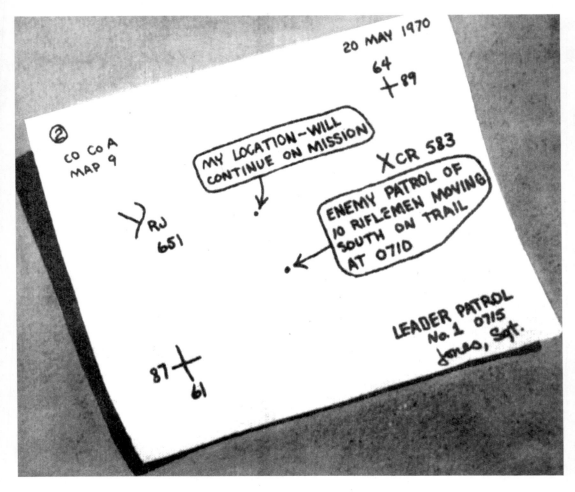

Figure 17-78.

out how far he should have traveled before taking the turn. Now if he had been careful enough to watch the odometer before starting on the trip, he would be able to figure out how far he had come and would know which of the two roads was the right one. If he had failed to note the odometer, he would not know which road to take.

Take Care of Your Map

In the field, a map is as important as your weapons. Take good care of it. Fold it small enough to slip into your pocket to protect it from rain. Fold it with face outward so that you can read parts of it without unfolding the whole map. The accordion fold (see Figure 17-81 on next page) makes it easy to use.

When you mark your map, mark it lightly. It may have to last you a long while. Many marks on it will confuse you. Erasures of heavy lines will smear it and make it difficult to read.

Covering your map with contact paper protects it from water damage. You can also write on it with a grease pencil.

Figure 17-79.

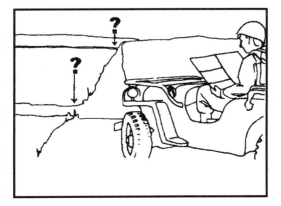

Figure 17-80.

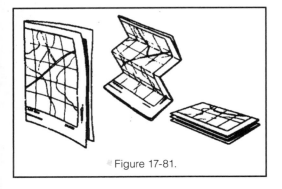

Figure 17-81.

CHAPTER 18

Combat Formations and Signals

Combat formations are designed to group individuals into effective fighting teams that can move up to and assault an enemy position. Their design provides for dispersion, teamwork, and the ability to fire at the enemy without hitting other Marines. Both close and extended formations are used, depending upon the situation, terrain and enemy activity. Movement into a formation or from one formation to another is executed on the signals or commands of fire team and squad leaders.

This chapter explains and illustrates the various combat formations used by Marines. Also pictured and explained are the arm and hand signals used in the execution of combat formations.

Fire Team Combat Formations

There are four combat formations for the fire team: *column, wedge, skirmishers right (left), and echelon right (left).*

The Column formation permits rapid, easily controlled movement and permits fire and maneuver to the flanks. It is vulnerable to enemy fire from the front. The ability to fire to the front from the column formation is limited. (See Figure 18-1 and 18-2.)

The Wedge formation is easily controlled, provides good all around security and permits fire and maneuver to both the front and the flanks. (See Figure 18-3 on next page).

Skirmishers Right (Left) permits maximum

firepower to the front but is a difficult formation to control. The ability to fire to the flanks is very limited. (See Figure 18-4 and Figure 18-5 on next page.)

Echelon Right (Left) is similar to skirmishers right and left except that one flank is angled to the rear (right or left) permitting fire to the

Figure 18-2. Column.

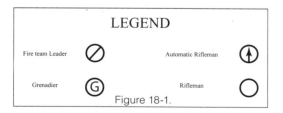

LEGEND — Fire team Leader ⊘ Automatic Rifleman; Grenadier Ⓖ Rifleman ◯

Figure 18-1.

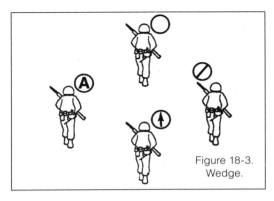

Figure 18-3. Wedge.

front and one flank. It is a difficult formation to control and is open to enemy fire from the flank that is not echeloned or angled back. (See Figure 18-6 and Figure 18-7.)

Squad Combat Formations

There are five combat formations for the squad: *squad column, squad wedge, squad line, squad echelon right (left), and squad vee.* The characteristics of the first four squad formations correspond generally to those of the fire team. There is no fire team formation similar to those of the squad vee, which is arranged with two fire teams forward and one fire team back in a "V" formation. The principal difference is that the individual Marine is the maneuver element of the fire team, while the fire team is the maneuver element of the squad.

Squad Column

The squad column, with fire teams arranged in succession one behind the other, is used to maintain speed and control when moving through thick terrain, such as a jungle or woods, during darkness or other periods of reduced visibility and along roads, trails or narrow routes of advance. Although easily controlled, it is open to enemy fire from the front and permits only a limited amount of fire to be returned to the front. The squad column does favor fire and maneuver to the flanks. (See Figure 18-8 on next page.)

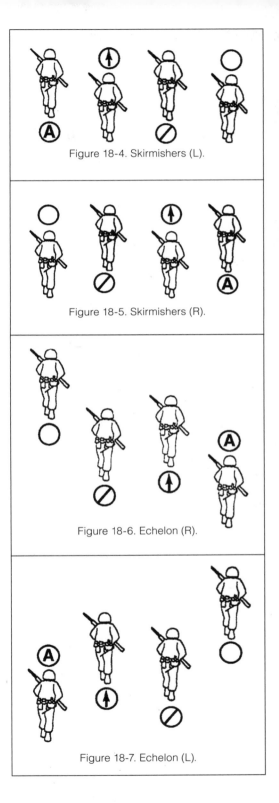

Figure 18-4. Skirmishers (L).

Figure 18-5. Skirmishers (R).

Figure 18-6. Echelon (R).

Figure 18-7. Echelon (L).

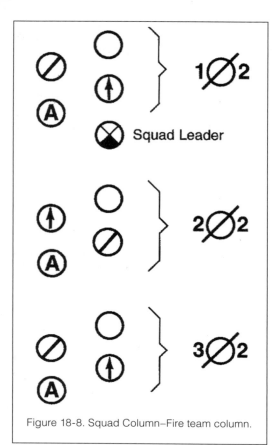

Squad Leader

Figure 18-8. Squad Column–Fire team column.

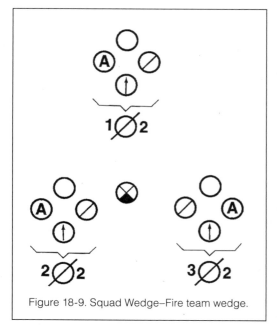

Figure 18-9. Squad Wedge–Fire team wedge.

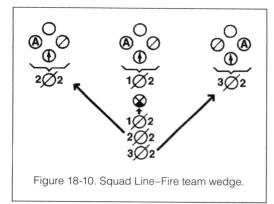

Figure 18-10. Squad Line–Fire team wedge.

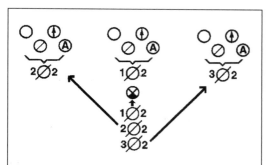

Figure 18-11. Squad Line–Fire team skirmishers (R).

Squad Wedge

The squad wedge, with one fire team forward and two fire teams back, is normally used when the enemy situation is generally unknown and the terrain and visibility require dispersion. Characteristics of the squad wedge are ease of control, all around security, and ability to fire and maneuver to both the front and flanks. (See Figure 18-9.)

Squad Line

The squad line places all three fire teams abreast or on line and is normally used in the assault or for rapid crossing of an open area exposed to hostile automatic weapons or artillery fire. The squad line is difficult to control and maneuver and is open to fire from the flanks. The ability to return fire to the flanks is limited. Maximum firepower is concentrated to the front, and the formation is less vulnerable

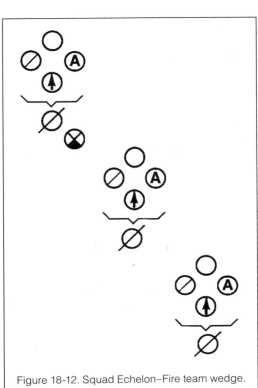

Figure 18-12. Squad Echelon–Fire team wedge.

to enemy fire from that direction. (See Figure 18-10 and Figure 18-11 on previous page.)

Squad Echelon Right (Left)

The squad echelon right (left) with fire teams echeloned or angled to the rear (right or left) is used to protect an open or exposed flank. It is a difficult formation to control and is open to enemy fire from the flank that is not echeloned. This formation can concentrate maximum firepower to the front and the flank that is echeloned or angled to the rear. (See Figure 18-12.)

Squad Vee

The squad vee has the same characteristics of control, all-around security, and ability to fire and maneuver to the front and flanks as the squad wedge. Arranged with two fire teams forward and one back, it is used when the enemy is located to the front, and the strength and location are generally known. It may also be used when crossing large, open areas. The squad vee facilitates movement into the squad line for the assault. (See Figure 18-13.)

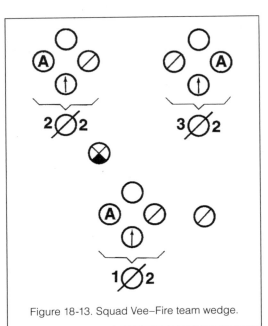

Figure 18-13. Squad Vee–Fire team wedge.

Positions of Individuals

The accompanying illustrations show the disposition of individuals in all of the basic combat formations. Squad leaders place themselves within the squad formation where they can best exercise control. The fire team leaders place themselves in the designated formations or as directed by the squad leader. Other members of the squad take their appropriate positions based on the location of the fire team leader or as they direct.

The distance between Marines varies within a formation, depending on threat visibility and terrain. While maximum dispersion is desirable to reduce vulnerability to direct and indirect fires, effective control must be maintained.

Use of Formations

Initial formations are usually ordered by the platoon commander for the squads and by the squad leader for the fire teams. Thereafter, each leader will normally determine the formation for the unit depending on the mission, situation and terrain. The squad and the fire teams do not have to be in the same formations. For example, the squad may be on *line* with the fire teams in *wedge* formation. Any other combination appropriate to the mission, situation, and terrain may be used.

The squad leader or fire team leaders should change formations as often as necessary to reduce casualties from enemy fire, to present a less vulnerable target or to cross difficul

or exposed terrain. Normally, all changes in formation are executed on the double.

Arm and Hand Signals

Distance and noise on the battlefield often make voice commands completely ineffective. For this reason, visual signals, using the arms and hands, are used to enable leaders to give commands to units. Arm and hand signals are the same as a voice order or command, and leaders must position themselves so that the signals can be seen. All arm and hand signals are executed with precision. The arm and hand signal illustrations commonly used to control and maneuver a fire team or squad are pictured on the following pages.

1. DECREASE SPEED–Extend the arm horizontally sideward, palm to the front, and wave arm downward several times, keeping the arm straight. Arm does not move above the horizontal.

2. CHANGE DIRECTION–or COLUMN (RIGHT/LEFT)– Extend arm horizontally to the side, palm to the front.

3. ENEMY IN SIGHT–Hold the rifle horizontally, with the stock in the shoulder, the muzzle pointing in the direction of the enemy.

4. RANGE–Extend the arm fully toward leader or Marine for whom the signal is intended with fist closed. Open the fist exposing one finger for each 100 meters of range.

5. COMMENCE FIRING–Extend the arm in front of the body, hip high, palm down, and move it through a wide horizontal arc several times.

6. FIRE FASTER–Execute rapidly the signal COMMENCE FIRING. For machine guns, a change to the higher rate of fire is prescribed.

7. FIRE SLOWER–Execute slowly the signal COMMENCE FIRING. For machine guns, a change to the next lower rate of fire is required.

8. CEASE FIRING–Raise the hand in front of the forehead, palm to the front, and swing the hand and forearm up and down several times in front of the face.

9. ASSEMBLE–Raise the hand vertically to the full extent of the arm, fingers extended and joined, palm to the front, and wave in large horizontal circles with the arm and hand.

10. FORM COLUMN–Raise either arm to the vertical position. Drop the arm to the rear, describing complete circles in a vertical plane parallel to the body. The signal may be used to indicate either a troop or vehicular column.

11. ARE YOU READY–Extend the arm toward the leader for whom the signal is intended, hand raised, fingers extended and joined, then raise arm slightly above horizontal, palm facing outward.

12. I AM READY–Execute the signal ARE YOU READY.

13. SHIFT–Raise the hand that is on the side toward the new direction across the body, palm to the front, then swing the arm in a horizontal arc, extending the arm and hand to the point in the new direction.

14. ECHELON RIGHT (LEFT)–Face the unit being signaled and extend one arm 45 degrees below the horizontal, palm to the front. The lower arm indicates the direction of the echelon. Supplementary commands may be given to ensure prompt and proper execution.

15. AS SKIRMISHERS (FIRE TEAM); LINE FORMATION (SQUAD)–Raise both arms laterally until horizontal, arms and hands extended, palms down. If it is necessary to indicate a direction, move in the desired direction at the same time.

16. WEDGE–Extend both arms downward and to the side at an angle of 45 degrees below the horizontal, palms to the front.

17. VEE–Extend arms at an angle of 45 degrees above the horizontal forming the letter "V" with arms and torso.

18. FIRE TEAM–The right arm should be placed diagonally across the chest.

19. SQUAD–Extend the hand and arm toward the squad leader, palm of the hand down; distinctly move the hand up and down several times from the wrist, holding the arm steady.

20. CLOSE UP–Start signal with both arms extended sideward, palms forward, and bring palms together in front of the body momentarily. When repetition of the signal is necessary, the arms are returned to the starting position by movement along the front of the body.

21. OPEN UP; EXTEND–Start signal with arms extended in front of the body, palms together, and bring arms to the horizontal position at the sides, palms forward. When repetition of this signal is necessary, the arms are returned along the front of the body to the starting position and the signal is repeated until understood.

22. DISPERSE–Extend either arm vertically overhead; wave the hand and arms to the front, left, right, and rear, the palm toward the direction of each movement.

23. I DO NOT UNDERSTAND–Face toward source of signal; raise both arms sidewards to the horizontal at hip level, bend both arms at elbows, palms up, and shrug shoulders in the manner of the universal "I dunno."

24. FORWARD; ADVANCE; TO THE RIGHT (LEFT); TO THE REAR (USED WHEN STARTING FROM A HALT)–Face and move in the desired direction of march; at the same time extend the arm horizontally to the rear, then swing it overhead and forward in the direction of movement until it is horizontal, palm down.

25. HALT–Carry the hand to the shoulder, palm to the front; then thrust the hand upward vertically to the full extent of the arm and hold it in that position until the signal is understood.

26. FREEZE–Make the signal for HALT and make a fist with the hand.

27. DOWN; TAKE COVER–Extend arm sideward at an angle of 45 degrees above horizontal, palm down, and lower it to the side. Both arms may be used in giving this signal. Repeat until understood.

28. INCREASE SPEED; DOUBLE TIME–Carry the hand to the shoulder, fist closed; rapidly thrust the fist upward vertically to the full extent of the arm and back to the shoulder several times. This signal is also used to increase gait or speed.

29. HASTY AMBUSH RIGHT (LEFT)–Raise fist to shoulder level and thrust it several times in the desired direction.

30. RALLY POINT–Touch the belt buckle with one hand and then point to the ground.

31. OBJECTIVE RALLY POINT–Touch the belt buckle with one hand, point to the ground, and make a circular motion with the hand.

32. ATTENTION–Extend the arm sideways, slightly above horizontal, palm to the front, wave toward and over the head several times.

33. LEADERS JOIN ME–Extend arm toward the leaders and beckon them with finger as shown.

34. DISMOUNT–Extend arm to the side at an angle of 45 degrees above horizontal, palm down, and lower it to side. Both arms may be used in giving this signal. Repeat until understood.

35. MOUNT UP–With the hand extended downward at the side with the palm out, raise arm to the side and upward to an angle of 45 degrees above horizontal. Repeat until understood.

36. DISREGARD PREVIOUS COMMAND– Face the unit or individual being signaled, then raise both arms and cross them over the head, palms to the front.

37. DANGER AREA–Draw the right hand, palm down, across the neck in a throat-cutting motion.

38. HEAD COUNT–Tap the top of the helmet with an open hand.

39. PACE COUNT–Reach down with either hand and tap the boot as you bend your knee.

CHAPTER 19

Individual Movement, Patrolling, Fundamentals of the Defense

In combat operations, frequent use of patrols provides commanders with needed information about the enemy, the local conditions, and friendly troops nearby. Various types of patrols provide security or accomplish specific tasks, such as ambushes and raids. In all cases, the use of stealthy movement procedures and careful use of the terrain will remain a constant requirement. All Marines depend upon each other in a patrol, and an individual error can cost lives and bring mission failure. Therefore, learn the rules of good individual movement and patrolling beginning with this chapter.

Individual Movement by Day

When you go out on patrol in daylight, there are several characteristics that are important to you. These are cover, concealment, camouflage, and the principles of movement.

Cover

In a combat environment, a Marine must be prepared to fire from any type of cover or concealment. Cover is anything that protects a Marine from enemy fire. Cover may be an existing hole, a hastily dug shelter or a well-prepared fighting position with overhead protection. Concealment is anything that hides a Marine from enemy view, but it may not afford protection. Concealment can be obtained from buildings, trees, crops, and skillful use of ground contours. A Marine can use any object or terrain feature that protects him from enemy fire, hides him from enemy view, allows him to observe the enemy, and provides support for a firing position.

As you move, you must continually pick out cover such as your surroundings afford. You may be in a place where no such objects are located. You must learn to study the ground and find protection where, at first, there seems to be none. The slightest depression or hump in the ground may give you shelter from enemy fire. Once you select your next position that offers cover, move to it and move fast.

Some cover will be good for one purpose and worthless for another. For instance, a reverse slope will give you protection from rifle or machine gun fire but will not give full protection from the high-angle fire of mortars and howitzers. If time permits, work to extend or improve natural cover. This means you dig fighting positions, pile rubble and so on. Setting in to a firm defensive position almost always requires these additional measures.

Common Cover Materials

Any material that protects a Marine from small arms fire can be used for cover. Some common materials include sandbags, trees, logs, and building debris. Table 19-1 presents some common materials and their minimum thickness required for protection from small arms fire.

MATERIAL	MINIMUM THICKNESS (IN INCHES)
CONCRETE	7
BROKEN STONE (RUBBLE)	20
DRY SAND	24
WET SAND	35
LOGS (OAK)	40
EARTH (PACKED)	48

Table 19-1. Minimum thickness for protection against small arms.

Concealment

While the word "cover" is used to mean protection from enemy fire, the word "concealment" means protection from observation by the enemy. Concealment may be natural or artificial. Natural concealment is that given by trees, grass, leaves, and so on, without any man-made changes. Artificial concealment is that which you construct yourself. You must become an expert in the use of concealment. Here are some rules to help you conceal yourself:

Rule 1. Remain motionless while you are observing. Movement can attract the eye of the enemy and give away your position.

Rule 2. Use all available concealment. Always act as though you are being watched and use the best available concealment.

Rule 3. Observe from the prone position. This position, lying flat on your stomach, gives you a low silhouette and makes it harder for the enemy to see you.

Rule 4. Expose nothing that glistens. Reflection of the sun flashing on bright objects like a wristwatch, knife blade, or bright button will attract the observation of the enemy at once.

Rule 5. Blend with the background. Be sure that the color of you and your clothes does not contrast too much with your surroundings.

Rule 6. Stay in the shade. When you are in the shade, you throw no shadow and you'll be harder to see.

Rule 7. Break regular outline of objects. If you put foliage around your rifle, twigs in your helmet, and use other tricks of camouflage, you break the regular shape of objects and make them harder to recognize.

Rule 8. Keep off the skyline. If you outline yourself against the sky at any time, you can be observed from a great distance.

Rule 9. Observing. When you are observing, look around one of the sides of an object unless you can look through it.

Rule 10. When you fire. You fire around the right side of an object, unless you are left-handed.

Rule 11. Never over the top. You never look or fire over the top of concealment or cover unless the outline of the concealment already is broken or you can otherwise blend in with a suitable background.

Rule 12. Enemy aircraft. When an aircraft approaches, you take a prone position, face down, and remain motionless. If the aircraft comes upon you by surprise, stand still and do not look up.

Rule 13. Good observation points. A small, thin bush in the shadow of a large bush makes a good observation point. Lone trees or rocks, fence corners, and other prominent landmarks are easily picked out as targets by enemy observers. Remember this when you are concealing yourself.

Camouflage

You already have seen by reading the above rules on cover and concealment that camouflage will be an important part of your individual movement. There are four things involved in successful individual camouflage. They are ability to recognize and take advantage of all forms of natural concealment available; knowledge of the proper use of the available vegetation, soil, and debris for camouflage purposes; knowledge of the proper use of artificial or issued camouflage materials; and camouflage discipline.

Helmets. Camouflage your helmet with the issue helmet cover or make a cover of cloth or burlap that is colored to blend with the terrain. The cover should fit loosely with the flaps folded under the helmet or left hanging. The hanging flaps may help break up the helmet outline. Leaves, grass, or sticks can also be attached to the cover. Use camouflage bands, strings, burlap strips, or rubber bands to hold those in place. If there is no material for a helmet cover, disguise and dull the helmet surface with irregular patterns of paint or mud. (See Figure 19-2(a) and Figure 19-2(b).)

Uniforms. Most uniforms come already camouflaged. However, it may be necessary to add more camouflage to make the uniform blend better with the surroundings. To do this, put mud on the uniform or attach leaves, grass, or small branches to it. Too much camouflage, however, may draw attention.

When operating on snow-covered ground, wear overwhites (if issued) to help blend with the snow. If overwhites are not issued, use white cloth, such as white bedsheets, to get the same effect. (See Figure 19-2(c).)

Skin. Exposed skin reflects light and may draw the enemy's attention. Even very dark skin, because of its natural oil, will reflect light. Use the following methods when applying camouflage face paint to camouflage the skin. (See Figure 19-3 on next page.)

When applying camouflage stick to your skin, work with a buddy (in pairs) and help each other. Apply a two-color combination of

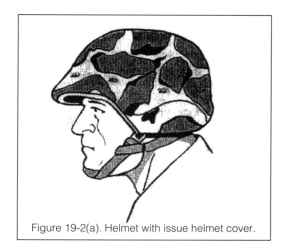

Figure 19-2(a). Helmet with issue helmet cover.

Figure 19-2(b). Helmet with issue helmet cover and camouflage.

Sand and light green for desert and dry areas

Loam and white for snow-covered terrain

Loam and light green for vegetated areas

Figure 19-2(c). Camouflage uniforms.

	SKIN COLOR	SHINE AREAS	SHADOW AREAS
Camouflage Material	Light or Dark	Forehead, Cheekbones, Ears, Nose and Chin	Around Eyes, Under Nose and Under Chin
Loam and Light Green Stick	All Troops in Areas With Green Vegetation	Use Loam	Use Light Green
Sand and Light Green Stick	All Troops use in Areas With Green Vegetation	Use Light Green	Use Sand
Loam and White	All Troops Only in Snow Covered Terrain	Use Loam	Use White
Burnt Cork, Bark Charcoal, or Lamp Black	All Troops, if Camouflage Sticks Not Available	Use	Do Not Use
Light-Color Mud	All Troops, if Camouflage Sticks Not Available	Do Not Use	Use

Figure 19-3. Application of camouflage materials.

camouflage stick in an irregular pattern. Paint shiny areas (forehead, cheekbones, nose, ears, and chin) with a dark color. Paint shadow areas (around the eyes, under the nose and under the chin) with a light color. In addition to the face, paint the exposed skin on the back of the neck, arms, and hands. Palms of hands are not normally camouflaged if arm-and-hand signals are to be used. Remove all jewelry to further reduce shine or reflection.

When camouflage sticks are not issued, use burnt cork, bark charcoal, lamp black, or light-colored mud.

Movement

Some of the principles of movement already have been mentioned. You should plan to move from one concealed location to another, and there are rules to help you move around successfully. Some of these rules are as follows:

Rule 1. Remain motionless when you are not changing your position.

Rule 2. When you are observing, lift your head slowly but steadily, without making any quick movements.

Rule 3. Select your next stopping place from each position. Avoid isolated or obvious places of concealment. Before you leave one position, make certain that your next stopping place does not contain an enemy. Hit the deck a few yards from your position and roll to it.

Rule 4. When you are changing your position by running, spring up, and run with your body bent low and drop to the earth quickly. Take advantage of any walls, ditches, or similar cover.

Individual Movement by Night

When you go on a night mission, some of your needs, such as cover, concealment, movement, and camouflage, are going to be similar to a day mission. Night will present special problems, however.

Night Vision

You have to adapt your eyes to seeing at night. This is night vision. The human eye adapts itself for seeing in the dark by enlarging the pupil in order to let in more light. If you are tired or have a vitamin deficiency, your night vision will not be as good as it could be.

You prepare your eyes for a night mission by staying in darkness for about an hour before you go out. If you cannot stay in the dark, keep out of the lights around you as long as possible and avoid looking straight at them. If it is possible, wear red goggles or keep one eye covered.

Appearance and Size

Darkness not only makes it hard or impossible for you to see objects, but it also changes their appearance and apparent size. Details are blotted out. You have to train yourself to identify objects by shapes at night.

- A tree seen against the night light looks much smaller than it does in the daytime, because the twigs at the tips of the branches cannot be seen at night. For the same reason, an airplane illuminated by city lights looks larger than the same plane when it is seen as a black mass against a dimly lighted sky.
- Special devices to aid night vision, which may be issued to you, make it possible to see objects or parts of objects that would otherwise be too small to be seen at all and help to identify objects already spotted.
- Any kind of light is quickly visible at night. Under ordinary conditions, a lighted match can be seen for several miles. Under ideal conditions of darkness and atmosphere, a candle may be visible for 10 miles.

Sounds

At night, the sounds of things will be very important. You depend mostly upon your ears to get information about the enemy, and you have to make every effort to keep the enemy from hearing you.

- When moving at night, stop frequently to listen. If you are required to wear a helmet, remove it when you stop so that sounds are not distorted by the helmet over your ears.
- By practicing a great deal, you can learn to listen for long periods in perfect silence.
- Remember that sounds are transmitted a greater distance in wet weather and at night than in dry weather and in the daytime.

- If you hold your ear close to the ground, you can hear much better such sounds as persons walking and the noise of vehicles.

Smells

Use your nose as well as your ears. Your sense of smell may warn you of enemy fires, cooking, motor parks, gasoline and oil engines, bodies of water, and the presence of troops.

Touch

Your sense of touch is going to mean much to you at night. Learn to operate and adjust your equipment by the sense of touch alone. You are also going to have to use your hands instead of your eyes to feel and recognize objects in the dark.

Concealment

Concealment at night is provided by darkness, unless there is bright moonlight or illuminated urban terrain. If there is light, however, you have to use the same methods of concealment that you use in daylight.

Movement

The principles of movement at night are somewhat different from those of daytime. At night, you must be able to move in absolute silence because your safety depends on your silent movement. The five principles of night movement are:

1. Move by bounds you have determined in advance.

2. Run at night only in an emergency.

3. Stop frequently and listen intently at each stop.

4. Take advantage of sounds that may distract the enemy to cover up your own movements.

5. If you fall down, don't cry out. Fall as silently as possible and then remain still.

Other Precautions

In addition to these principles for movement at night, there are other methods that you can use to avoid detection:

- If you feel you are about to sneeze, press upward on the end of your nose with your fingers. This may stop the sneeze.
- If you feel a cough coming, press lightly on your Adam's apple. This may stop it.
- Sometimes you may have a ringing noise in your head that interferes with your hearing. Try yawning to stop this.
- If it is necessary for you to whisper, expel most of the air from your lungs before you do. This does away with the hissing sound usually made by a whisper.
- If the enemy has been using chemical weapons, keep away from depressions in damp and rainy weather. Gas can remain in these places quite a while.
- Whenever you stop, look and listen.
- Do not look at an object too long. This strains your eyes.
- If caught in a flare's light, drop quickly in the split second that the enemy is blinded after the flare ignites. If you hear the flare fired, drop to the ground before it ignites. Never look at a flare; you will impair your night vision for nearly an hour. Close one eye to preserve your night vision.
- When you come upon patrols or persons, consider all of them to be unfriendly until you identify them. When you meet someone, crouch low in order to get the person silhouetted against the sky and to offer only an indistinct target if the person proves to be an enemy. If you are fired upon, do not return the fire except to avoid capture.
- If you are carrying a luminous compass or watch, be sure that the dial has some covering on it.

Passing Obstacles

The proper passing of obstacles, such as wires and trenches, is another thing you need to know about night movement. Whenever possible, avoid enemy obstacles, which are frequently covered by their weapons.

- All of your movements near wire must be slow and cautious because of the danger of booby traps and mines. Walk over low wire at night by grasping the first strand with one hand and reaching forward with the other to feel for a clear spot on the ground. Feel for a spot where you can place your foot without touching another strand, or a mine, booby trap or any object that might make a noise. When you find such a spot, lift your foot up and over, close to the hand grasping the wire. Place your foot beside your other hand to avoid catching it on another strand. If you are armed, sling your rifle across your back and follow the same procedure.
- You can move under wire on your back by feeling ahead and above for the strands of wire and inching yourself along, holding the wire clear of your body. Be careful not to tug on the wire or jerk it. You might make a noise or set off a booby trap. If you have a rifle with you, you can put it on your stomach, or you can place it between your body and right arm.
- When cutting wire, if you are alone, cut the wire near a picket to avoid having a loose end fly back. When you are operating with another Marine, one of you can hold the wire in both hands while the other cuts the wire between the hands. Then you bend or roll back the wire to make an opening sufficient for passage. When cutting wire, wrap a cloth around it to muffle sound. If a gap is cut in enemy wire, it is best to leave the top wires intact. This lessens chances of discovery.
- The proper way to cross a narrow trench at night is explained here. You should crawl silently up to the edge of the trench, look into it, and remove all loose dirt and rocks from the edge. Then spring up from the prone position and jump across, sinking quietly to the ground on the other side. Remain there quite still for a moment and listen before you proceed any farther.
- If the trench is too wide for you to jump it in this manner, you must climb into it silently and slowly and then climb out the other side, using the revetment of the trench for support.

Observing

Special actions are needed when your mission is to observe and report. So far, we have studied ways to protect yourself and get around on your job. Now we come to the job itself.

Selecting Observation Posts

When looking for a place from which to observe, study it closely before you occupy it just to be sure the enemy does not already occupy it.

After you have occupied the position, avoid unnecessary movement. Leave the position by a route different from the one you used to approach it. Be careful not to make paths that would reveal your position.

When you search the ground about your position, there are certain methods you can use to assure that you do a good job.

- In daylight, look first at the ground nearest you. Begin close to your position and search a narrow strip 50 yards or less wide, going from left to right parallel to your front. Then search from right to left a second and similar strip farther away but overlapping the first. You continue in this manner until you have covered your entire field of view.
- At night, you should search the horizon with short, jerky movements and short pauses. Look a little to one side of an object and then to the other side to see it best on a dark night. Low-powered field glasses also increase the range of your vision.
- Look at Figure 19-4, which shows you how terrain is searched. You can see troops as far away as 2,000 meters in the daytime. At 600 meters, you can count the files of a squad, and at 400 meters, the movement of arms and legs can be seen plainly.

Interpretation of Signs

You can identify trained combat Marines by their powers of observation. When they return from a mission, they can describe what sort of country they have passed through, all noticeable landmarks, and any indications of the enemy in the vicinity. These Marines have acquired a keen sense of interpretation by constant practice in observing. The ability to do this is valuable.

They have learned that the enemy, in its movements, leaves slight indications that show strength, the character and condition of troops, and direction of march.

- The size of a bivouac area usually indicates the number of the enemy there. You can check laundry, ration tins, dumps, and so on for clues as to the size of the enemy force.
- Tracks on a road can show you what kinds of troops or vehicles are in the body and their directions of march.

Figure 19-4. How to search terrain.

• The state of the bivouac and the amount of abandoned material lying about can reveal the enemy's condition to you. For instance, if you find food left uneaten, you can assume that they are well supplied. If all scraps of food have been eaten, you can assume that they are short on supplies.

• You can check a track for the time it was made. A freshly made track has sharp edges and ordinarily has signs of moisture, which disappear in about 15 minutes.

• You can tell whether a footmark was made by a running or walking person. A running person digs the toes into the ground. The walking footprint is fairly even.

• You can easily tell the direction of travel of a car by the way its tracks pass across ruts or splash water from puddles.

• You can estimate the speed of a vehicle by the amount of mud splattered about or the dirt scattered by it. Slow-moving vehicles leave shallow, smooth tracks. Faster moving wheels cut deeper.

• You can observe carefully your own unit, when you are on the march, in camp or deployed, in order to develop your power to estimate the size of enemy forces, even at a distance. Here are a few of the things you can learn. If a column is so far away that you cannot count it, you can estimate its size by the length of time it takes the column to pass a given point; infantry on the march usually raises a low, thick cloud of dust; a broken cloud indicates artillery on the move; trucks and mechanized vehicles raise a heavy, rapidly moving cloud of dust

Reporting

You send messages in the field to get information to your commander. A message can be either oral—that is, sent by word of mouth—or can be written. But whether it is spoken or written, you must learn to give accurate, clear and complete information, and you have to get

it to your commander in time for them to use it. Figure 19-5 shows a message that is correctly written.

Oral Messages

You send an oral message when it is impractical to write out a message, when the information is just one simple idea or when there is greater danger that the enemy might seize a written one. Oral messages have to be as simple and clear as possible, and you should avoid having a series of numbers or names in them. Always have the person who is delivering an oral message for you repeat it back to you, so that you can be certain he has it correctly memorized.

Written Messages

When you write a message, you should include all information of value about the enemy and about yourself. You should be brief, accurate and clear. Distinguish carefully between facts and opinion. If you send in hearsay information, give the source somewhat in this manner: "Friendly farmer states four-man patrol crossed bridge at 36544273 at 0930 traveling south."

Regardless of the type of message, there are six kinds of facts that your commander always wants to know about the enemy. These are size, activity, location, unit, time, and equipment.

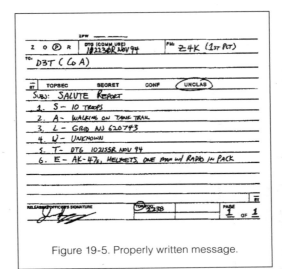

Figure 19-5. Properly written message.

The key word for remembering what information is needed on the enemy is SALUTE.

1. Size.
2. Activity.
3. Location.
4. Unit.
5. Time.
6. Equipment.

Number each item of information. This makes it clearer for your commander when it is read or sent over voice radio.

If you suspect that your commander did not get a message you sent, include a summary of it in your next message.

You indicate for your commander the place from which the message is being sent. You can do this by reference to an important terrain feature, by map coordinates, by the magnetic azimuth from each of two definitely located points or by the azimuth and distance from one known point. Sometimes you can describe your position best by using a simple sketch or overlay, which also makes other information in your message clearer.

Your commander will want to know what you plan to do next, so include in your message your intentions. If you plan to remain in observation, continue your mission or take other action, you must tell your leader. If you think the message might fall into enemy hands, have a messenger give this information orally.

After you have written your message, reread it carefully. If it is possible, have someone else read it to see that it is complete and easily understood.

Messengers

Information will be valuable to your commander only if it is received in time to act upon it. If you are in doubt about when to send a message, send it at once. If radio silence has been imposed, a messenger is employed. Here are some suggestions about messengers:

- When you are in friendly territory or close to friendly troops, one messenger is all you need. However, if you are in enemy territory or when it may be necessary to pass through heavy artillery concentrations,

you should use two messengers if possible. They should leave at different times and travel by separate routes.

- The messenger must know where the message is to be delivered and the route to take. If there is a map available, the messenger marks a starting point and selects landmarks to help find the way.
- A messenger always travels light and takes only the necessary food and arms.
- If delayed or lost, the messenger should show the message to an officer, if it is possible, and ask the officer's advice. Messengers have the right of way and must be given all practical assistance.
- When there is danger of being captured, the messenger immediately destroys the message. To avoid detection, the messenger uses different routes in entering and leaving a message center or command post.
- If the messenger picks up any information along the route of interest to the commander, it should be reported at the time the message is delivered.

Sketches and Overlays

Sketches are valuable in getting information to your commander. Sometimes your information can be carried in no other manner. You can make two kinds of sketches, panoramic and topographic.

Panoramic Sketches

A panoramic sketch is a picture of the ground (terrain) showing the height and view from your point of observation. A panoramic sketch made by one scout can assist another scout in finding oneself quickly in the same location. Figure 19-6 (on page 271) shows how a panoramic sketch looks.

A panoramic sketch is made as follows:

- You first determine what information you want to give, then draw in the landscape lines that are more or less horizontal.

- Put the prominent points of your area on the sketch, but leave out unimportant details that might be just confusing.
- Do not show the foreground.
- Show on your sketch the location of the information you are sending and place any explanatory notes above the sketch in the margins with arrows pointing to the features explained.
- Select as a reference point the most prominent point in your sketch and indicate the azimuth to it.
- Then place a title on the sketch, show where it was made, indicate the date and time it was made and sign it.

Topographic Sketches

A topographic sketch is made so that the person receiving it can plot on a map your scouting position or the information you desire to convey. To make a topographic sketch, you need a map similar to one your commander has. This is the way you make a topographic sketch:

- You find the azimuth from your position to the position of an object you can easily see and describe. Estimate the distance by the most accurate means available.
- Draw the azimuth line from you to the object. Mark the azimuth above this line and the distance below the line.
- At the proper end of the line, show the object, and at the other end, indicate your own position.
- Find the azimuth and the distance to some other point on your map or to the position of the command post. Then draw this line on the sketch and indicate the azimuth, the distance, and the object to which it is drawn. Sign the sketch.

Overlays

The topographic sketch is drawn on a piece of translucent paper or clear plastic, which is called an overlay. The overlay can be placed over a map or chart on which locations, such as targets or enemy positions, are shown. Your commander can take the overlay you made with your map, place it over the map, and see clearly

the information you are giving. You can use any kind of thin paper–tracing paper, overlay sheets from a message book or acetate–for your overlay. Figure 19-7 (on page 272) shows you a brief and accurate overlay. Here is the way to make a simple one:

- Place your map on a hard, flat surface.
- Put the transparent paper over the part of the map you are using and fasten the paper with clips, thumbtacks, or pins.
- Next, identify the section that you are reporting on. To do this, trace the intersecting grid lines at two opposite corners of the overlay and give their correct number designations. If there are no grid lines on your map, trace in at least two clearly defined map features, such as road junctions, towns, or streams. This lets your commander know the exact area on the map that is covered by your overlay.
- On the overlay, sketch in the object or information you wish to tell your commander about. If some of the information on the map is needed to complete your information, be careful to make your sketches so that the map's information shows through when the overlay is on it.
- Put all of your explanatory notes along the margin of the overlay with arrows pointing to the objects mentioned.
- Indicate on your overlay the position on the map from which you saw the object or obtained the information.
- Indicate the title and the scale of the map from which the overlay was made, so your commander will know which map the overlay belongs.
- Give the date and hour you obtained the information shown on the overlay.
- Sign the overlay.

Patrolling

In the field, small groups are sent out from time to time on special missions that are called patrols. A patrol is a detachment of troops sent

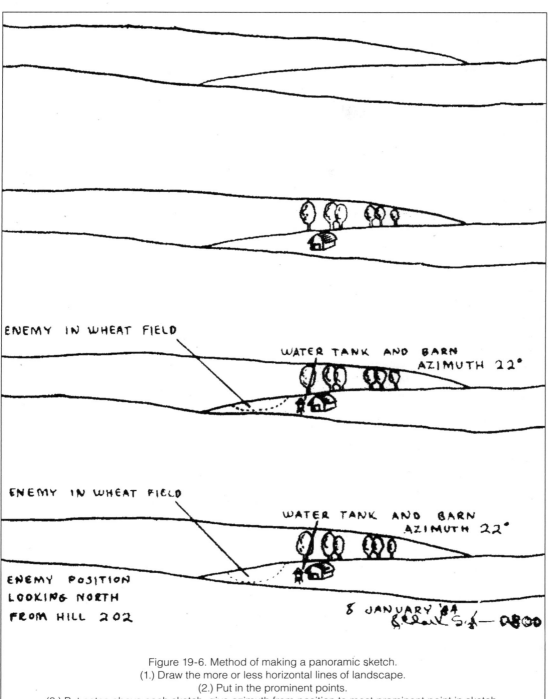

ENEMY IN WHEAT FIELD

WATER TANK AND BARN
AZIMUTH 22°

ENEMY IN WHEAT FIELD

WATER TANK AND BARN
AZIMUTH 22°

ENEMY POSITION
LOOKING NORTH
FROM HILL 202

8 JANUARY '84 — 0800

Figure 19-6. Method of making a panoramic sketch.
(1.) Draw the more or less horizontal lines of landscape.
(2.) Put in the prominent points.
(3.) Put notes above each sketch, give azimuth from position to most prominent point in sketch.
(4.) Give sketch a title and show where made, date and time, sign it.

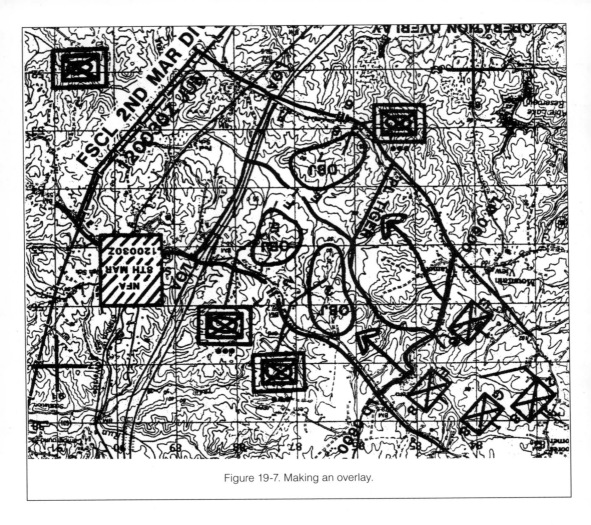

Figure 19-7. Making an overlay.

out from a larger body on a mission of reconnaissance, security, or combat. There are two general classes of patrols, reconnaissance, and combat, either of which might have a mission of security. The classification is derived from the mission assigned a patrol.

Reconnaissance Patrols

Reconnaissance patrols are sent out to gain information about the enemy or the terrain. Such patrols engage in combat only when it becomes necessary to accomplish their assigned mission or in order to protect themselves. In general, they avoid combat and accomplish their missions by stealth.

Reconnaissance patrols have a great variety of tasks, but their primary mission is to obtain and report information in time for it to be of value to the commander who dispatched the patrol.

Some of the tasks that may be assigned to reconnaissance patrols are (1) to locate and observe the characteristics of a hostile position or installation, (2) to reconnoiter a route of march for a larger force, (3) to reconnoiter a safe and fordable stream crossing for an advancing unit, (4) to reconnoiter a certain terrain feature or the general nature of the terrain in a given locality, and (5) to maintain contact with a rapidly withdrawing force. The tasks mentioned are by no means all-inclusive but are given as examples.

Combat Patrols

Combat patrols are assigned missions that usually require them to engage actively in combat. They are fighting patrols. Every combat patrol, no matter what its primary mission, has a secondary mission—that of gaining information about the enemy and the terrain.

A combat patrol may be dispatched with the mission of (1) capturing prisoners, (2) destroying an enemy installation, (3) protecting an exposed flank of an advancing unit, (4) seizing and holding a piece of commanding ground to prevent enemy occupation of the terrain feature, and (5) ambushing the enemy. Again, the missions mentioned are not all-inclusive but are given merely as examples.

Patrol Formations

In Chapter 18, "Combat Formations and Signals," you saw a number of fire team formations. While on patrol as a unit, as part of a squad or as part of a larger force, the fire team leader may use any or all of these formations from time to time. The factors determining which formation will be used include mission, terrain, visibility, control, and security. The leader must be able to move the team in any direction and to change quickly to another formation by signals. Each member of the patrol is assigned a sector of observation. In order to be sure of security when the patrol halts, each member takes up a firing position from which the sector assigned can be observed.

Duties as a Patrol Member

As a patrol member, you must respond quickly to the decisions and orders of your leader. You must have complete confidence in all members of the patrol and confidence that your team will succeed in its mission.

Your patrol goes in a formation that can be changed to suit conditions you meet. The leader of your patrol tells you by signal where to place yourself in the formation as you proceed.

One member of the patrol remains inside the group where the patrol leader can always be seen. Other members on the points and flanks move in and out to look for any cover that might

hold an enemy. They can carefully observe an area up to 100 meters in open terrain to protect the entire patrol.

Members of your patrol automatically move closer together in thick cover, fog, and at night. When you are in open country in daylight and the weather is clear, you can move farther apart. However, your flank groups usually are not more than 100 meters from the center of the advancing patrol.

Your patrol leader tries to locate so that all members of the patrol can see signals quickly. The leader uses arm-and-hand signals shown in Chapter 18 during the daytime. At night, touches and the arm-and-hand signals are used.

Patrol Reports

When your patrol returns, the leader makes a report to cover your activities. This report is written, unless there is not enough time to write it, and the patrol leader must also be prepared to answer questions that the commander or intelligence officer may ask. In case you become a patrol leader, the following is the information you are expected to give either by word of mouth or in writing:

Routine Information. Certain information is gathered as a matter of course and delivered without specific questions being asked.

- The name or number of your patrol, its size, and mission are given first.
- The time the patrol departed and the routes it took are reported.
- You detail the character of the terrain you covered—that is, was it dry, swampy? Could vehicles cross it?
- Tell what you observed. That is, give the number, composition, equipment, and attitude of the enemy.
- Where and when the enemy was observed. This includes what the enemy was doing when spotted, the direction of the movement, if the enemy was moving, and any changes in dispositions.
- The location and condition of enemy defenses is described.
- If your patrol met any of the enemy, give the results of the encounter.

- The return route and time of the patrol's return are furnished, and the condition of your patrol, including the disposition you made of any dead or wounded, is described.
- Finally, you give your conclusions, including to what extent your mission was accomplished.

Special Information. In addition to this routine information, the patrol leader should be able to answer special questions from the commander or an intelligence officer.

- Your commander might ask you to show on the map just where you went.
- You might be asked to give the routes of approach to your outfit's position.
- You also might be asked if you saw any assembly places close to your front lines from which an enemy assault could be launched.
- Someone might want your opinion as to whether the enemy could use armored vehicles on the ground you covered.
- Other questions could concern whether the security measures taken by your outfit are good or whether there are some particular weaknesses in your unit's positions that you have observed during the patrol.

Preparing for Combat

Prior to conducting a patrolling mission or any operations, Marines must ensure they are properly prepared to successfully execute the mission. Preparation for combat includes receiving a warning order, receiving an operations order, rehearsals, pre-combat checks (PCC), and pre-combat inspections (PCI).

Warning Order. The warning order is issued as soon as practical with all information available included to assist in the conduct of a mission. (See Figure 19-8.) It is posted in a common area where all members of the unit will see it or given orally to all members of the unit. The warning order consists of the following elements and information:

Warning Order

Situation
Enemy (SALUTE)
Size:
Activity:
Location:
Unit:
Time:

Friendly (HAS)
Higher:
Adjacent:
Supporting:

Attachments:
Detachments:

Mission (5 Ws)
Who:
What:
When:
Where:
Why:

General Instructions

Unit	Gen Org	Duties	Arms, Ammo, Equip	Gear common to all	Time Schedule			
					When	What	Where	Who

Specific Instructions

Figure 19-8.

1. Situation. Friendly and enemy situation and troop activity information is necessary for initial preparation.

2. Mission. A statement of what the unit is to accomplish its purpose for accomplishing it. It should include who, what, when, where, and why.

3. General Instructions.

- Task Organization. How the unit will be organized to accomplish the mission.
- Tasks. Alert subordinate leaders to specific key tasks.

4. Specific Instructions. Designate specific equipment or individuals. For example:

- Designation of assistant patrol leader and his role in preparation.
- Designation of navigators and radio operators.
- Designates specific tasks for fire team and or fire team members, such as aid and litter team, or rear security.

Receive the Operations Order. At some point after the warning order is received, the unit will receive a full operations order. When receiving the five-paragraph order, all members of the unit should be present with note taking material. The unit leader will use a terrain model to assist in his presentation of the order and to allow members to visualize the operation as it is being briefed. The operation order consists of five paragraphs: Situation, Mission, Execution, Administration and logistics, Command and signal (SMEAC). Below describes the five paragraphs of an operations order.

Situation

Enemy Forces. Consists of the composition, disposition, location, movement, and recent activities of enemy forces. The acronym SALUTE can be used to describe the most recent information on the enemy. The acronym DRAW-D can be used to describe the capabilities of the enemy:

1. SALUTE.
   Size. What is the size of the force?
   Activity. What is the enemy doing?
   Location. Where is enemy known or suspected to be?
   Uniform. What is the enemy wearing?
   Time. When were they last seen?
   Equipment. What type of weapons and gear they have?
2. DRAW-D.
   Defend. Will they defend?
   Reinforce. Can they be reinforced, if so from where?
   Attack. Will they attack?
   Withdraw. A form of way the enemy disengages from the fight?
   Delay. To slow and defeat as much as possible without sacrificing the tactical integrity of the unit; presents low risk to the unit?

Friendly Forces. A statement of the mission of the higher unit, location and mission of adjacent units, and mission of supporting units. The acronym HAS can be used to describe friendly forces. The acronym HAS stands for:

1. Higher.
2. Adjacent.
3. Supporting.

Attachments and Detachments. Units attached or detached from the squad by higher HQs, including the effective time of attachment or detachment.

Mission

The mission is a clear concise statement of the task that the squad must accomplish. Who, What, When, Where, and Why. For example: "At 0800, 1st squad attacks to clear Objective A in order to prevent the enemy from interfering with convoy operations."

Execution

1. Commander's Intent. This is a brief statement concerning what the commander is trying to achieve, thus amplifying the mission statement. It should include the end state of what the commander wants to happen.

2. Concept of Operations. The concept of operations is a brief summary of the tactical plan.

3. Subordinate Tasks. The tasks to the subordinate unit. These will form the mission statements for these subordinate elements.

4. Coordinating Instructions. Amplifying information to tie everything together. Tasks that are common to all in the execution. This contains various things such as timelines, SOP's, control measures, and contingency plans.

Administration and Logistics

This paragraph contains information or instructions pertaining to logistical sustainment for the mission. It should include the location of the distribution points, corpsman, and aid station. It also includes the handling of POWs and other administrative and supply matters. The phrase, "the five B's," is used to describe this paragraph. The 5 B's:

1. Beans.
2. Bullets.
3. Bandages.
4. Bad guys.
5. Batteries.

Command and Signal

1. Command. Should include the location of leaders throughout the operation, the succession of command, and amplify command relationships.

2. Signal. This section includes the communication plan and includes items such as radio frequencies, use of signal plans, and challenge and passwords.

Conduct rehearsals. After receiving the operations order the unit will begin conducting rehearsals. Units should conduct at a minimum the key phases of the operation and immediate action drills. Rehearsals can also include the following drills or events:

- Guided discussions.
- Walk-throughs.
- Sand Table Exercise.
- Map Exercise.
- Rehearsal of Concept (ROC) Drill or "ROC walk."
- Combined Arms Rehearsal (CAR).

Pre-Combat Checks (PCCs). Prior to execution of the operation, Marines will check to ensure they have the proper equipment and knowledge to be successful. These checks include but are not limited to the following:

1. Having prescribed uniform, weapons, ammunition, ordnance, and equipment as indicated in the warning order. Ensure that all items are available and operational.

2. Ensure Marines are correctly camouflaged.

3. Silenced gear and equipment.

4. Having identification tags and Military Identification Card.

5. Not taking any unnecessary equipment and personal items.

Pre-Combat Inspections (PCIs). During PCIs leaders will physically inspect the Marines and equipment in their unit. For example, test optics, conduct radio checks, inspect vehicles, inspect combat loads, and test fire weapon (when feasible).

During the check, the leader will question each member to ensure they know key pieces of information such as:

1. The mission, routes, and fire support plan.

2. Individual assignments during the mission.

3. Casualty evacuation plan.

4. Challenge and passwords, call signs, frequencies, code words, reporting procedures.

Fundamentals of the Defense

Defensive missions of Marine Rifle Squad. Defensive missions of squads are normally one of three missions: the front-line squad, the squad as part of the reserves, and the squad as a security element.

The Front Line Squad. The mission of the front line squad is to stop the enemy by fire forward of the platoon battle position and to repel him by close combat if he reaches the platoon battle position. The mission requires that the squad be assigned a fighting position and a sector of fire.

Squad as Part of the Reserves. As part of the company reserve platoon, the squad is normally assigned a fighting position to the rear of the frontline units and supports them by fire. The fighting position and sector of fire is assigned to concentrate fire in the rear, on the flanks, or into a gap between frontline platoons. The squad as part of company's reserve platoon may participate in a counterattack to expel the enemy from the company battle position.

Squad as a Security Element. During the defense, the squad may serve as part of the security element located forward of the platoon battle position. The squad's mission in this capacity is to gain information about the enemy and to deceive, delay, and disorganize his advance. An example of a security element would be security patrols.

Sectors of Fire. While conducting a defensive mission, Marines are assigned sectors of fire. A sector of fire is an area required to be covered by an individual, fire team, squad, or a crew-served weapon. It is a pie-shape area enclosed by two lateral limits and a forward limit. Marines will report any activity within their sectors of fire to their higher HQs.

Final Protective Fires (FPF). Final protective fires are the final attempt to stop the enemy attack before he reaches the platoon's battle position. When final protective fires are called for, all squad members fire in their assigned sectors. Service rifles and grenade launchers continue to fire at the average rate; the automatic riflemen will increase their volume of fire to the rapid rate.

Fighting Positions. A fighting position is a location on the ground from which fire is delivered by an individual, a fire unit (squad or fire team), or a crew served weapon; see Figure 19-9 and Figure 19-10.

1. *Primary Fighting Position.* The primary position is the best available position from which the assigned sector of fire is covered.
2. *Alternate Fighting Positions.* An alternate position is located so that a crew-served weapon can continue to accomplish its original mission when the primary position becomes untenable or unsuited for carrying out that mission. (See Figure 19-11.)
3. *Supplementary Fighting Positions.* These positions are oriented in a different direction than the primary positions. (See Figure 19-12 and Figure 19-13 on next page.)

Priorities in the defense. Priorities of defensive operations can be remembered using the acronym SAFESOC.

S-Security.
A-Automatic weapons/avenues of approach.
F-Fields of fire.
E-Entrenchment.
S-Supplementary and alternate positions.
O-Obstacles.
C-Camouflage and cover and concealment.

Security. To prevent surprise attacks and deny the enemy information. All-around security and protection against surprise are gained by:

1. Posting a sentinel for surveillance.
2. Enforcing noise and light discipline.

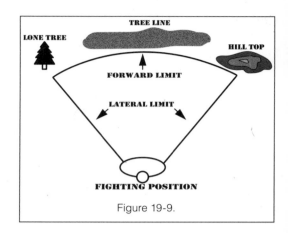

Figure 19-9.

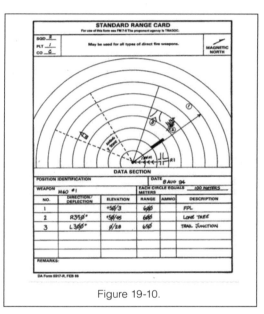

Figure 19-10.

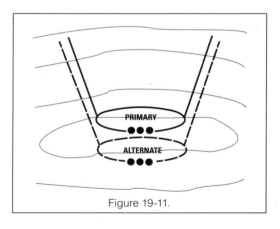

Figure 19-11.

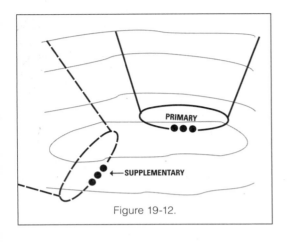

Figure 19-12.

Figure 19-14.

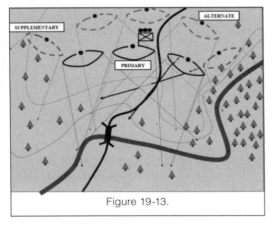

Figure 19-13.

Figure 19-15.

3. Keeping movement in the fighting positions to a minimum.

Automatic weapons/avenues of approach. Automatic rifles are positioned to cover the most likely avenues of approach. Their positions should enable them to cover the fire team's sector of fire, provide support for adjacent fire teams, and effectively deliver final protective fires.

Fields of Fire. Clear fields of fire forward of each fighting position to allow maximum firepower to be delivered on the enemy entering the battle area.

Entrenchment. Fighting holes are dug by Marines at their fighting positions. Fighting positions provide excellent protection against small arms fire, shell fragments, aircraft strafing and bombing, effects of nuclear detonations, and the crushing actions of a tank. (See Figure 19-14.)

Supplementary and Alternate Fighting Positions. Supplementary and alternate fighting positions provide flexibility to the defensive line. They are used in the event that the enemy attacks from a different location other than that which the primary positions are oriented.

Obstacles. Obstacles are designed to break up the enemy's attack, canalize him into heavy weapons fire, and disorganize his assault.

Camouflage. Concealment from enemy ground and aerial observation is very important in selecting and organizing each fighting position. Camouflage measures begin from the moment the position is occupied and are continued as long as the Marines are there. The "C" also stands for "Continuing Actions." You should always be improving your positions in the defense.

Cover. Cover is made of natural or man-made materials, gives protection from bullets, fragments of exploding rounds, flame, nuclear effects, biological and chemical agents, and enemy observation. (See Figure 19-15 on previous page.)

Concealment. Anything that hides you from enemy observation is considered concealment. Concealment does not protect you from enemy fire. Natural concealment includes bushes, grass, and shadows. If possible, natural concealment should not be disturbed because they are already prepared, seldom attract enemy attention, and need no replacement. (See Figure 19-16.)

Figure 19-16.

CHAPTER 20

Chemical, Biological, Radiological, and Nuclear Defense

Enemy states or groups may seek to employ chemical, biological, radiological, or nuclear (CBRN) weapons to counter the qualitative military superiority of the Untied States. Historically, CBRN use has generally occurred when conventional munitions were unable to provide the necessary advantage to one side or the other. Use of these weapons requires both the capability (i.e., having the weapons) and the political will to use them. For a nation, that decision has high potential for significant retribution, in the form of the massive U.S. deterrent arsenal. Stateless groups, unless they have defined territory and assets, remain far more difficult to deter. CBRN weapons in the hands of our adversaries may pose grave danger to the United States at home and abroad.

For this reason, Marines must be familiar with the effects of these weapons and the defensive measures necessary to counter them. Current U.S. policy is to deter enemy CBRN use through a strong nuclear force and conventional capabilities that include counterforce, active and passive defense, and consequence management to enable U.S. forces to survive, fight, and win in a CBRN environment. In shaping a peaceful international environment favorable to U.S. interests, U.S. policies and strategies are continually adapted to prevent and limit the proliferation of CBRN capabilities. Commanders organize, train, and equip to ensure that their forces and supporting activities are prepared to advance and defend U.S. interests; however, the overriding mission of the U.S. Armed Forces is to deter war. Should deterrence fail, the United States will pursue war to a successful conclusion.

The United States may use nuclear weapons to terminate a conflict or war at the lowest acceptable level of hostilities. The United States will never use chemical weapons. The Chemical Weapons Convention, ratified by the United States on April 29, 1997, bans the acquisition, development, production, retention, stockpiling, transfer, and use of chemical weapons. The United States will never use biological weapons. Under the terms of the Biological Weapons Convention, ratified by the United States on March 29, 1975, parties agreed not to develop, produce, stockpile, or acquire biological agents or toxins of types and in quantities that have no justification for prophylactic, protective, or other peaceful purposes.

Nuclear Defense

The introduction of nuclear weapons in modern warfare has placed greater responsibility on the unit leader. While nuclear fires produce casualties through blast, heat, and radiation, their effect depends upon many variables. Such variables include the size or yield of the weapon, height of burst (subsurface, surface or air burst), distance from ground zero (GZ), and the protection afforded Marines by fighting holes or armor.

Marines with a basic knowledge of nuclear weapons and their effects can survive and still function as an effective part of a combat unit. Tests have proven that troops with adequate protection can operate within a matter of minutes in an area where a nuclear explosion has occurred.

Conventional and Nuclear Explosions

There are several basic differences between a nuclear and a high-explosive detonation.

First, a nuclear explosion may be thousands or millions of times more powerful than that of the largest conventional weapon.

Second, a fairly large portion of the energy of a nuclear explosion takes the form of heat and light or thermal radiation, capable of producing injury or starting fires at considerable distances from the point of detonation.

Third, and probably the greatest difference, are the highly penetrating and harmful rays called "initial nuclear radiation."

Finally, the substances left after the explosions are radioactive, giving off harmful radiation over an extended period of time. This effect is known as the "residual nuclear radiation" or "residual radioactivity."

These differences between the conventional and nuclear explosions require special considerations. (See Figure 20-1.)

Effects on Individuals

Casualties from nuclear fire result from blast, thermal radiation, and nuclear radiation effects. Each is discussed below.

Blast. Causes injuries by both direct and indirect effects. Direct effect injuries, such as ruptured eardrums and internal injuries, result from very high-pressure waves generated by the blast. Indirect effect injuries occur from impacts of collapsing structures, flying objects, shattered glass, and fires started from short circuits, overturned stoves, and ignited fuels.

Most blast injuries will normally result from indirect effects.

Thermal Radiation and Other Burns. Studies indicate that burns of one kind or

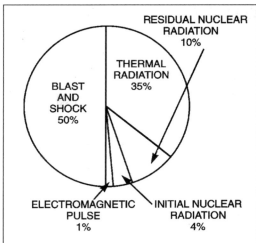

Figure 20-1. Energy distribution contained in a low air burst type of nuclear explosion.

another cause approximately 30 percent of the deaths that occur as a result of a nuclear weapons detonation.

Persons in the open within two miles of a medium-sized nuclear weapon will receive painful flash burns on exposed skin.

Fires resulting from blast cause other burn injuries. People looking directly at a nuclear explosion may receive eye damage, which is usually temporary in nature. Flash and flame burns resulting from nuclear explosions are treated like other burns.

Nuclear Radiation. The damage done by nuclear radiation depends on the dosage received and the time of exposure.

Exposure to nuclear radiation does not necessarily cause radiation sickness. It takes a large amount of nuclear radiation whether initial or residual, to immediately harm an individual. Normally, the effects of nuclear radiation are not noticed during or immediately after exposure.

If a Marine receives an excessive amount of nuclear radiation, such symptoms as nausea, vomiting, and a feeling of weakness occur within a few hours. Bear in mind, however, that a person can have nausea, vomiting, and weakness and still continue to do duties.

The effects of nuclear bursts vary among their type: designated air, surface, and subsurface, depending upon where the explosion occurs in relation to the surface of the earth. The height of the burst has much importance because it influences the amount and kind of damage that occurs. (See Figure 20-2 and Figure 20-3).

Air Burst. An air burst is a nuclear explosion in which the fireball does not touch the

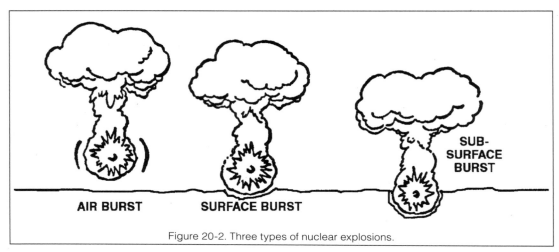

Figure 20-2. Three types of nuclear explosions.

Type of Burst	Initial Nuclear Radiation	Residential Nuclear Radiation Contamination (target area and/or fallout)	Blast	Heat (thermal radiation)
Air	Extensive and hazardous Hazard exists, however, only during explosion.	Negligible except as induced radioactivity in soil in target area following low air bursts.	Extensive.	Extensive.
Surface	Generally less extensive than from air burst of the same size, but still hazardous.	Generally extensive. Occurs in target area as induced radioactivity in soil and as fallout in target area and in areas miles downwind of target area. Hazard lasts for long periods of time; fallout may not reach your position until several hours after explosion.	Concentrated in smaller area than in air burst.	Affects smaller area than does air burst.
Subsurface	So little it is not considered hazardous.	Generally extensive and more dangerous than from a surface burst of the same size. Occurs as induced radio-activity in soil and as fallout, just as from a surface burst. Hazard lasts for long periods of time; fallout may not reach your position until several hours after explosion.	Concentrated in smaller area than in air burst.	Negligible because most of it is absorbed or deflected by ground or water.

Figure 20-3. Characteristics of nuclear explosions.

GUIDEBOOK FOR MARINES

surface of the earth. Blast and heat present the greatest danger from this type of burst. The primary nuclear radiation hazard comes in the initial nuclear radiation, but a residual surface hazard may exist out to several hundred meters from GZ (further with larger yield weapons) and should be avoided or passed through rapidly if attack through or reconnaissance of this area is necessary.

Surface Burst. A surface burst is one in which the fireball touches, but is not beneath, the surface of the earth. Damage from blast is less widespread, and damage from heat is approximately the same as for an air burst of the same size. About the same initial nuclear radiation is present. Residual nuclear radiation is present. Residual nuclear radiation is created in the target area and may occur as fallout in downwind areas.

Subsurface Burst. A subsurface burst is one in which the center of the fireball is beneath the surface of the earth. Most of the blast effect appears as ground or water shock waves. The majority of the heat and initial nuclear radiation is absorbed by the surrounding earth or water. However, considerable residual radiation is produced in the target area and later as fallout.

Individual Protection

The effects of a nuclear explosion may be divided into two broad categories, immediate and delayed. The immediate effects are those that occur within a few minutes of detonation and include blast and shock, thermal radiation, and initial nuclear radiation. The delayed effects comprise the radioactivity present in fallout and neutron-induced activity. The early fallout from a surface burst will begin to reach the ground within a few minutes after the explosion at close-in locations and later at greater distances from GZ.

Protection From Blast

Since the effects of blast are immediate, consider the individual in each of two circumstances: when adequate warning is given prior to the attack and when no warning is forthcoming.

When adequate warning is given, the individual has time to prepare defenses. The fighting hole is good protection. It should be deep and strong with the cover well secured. Bunkers, fortified positions, and shelters are excellent protection from all effects of blast.

When there is no prior warning, individual reaction is mandatory. The individual should immediately drop to the ground with feet facing towards the blast. All efforts should be made to look away from the blast which can cause retinal damage. Ditches, culverts and reverse slopes of hills offer good protection. As the distance from GZ increases, Marines can find good protection from walls, slight depressions in the ground or anything that breaks the pattern of the shock wave.

Protection From Thermal Radiation

Another of the immediate effects that requires reaction on the part of the individual is the thermal radiation that is emitted from the fireball. Thermal radiation has a line of sight effect, so protection from it is the same as for blast. If prior warning of a nuclear attack is received, preparation both for blast and thermal radiation should be complete. If a weapon goes off with no warning, drop flat on the ground or to the bottom of a fighting hole. Keep your eyes closed and protect exposed skin from heat rays as much as possible (keep hands and arms near or under your body and helmet on). This immediate reaction will minimize serious burns.

Protection From Nuclear Radiation

The different effects of nuclear radiation require both immediate and delayed action. Initial nuclear radiation is spent in the first minute or two after the burst, so protection from it is the same as for thermal radiation and blast. Any material will afford some protection from initial radiation, but denser items are better. For example, earth is a better shield than water, and steel is better than concrete.

Residual Radiation. Under conditions where the explosion takes place either on or beneath the surface, the resulting residual radiation hazard is high. Particles of water spray, dust and other debris that become radioactive through contact with the nuclear reaction of the weapon will contaminate large areas. Individual protection consists of avoiding the fallout particles. This may be accomplished in the field by covering fighting holes with earth, canvas or tenting. Open food and water supplies should be disposed of by burying if contaminated. Personnel and equipment should be checked and decontaminated if necessary.

Nuclear Decontamination

At the small unit level, decontamination is usually confined to personnel, equipment, and food.

Personnel

Personal decontamination should be accomplished as soon as the tactical situation permits.

Normal Procedure. In rear areas, and when permitted in the tactical area, personnel bathe using plenty of soap and water, warm if possible. Particular attention should be given to skin creases, hairy parts of the body, and the fingernails.

Field Expedient Procedures. When the tactical situation prohibits normal procedures, field expedient procedures are used. Clothing should be removed and shaken vigorously downwind. Shrubbery can be used to brush radioactive particles from the clothing. Personnel should put on protective masks or cover their noses and mouths with a damp cloth to prevent inhalation of the radioactive dust. Care must be taken to avoid secondary contamination of food or water supplies during the shaking of clothing. Personnel then wipe all exposed skin with a damp cloth and remove as much dust as possible from the hair and from under the fingernails. Personnel should bathe and change clothing when the tactical situation permits.

Equipment

The squad may be required to decontaminate individual items of equipment. The decontamination of equipment may be accomplished by particle removal (brushing and washing), sealing and aging. In some cases, brushing will reduce dry contamination to a permissible level. In most cases, washing will be adequate even though brushing has not been effective. When speed in the decontamination of equipment is important, brushing is performed first, followed by washing as time and circumstances permit.

Food

Food and water that have become contaminated should be disposed of by burying.

Biological Defense

The individual Marine's primary concern during a biological operation will be that of protection and continuing the mission. Protection is provided by keeping shots up to date and wearing the protective mask and protective clothing when an attack is suspected. These protective items are described in more detail under the section on chemical defense.

Protective Measures To Take Before a Biological Attack

Maintain Natural Body Defenses. A healthy body can better resist disease and infection from any source. Therefore, keep yours in top physical shape. A high standard of personal cleanliness and careful attention to field sanitation is essential. Protection is provided by keeping body, clothes, and living area as clean as possible.

Care of minor wounds, cuts, and scratches by keeping them clean and using available first-aid supplies is important. Such care speeds healing and reduces the possibility of infection from any source. Soap and water are very effective in keeping cuts and scratches clean.

DON'T...

1. Consume native or civilian food or drink of any kind. Eat and drink only approved food and water.
2. Put anything in your mouth unless you are certain it is not contaminated.
3. Bathe in lakes or ponds.
4. Take souvenirs.

DO...

1. Keep immunizations current and use prescribed medications
2. Be able to recognize the biological contamination marker. Know what it means

Figure 20-4. Precautionary measures to take before a biological attack.

Biological agents can enter your body through your nose, mouth, and skin, depending on the type of agent released. The main danger in a biological agent attack is breathing the agents in an aerosol form. Your protective mask, if properly fitted and worn, will prevent agents from entering your body by inhalation.

Take All Prescribed Immunizations or Other Medication. The Marine Corps has a varied and effective immunization program. In the event of biological weapons employment, additional immunizations may be given or special medications issued.

Immunizations are valuable because they strengthen the body's defense against certain diseases. If attacked with biological agents, immunizations may prevent diseases and will certainly reduce the severity of the disease. (See Figure 20-4.)

Train in the Use of the Protective Mask. All Marines must know how to use and care for the protective mask. This mask is so important that it will be dealt with separately.

Detection of a Biological Attack. Detection of a biological warfare attack can be very difficult. Figure 20-5 lists out of the ordinary occurrences that should be reported if observed.

Decontamination and First Aid

The simplest and most effective method of decontaminating the body after a biological agent attack is the use of soap and water. There are no first-aid measures for biological agents because there are no immediate effects.

On observing any of the items in Figure 20-5, mask, pass the word, and:

- Button cuffs and collar.
- Turn collar up.
- Apply insect repellent if available.

Chemical Defense

The enemy may use toxic chemical agents at any time, so the Field Protective Mask (FPM) and protective clothing are very important pieces of equipment.

A chemical attack can be disastrous to those not prepared for it. A properly trained Marine, using the equipment issued, can survive a chemical attack.

DETECTION OF A BIOLOGICAL ATTACK

a. **Enemy aircraft dropping unidentified material or spraying unidentified substances.**

b. **New and unusual types of shells and bombs, particularly those which burst with little or no blast.**

c. **Smoke from an unknown source or of an unknown nature.**

d. **An increased occurrence of sick or dead animals.**

e. **Unusual or unexplained increase in the number of insects, such as mosquitoes, ticks or fleas.**

f. **Any weapon not seeming to have an immediate casualty effect.**

Figure 20-5. Early warning signs.

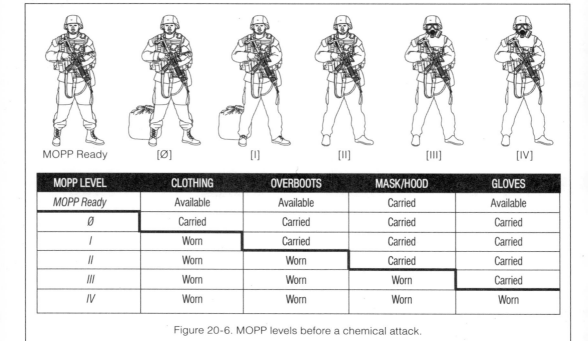

MOPP LEVEL	CLOTHING	OVERBOOTS	MASK/HOOD	GLOVES
MOPP Ready	Available	Available	Carried	Available
Ø	Carried	Carried	Carried	Carried
I	Worn	Carried	Carried	Carried
II	Worn	Worn	Carried	Carried
III	Worn	Worn	Worn	Carried
IV	Worn	Worn	Worn	Worn

Figure 20-6. MOPP levels before a chemical attack.

Protective Equipment

In addition to the protective mask, which will be discussed in more detail later, you may be issued protective clothing. This clothing consists of the chemical protective suit, glove set, and overboots, which have been developed to provide the individual Marine with protection against all forms of chemical and biological dissemination.

The suit is a two-layer, two-piece overgarment consisting of a coat and a pair of trousers. The outer layer of the coat and trousers is fabricated of nylon-cotton twill fabric that is treated with a water repellent finish. The inner layer is fabricated of charcoal-laminate impregnated polyurethane tricot laminate.

The glove set consists of an outer glove to provide chemical protection and an inner glove to assist in absorption of perspiration. The outer five-fingered glove is fabricated of impermeable black butyl rubber. The inner glove is fabricated of thin white cotton material and can be worn on either hand.

The black rubber overboots are made to slip over the combat boots.

The suit, glove set, and footwear covers, together with the protective mask, provide protection against both biological and chemical agents. However, they can reduce your efficiency and cause heat exhaustion, fatigue, or other adverse reaction. The protective equipment will only be worn when the mission and the threat so indicate.

Mission-Oriented Protective Posture

Mission-oriented protective posture levels (MOPP levels) are established to tell you what level of mission-related threat there is against you. Figure 20-6 shows what protective equipment you must use relative to the threat.

The charts on the next two pages (page 287 and 288) (Figure 20-7) depicts some of the chemical agents the enemy may use. The enemy may disseminate those agents in liquid, vapor, or aerosol form.

TYPE AGENT	HOW NORMALLY DISSEMINATED	MEANS OF DETECTION	SYMPTOMS	EFFECTS	RATE OF ACTION
A. TYPES OF ENEMY CHEMICAL AGENTS					
NERVE	Aerosol or vapor	Automatic chemical agent alarm and chemical agent detector kits to defect vapors and aerosols; chemical agent detector paper to detect liquids.	Difficult breathing, drooling, nausea, vomiting, convulsions and sometimes dim vision.	Incapacitates; kills if high concentration is inhaled.	Very rapid by inhalation; slow through skin.
	Liquid droplet			Incapacitates; kills if contaminated skin is not decontaminated in time.	Delayed through skin; more rapid.
BLISTER	Liquid droplet		Mustard; nitrogen mustard – no early symptoms. Lewisite; mustard-lewisite – searing of eyes and stinging of skin. Phosgene oxime - irritation of eyes and nose.	Blisters skin, is destructive to upper respiratory tract; can cause temporary blindness. Some agents sting and form welts on skin and others sear eyes.	Blistering delayed hours to days; eye effects more rapid. Mustard-lewisite and phosgene oxime very rapid.
BLOOD	Vapor		Convulsions and coma.	Incapacitates; kills if high concentration is inhaled.	Rapid
CHOKING	Vapor		Coughing, choking, nausea, and headache.	Damages and floods lungs.	Immediate to 3 hours.
INCAPACITATES	Aerosol	May look like smoke at point of release.	Unpredictable, irrational behavior.	Temporarily incapacitates mentally and physically.	Delayed
B. TYPES OF ENEMY IRRITANT AGENTS					
VOMITING	Aerosol	May look like smoke at point of release.	Coughing, nausea vomiting, and headache.	Irritates and physically incapacitates.	Rapid
IRRITANT	Aerosol	May look like smoke at point of release, turning colorless. Instant eye irritation.	Coughing and copious tears.	Irritates respiratory tract, eyes, and skin.	Instantaneous

Figure 20-7. Characteristics of and defense against types of chemical and irritant agents.

TYPE OF AGENT	INDIVIDUAL		PROTECTION REQUIRED	EQUIVALENT US AGENT	
	First Aid	Decontamination		Symbol/Name	Characteristics in the field
A. TYPES OF ENEMY CHEMICAL AGENTS					
NERVE	ATNAA Injection. Artificial respiration or resuscitation may be necessary.	None needed	Protective mask and protective clothing.	GA – Tabun GB – Sarin GD – Soman	Colorless
		Flush eyes with water, use skin pad from a RSDL, or M291 or wash skin with soap and water.		VX	
				Thickened G-agent	
BLISTER	None	Flush eyes with water, use skin pad from a RSDL, or M291 or wash skin with soap and water.	Protective mask and protective clothing.	HD – Mustard	- Pale yellow droplets
				HN – Nitrogen mustard	- Dark droplets
				L – Lewisite	- Dark, oily droplets
				HL – Mustard lewisite	- Dark, oily droplets
				CS – Phosgene chloride	- Colorless droplets
BLOOD		None needed	Protective mask		Colorless
CHOKING	For severe symptoms, avoid movement and keep warm.	None needed	Protective mask	CG – Phosgene	Colorless
INCAPACITATING	Remove excessive clothing in temperatures above 78°F.	Wash with soap and water.	Protective mask	BZ	White to grayish smoke
B. TYPES OF ENEMY IRRITANT AGENTS					
VOMITING	Move vigorously to lessen duration of effects.	Wash with soap and water.	Protective mask	DM – Adamsite	White to grayish yellow smoke
IRRITANT	Face the wind with eyes open; do not rub eyes.	Flush eyes, face and skin with water.	Protective mask	CS and CN – Riot control agents.	White cloud

Figure 20-7. Continued.

Each Marine, in addition to being equipped with a properly fitting protective mask and protective clothing, must also be equipped with a basic knowledge of toxic chemical agents, their uses, and effects.

Types of Chemical Agents

Chemical agents are divided into the following general classifications:

Toxic Chemical Agents. Chemical agents designed to kill or incapacitate are known as toxic agents. They may enter the body through the lungs or by contact with the eyes and skin. The current groups of toxic agents are:

• **Nerve Agents.** These agents are quick acting. Entering the body through breathing or by skin contact, they are very rapid in action and produce immediate casualties.

- **Blister Agents.** These are delayed action chemicals that produce blisters on exposed skin, in the eyes, or in the respiratory system. Symptoms may appear within 4 hours or as long as 36 hours after exposure.
- **Blood Agents.** These are rapid acting agents that deprive the body of oxygen. They must be inhaled to be effective, so the FPM affords complete protection.
- **Choking Agents.** These are delayed action casualty producers that are very damaging to the lungs. Low concentrations may be difficult to detect. The protective mask provides adequate defense.
- **Incapacitating Agents.** These chemicals will cause temporary casualties that may be extremely difficult to control. Symptoms of mental confusion may take several hours to appear and may last for several days. Restraint and immediate medical assistance is necessary.
- **Irritant Chemical Agents.** The irritant agents produce temporary irritating or disabling effects if they are inhaled or contact the eyes and skin. The standard agents of this group range from CS (tear agents) through chlorine.

Detection of Chemical Agents

The success of chemical defense depends to a great degree on the thoroughness of the training program conducted by the small unit leader. This training must consider the various characteristics of the agents as stated above and the three phases of defensive operations: detection, protection, and decontamination.

Intelligence Sources. Intelligence sources may warn of expected attacks. These reports are usually based on enemy preparations and capabilities.

Individual Marines. Marines may be able to identify a chemical attack by the use of their physical senses. Agents may have characteristic odors, create a visible cloud, appear as droplets on vegetation, or be detectable only by early recognition of symptoms.

Because of this variety and the risk of rapid casualty effects, an automatic masking procedure will be put into effect once chemical operations are initiated.

Any suspicious occurrence (low-flying aircraft, smoke screen, unaccountable liquid and unusual physical or mental symptoms) will be considered a potential threat, and all Marines will mask. The situation can then be checked in comparative safety and the decision made to unmask or continue a protected posture as required.

Special Equipment. There are several items of special equipment designed for the identification and detection of chemical agents. The squad should be basically familiar with this equipment and its uses.

- **ABC-M8 Paper, Chemical Agent Detector, VGH.** ABC-M8 chemical agent detector paper is a component of the chemical agent detector kits. The sheets consist of paper impregnated with chemical compounds that vary color when in contact with V- or G-type nerve agents or blister (mustard) agents in liquid form. This paper does not detect vapor and must touch the liquid agent to ensure a positive test.

  Because some solvents cause a change in the color of paper, it is unreliable for determining the completeness of decontamination by the use of solvents. A color chart is included in the kit to aid in interpreting the tests.
- **M9 Paper, Chemical Agent Detector.** M9 paper is issued in a roll with a sticky side and is designed to be worn on the wrist (on which watch is worn), arm (opposite wristwatch arm), and ankle (just above the boot). If it detects chemicals, pink or red spots will appear on the paper. It does not determine the type of chemical. Some ordinary solvents also will cause the pink or red spots to form.
- **M256A1 Kit.** This item is designed for company and larger sized units and provides the means of detecting and identifying vapor concentrations of most chemical agents. Color changes occur in select detector spots and tickets. This device is designed for rapid identification of agents,

but cannot be used as a warning device because test reactions may take 15 minutes to complete.

Protection

Protective Mask. When properly fitted, the protective mask protects against inhalation and facial contamination by toxic agents. This is the primary means of protection in chemical defense.

Protective Clothing. Protective clothing is available for those persons required to enter or remain in a contaminated area for a length of time.

Antidote and Personnel Decontamination Kits. Antidotes for blister and nerve agents are found in the protective mask carrier when issued.

• The antidote treatment, nerve agent autoinjectors (ATNAA) is used as a treatment for any exposure to a nerve agent. It may be given by medical personnel or self-administered by the individual. The effects are immediate.

First Aid and Individual Decontamination

First aid includes the immediate action required to prevent further injury or complications from the effects of chemical agents. This necessarily includes the prompt removal of agents from the eye and decontamination of skin to avoid casualties from lethal liquid agents. Therefore, first aid must include individual decontamination automatically and without orders when it is required, and the use of appropriate medications or actions to reduce the effects of the agent, such as the use of the nerve agent antidote injector for nerve agent poisoning. Each Marine must be thoroughly trained in both first aid and decontamination so that these actions can be performed quickly.

Unidentified Chemical Agents. In most cases the individuals will not be able to immediately identify the chemical agent used in the attack. When exposed to an enemy chemical attack while dressed in chemical protective clothing and equipment, they will not normally be concerned with immediate decontamination. However, if an unidentified agent has contaminated an individual, perhaps while unmasked, the following actions are taken:

Decontamination of Eyes and Face. Use the buddy system to decontaminate each other, if alone, proceed as follows. If the eyes and face have been contaminated, the individual must immediately try to get under cover. Shelter is necessary to prevent further contamination during the decontamination process. If no overhead cover is available, throw a poncho or canvas over the head before beginning decontamination. Then decontaminate the eyes by turning the side of the face upward and, using water from a canteen, repeatedly flush the eyes. The facial skin decontamination should be done by using the reactive skin decontamination lotion (RSDL).

Caution: Do NOT let the solution from the RSDL get in the eyes!

Nerve Agents. It is imperative that nerve agents in contact with the skin or eyes be neutralized or removed immediately if the individual is to avoid becoming a casualty. These agents are lethal and rapidly absorbed by the eyes and through cuts in the skin. They are absorbed through unbroken skin somewhat more slowly. The most unique symptoms of nerve agent poisoning is pinpointing of the pupils of eyes.

First Aid. The injection of nerve agent antidote and the giving of artificial respiration are first-aid measures necessary for individuals showing symptoms of nerve agent poisoning.

Decontamination. RSDL decontamination kits are used to remove contamination from the skin. Plain water only is used to repeatedly flush the eyes. The skin in contact with contaminated clothing should be decontaminated as soon as the clothing can be removed.

Blister Agents. Casualties of blister agents, such as HD (distilled mustard), will exhibit redness and inflammation of the eyes. Usually several hours after exposure, reddening of the skin will appear, followed by the appearance of blisters. There is no first aid for blister agents other than decontamination. Blister agent effects will be delayed for several hours to days. To decontaminate the eyes, flush with plain water repeatedly. Any blister agents on the skin and clothing should be removed using the RSDL decontamination kits and then seek medical care as soon as possible. If evacuation to a medical facility is required, blister agent casualties will receive the same treatment given other burn victims.

Blood Agents. Agents, such as AC and CK, enter the body by inhalation and produce symptoms ranging from convulsions to coma. They act on the body by interfering with the ability of oxygen carrying cells to transfer oxygen to other body tissue. They may have an irritating effect on nasal passages. First aid remains immediate masking. This may prevent further damage. No specific treatment other than basic first aid is available.

Choking Agents. This agent will produce coughing, choking, nausea, and headaches in casualties. Delayed effects include rapid and shallow breathing, painful cough, discomfort, fatigue, and shock. First aid is immediate masking. This may prevent further damage. No specific first aid other than efforts to prevent shock is available.

Decontamination

Decontamination can be accomplished by the removal, neutralization, absorption, or weathering of the chemical agent. Decontamination's primary purposes are to prevent casualties and to remove obstacles that may prevent mission accomplishment.

Levels of Decontamination. Individual decontamination is performed by the individual, with material on hand, on the body, clothing and the equipment they use. It is performed as soon as practical and is usually sufficient to allow the individual to carry on the assigned mission. Individuals are issued the RSDL decontamination kits. Each tactical vehicle is authorized one M100 portable decontamination apparatus that uses reactive sorbent powder to remove and neutralize chemical agents from surfaces. It is used to decontaminate parts of the vehicle that must be touched during vehicle operation, such as the controls.

Unit decontamination is an organized effort performed by personnel of the unit, with equipment available to the unit, when directed by the commander and under supervision of trained CBRN specialists. All officers, NCOs, and qualified CBRN specialists should be prepared to act as supervisors of decontamination teams when required.

Decontamination that is beyond the capabilities of the unit is performed by specialized teams equipped with the M26 Joint Service Transportable Decontamination System-Small Scale (JSTDS-SS). Communication equipment should be decontaminated by using hot air, if available. The next best method is by airing or weathering. The metal parts of field telephones and radios may be decontaminated by the heat given off during operation.

Use and Care of the Protective Mask

The Marine Corps-issued FPM is the best that modern science can produce.

In the event of a chemical or biological attack, commands are not used. The mask is put on and checked as rapidly as possible because each second can mean the difference between survival and serious injury or death. Individual proficiency standards call for the Marine to properly put on, seal, clear, and check the mask within nine seconds.

Because of the dangers of chemical and biological operations, care of the protective mask is essential. Water damages the filter elements of the mask and destroys efficiency. The waterproof bag issued with the protective mask must be used to protect filter elements against submergence in water. Never sit or lie on the mask. Treat the mask with the same respect shown a weapon, and it will perform properly when needed.

The FPM may be carried in one of the following positions: shoulder carry, leg carry, or cartridge belt carry.

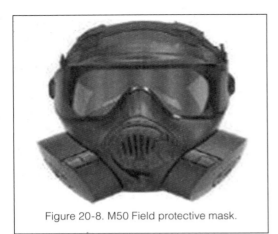

Figure 20-8. M50 Field protective mask.

Field Protective Mask Characteristics. The joint service general purpose mask (JSGPM) or M50 series FPM has replaced the M40 series FPM, mask carrier, and accessories for the Marine Corps ground and combat vehicle operations. The M50 series FPM incorporates state-of-the-art technology to protect U.S. forces from all known threats. The mask components are integrated to reduce the impact on the wearer's performance and to minimize equipment compatibility issues. (See Figure 20-8.)

Sighting Rifle
While Wearing the
Protective Mask

Special procedures are recommended for sighting a rifle while wearing the protective mask. Speed and accuracy in obtaining a proper sight picture may be achieved by repeated sighting of the rifle using the following procedures:

• Aim the rifle in the same manner as when unmasked except that the mask should slide up the stock of the rifle to the sighting position.

• If a sight picture is not readily obtained, move the rifle butt around (higher or lower, inward or outward) in the shoulder and resight the rifle. Adjust the position. (In

some instances, a slight canting inward of the weapon will be required.)

Drinking Water While
Wearing the Mask
in a CBRN Area

When the mask is connected to a water canteen with a water canteen cap, a drinking system is formed. The wearer of the mask can then drink safely through the drinking tube inside the mask. When the drinking system is disconnected, self-closing valves seal off both the mask and the water canteen.

Warning: Do not connect the drink tube to your canteen until all mating surfaces are checked and are free of contamination. Chemical agents could be swallowed, resulting in sickness and death.

To use the drink tube, your canteen must be equipped with a water canteen cap.

  a. Fill your plastic water canteen before entering contaminated area, or if in a contaminated area, work inside a protective shelter.

  b. Use M8 chemical agent detector paper to check for contamination before using the drink tube.

Warning: Care should be taken not to break the facepiece seal while pressing in on the outlet valve body. Water may leak into the facepiece if the mouth is taken off the internal drink tube.

  c. Press in on top of outlet valve until internal drink tube can be grasped between your teeth.

  d. Steady facepiece and pull quick disconnect coupling out of outlet valve cover.

  e. Remove canteen from canteen carrier.

  f. Flip open cover on water canteen cap.

  g. Push quick disconnect coupling into water canteen cap so that pin enters coupling.

Warning: If resistance is not felt, your drinking system is leaking. Do not drink. Notify CBRN specialist to replace mask as soon as possible.

    h. Blow to create positive pressure. You should feel some resistance. Do not tilt head back while drinking.

    i. If system does not leak, raise and invert canteen and drink water from canteen.

    j. After several swallows, stop sucking and lower canteen. Blow into internal drink tube to prevent canteen from collapsing. Repeat drinking procedure as required.

    k. Disconnect drinking system.

Protection against the effects of chemical and biological agents and nuclear radiation may depend on avoiding contaminated areas. Figure 20-9 describes the design, lettering and color of the CBRN marking signs used to identify contaminated areas. Remember, however, that contaminated areas may not be marked, requiring constant alertness to any signs of possible contamination.

The markers will be placed above the ground suspended from wires, trees, or rocks with the right-angled point downward and the front facing away from the contaminated area. When you can see the word GAS, BIO, or ATOM, you are outside the contaminated area. Where more than one kind of contamination is in an area, the appropriate markers will be used near each other.

Decontamination Material and Procedure

In emergencies, Marines may be called upon to accomplish personal decontamination measures. Some will be called upon to act as members of decontamination teams, in which case specially trained personnel will act as supervisors. Decontamination of large areas will be accomplished by specially trained units.

Reactive Skin Decontamination Lotion

Each RSDL operational pouch consists of a green colored pouch containing three green colored individual decontamination packets. Each packet contains a lotion-impregnated applicator pad. The lotion is the decontaminant and the applicator pad is used to apply the lotion. Allow RSDL to remain on skin for at least 2 minutes. (Consult the outside package of the RSDL kit.)

Self-Aid for Nerve Agents

Mask at once if you notice any of the following symptoms:
• A faint, sweetish, fruity odor.
• The pupils of someone else's eyes shrinking to pinpoint size.
• Your sight blurring or diminishing.
• Running nose.
• Salivation.
• Tightness in your chest and difficulty in breathing.

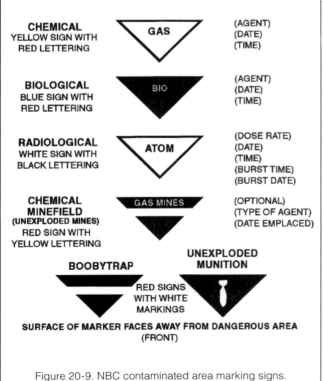

Figure 20-9. NBC contaminated area marking signs.

If you are told that your pupils are getting very small, or if you are having trouble breathing and your chest feels tight, use the ATNAA.

(*Caution:* For use ONLY in NERVE agent poisoning.)

The injector contains medication to treat the initial symptoms of nerve agent poisoning. But most importantly it will check the more serious effects of nerve agent sickness. The injector is an antidote, not a preventive device–so only use the injector if you actually experience symptoms of nerve agent poisoning.

The directions for use are:

- Pull off the injector's ridged safety cap.
- Place the opposite end of the injector against your thigh.
- Press down hard. Continue to press for at least four seconds to make sure you give yourself the whole injection.
- After you remove the injector, rub the area for a couple of minutes. This will help the antidote to be better absorbed. In about five minutes you should feel better. If you don't improve or you feel worse, use a second antidote injector. In time of war, you will be issued three ATNAA.

Complete directions for its use will be included with the injector.

Tips on the use of the ATNAA:

- Inject the needle into a large muscle in the meaty portion of your thigh.
- The needle may be injected through clothing.

Precautions in Applying Self-Aid for Nerve Agents

Do not take an injection of ATNAA until you are sure you need it. Pinpointing of the eye pupils or blurred vision along with a tightness in the chest and a hard time breathing are signs that you need it. If you get excited and inject yourself when you have not been exposed to a nerve agent, you will become ill, particularly in hot weather. This would be a real danger in combat. However, if you really do inhale some nerve agent, the injector counteracts it and will make you feel better.

If you have inhaled a really large dose of nerve gas vapor, you may need more than one injection to relieve your symptoms. If nerve agent symptoms persist, you may give yourself two more injections for a total of three. More than three injections may be given under supervision of medical personnel, if available, or under direction of your NCO or officer in charge.

If you get good relief from the injector and can breathe freely again, carry on with your duties. *Dryness of the mouth is a good sign.* It means that you have had enough ATNAA to overcome the dangerous effects of the nerve agent.

If you should get a drop or splash of liquid nerve agent in your eye, instant action is necessary to avoid serious injury. Get some water as fast as possible, tilt your head back so that your eyes look straight upward, and slowly pour water into the contaminated eye to flush it out. Hold the eye open with the fingers if necessary. Pour the water slowly so that the irrigation will last not less than 30 seconds. Do not breathe as you are irrigating/decontaminating your eyes. Get your mask on quickly after completing the irrigation. Then if symptoms of nerve agent develop, give yourself an injection.

If liquid nerve gas gets on your skin or clothing, get rid of it. Immediately use the RSDL decontamination kit. Then carry on with your combat duties. Meanwhile, notice if there is any twitching of the muscles under the contaminated area. If none develops in the next half hour and you have no tightness in your chest, your decontamination was successful.

If twitching of the muscles under the area of contaminated skin does develop, do not wait for the appearance of other symptoms, but give yourself an injection of the ATNAA at once. If no other symptoms develop, one injection is enough.

Alarms

Two types of CBRN alarm systems may be used to alert Marines in the event of CBRN attack.

General Alarm. Will be spread by normal communication means, such as computer, telephone, and radio.

Local Alarm. Will be initiated within the unit in accordance with the local CBRN SOP and may be spread by striking metal on metal, a triangle, a bell, or a hand siren or using the vocal alarm of shouting "GAS," "GAS," "GAS" once masked or using the hand and arm signal (once masked) with extending both arms to the side horizontally with doubled fists facing up, and moving the fists rapidly up to the head and back down to the horizontal position. As a supplement to this alarm, certain visual signals, such as putting on the mask, are used to give emergency warning of an attack. In the event of a chemical or biological attack, all Marines should mask immediately to protect themselves from becoming casualties.

CHAPTER 21

Drill

The object of close order drill is to teach Marines by exercise to obey orders and to do so immediately in the correct way. Close order drill is one foundation of discipline and esprit de corps. Additionally, it is still one of the finest methods for developing confidence and troop leading abilities in our subordinate leaders.

Purposes of Drill

The purposes of drill are to:

- Move a unit from one place to another in a standard, orderly manner.
- Provide simple formations from which combat formations may be readily assumed.
- Teach discipline by instilling habits of precision and automatic response to orders.
- Increase the confidence of junior officers and noncommissioned officers through the exercise of command, by the giving of proper commands, and by the control of drilling troops.
- Give troops an opportunity to handle individual weapons.

Purposes of Formations

The purposes of formations are to:

- To build unit cohesion and esprit de corps by recognizing Marines during awards and promotion ceremonies.
- To maintain continuous accountability and control of personnel.
- To provide frequent opportunities to observe the appearance and readiness of the uniforms, arms, and equipment of the individual Marine.
- To keep the individual Marine informed by providing the means to pass the word.
- To develop command presence in unit leaders.
- To instill and maintain high standards of military bearing and appearance in units and in the individual Marine.

General Rules for Drill

- Certain drill movements may be made toward either flank. This *Guidebook* explains such movements in one direction only. To move to the other direction, it is necessary to substitute the word "left" for "right" as shown in parentheses.
- The command, "AS YOU WERE," cancels a movement or order started but not completed. At this command, troops should resume their former positions.
- While marching, the guide and alignment is maintained to the right except:
- Upon command "GUIDE LEFT" or

"GUIDE CENTER," guide is maintained toward the left or center, as the case may be, until "GUIDE RIGHT" is given.

• Regardless of the direction in which alignment is established, at the command of execution for a drill movement involving marching, the direction toward which alignment is obtained is the flank toward which the movement is made. Upon completion of the drill movement, alignment will be in the direction established before commencing the movement.

• Slight changes in direction are made by adding, "Half" to the preparatory command for turning or column movements; for example, "Column Half Right (Left)" changes direction 45 degrees. When given the command "INCLINE TO THE RIGHT (LEFT)," the guide changes direction of march slightly to the right (left).

• Platoons in a company and Marines in a squad are numbered from right to left (the company's or squad's own right) in line by squad and from front to rear by squad in column. Squads in a platoon are numbered from front to rear in line and from left to right in column.

• Whenever drill movements are executed while troops are marching, the command of execution "(MARCH)," is given as the left foot strikes the ground if the movement is to the left, and as the right foot strikes the ground if the movement is to the right. The only exception to this rule is when moving from "Port Arms" to "Left Shoulder Arms" while marching, the command of execution is given as the right foot strikes the ground in order to take advantage of the natural swing of the arms.

• Drill movements may be divided into individual motions for instruction. When drills are executed by the numbers, the first motion is made on the command of execution. Subsequent motions are made in proper order on the commands ("TWO"), ("THREE"), ("FOUR"), the number of counts depending upon the number of motions in the movement. To use this method, the command "By the Numbers" precedes the preparatory command. All movements then are executed by the numbers until the command "Without Numbers" is given.

Close Order Drill Definitions

The terms defined herein are used in drill for foot troops.

• **ALIGNMENT**—The dressing of several elements on a straight line.

• **ASSSEMBLY AREA**—A designated location for forming units of platoon size or larger in preparation for a parade, review, or ceremony.

• **ARMS**—A term used to normally designate the service rifle but can refer to any weapon. When in formation and a mix of weapons is carried the term arms will be used to designate all types of weapons.

• **BASE**—The element on which a movement is regulated.

• **CADENCE**—A rhythmic rate of march at a uniform step.

• **CENTER**—The middle element of a formation with an odd number of elements or the left center element of a formation with an even number of elements.

• **CEREMONY**—A formal military formation designated to observe a specific occasion.

• **COLUMN**—A formation in which the elements are placed one behind the other. A section or platoon is in column when members of each squad are one behind the other with the squads abreast of each other.

• **COMMANDER OF TROOPS (COT)**—The COT is the senior officer taking part in the ceremony. If an enlisted ceremony the COT is the senior enlisted.

• **DEPTH**—The space from head to rear of an element or a formation. The depth of an individual is considered to be 12".

• **DISTANCE**—The space between elements in the direction of depth. Between individuals, the space between your chest and the person to your front. Between vehicles, the space between the front end of a vehicle and the rear of the vehicle to its front. Between troops in formation (either on foot, mounted, or in vehicles), the space from the front of the rear unit to the rear of the unit in front. Platoon commanders, guides, and others whose positions in a formation are 40" from a rank are, themselves, considered a rank. Otherwise, commanders and those with them are not considered in measuring distance between units. The color guard is not considered in measuring distance between subdivisions of the unit with which it is posted. In troop formations, the distance between ranks is 40".

• **DOUBLE TIME**—Cadence at 180 steps per minute.

• **ELEMENT**—An individual, squad, section, platoon, company, or other unit that is part of a larger unit.

• **EXTENDED MASS FORMATION**—The formation of a company or larger unit in which major elements are in column at close or normal interval and abreast at a specified interval greater than normal interval.

• **FILE**—A column of individuals or vehicles one behind the other. (See Figure 21-1.)

• **FLANK**—The right or left extremity of a unit, either in line or in column. The element on the extreme right or left of the line. A direction at a right angle to the direction an element or a formation is facing.

• **FORMATION**—Arrangement of elements of a unit in line, in column, or in any other prescribed manner.

• **FRONT**—The space occupied by an element or a formation, measured from one flank to the other. The front of an individual is considered to be 22".

• **GUIDE**—The individual (base) upon whom a formation or elements thereof regulates its march. To guide: to regulate interval, direction, or alignment; to regulate cadence on a base file (right, left, or center).

• **HEAD**—The leading element of a column.

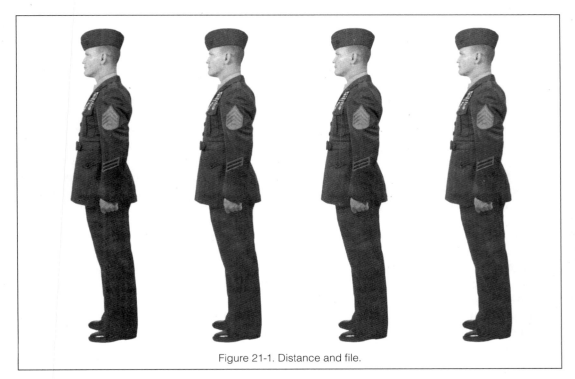

Figure 21-1. Distance and file.

Figure 21-2. Interval and rank.

- **INTERVAL**—The lateral space between elements on the same line. Interval is measured between individuals from shoulder to shoulder. It is measured between elements other than individuals and between formations from flank to flank. Normal interval between individuals is one arm's length. Close interval is the horizontal distance between shoulder and elbow when the left hand is placed on the left hip and is considered to be 4". (See Figure 21-2.)
- **LINE**—A formation in which the elements are abreast except that a section or platoon is on line when its squads are in line and one behind the other.
- **LINE OF MARCH**—The line on which individuals or units are to march on.
- **LINE OF TROOPS**—The line on which individuals or units are to march on.
- **MASS FORMATION**—The formation of a company or larger unit in which the major elements are in column at close interval and abreast at close interval.

- **MUFFLING**—The procedure of draping colors for mourning with a mourning streamer or black bunting. It also refers to the process of muffling the musical instruments of a band for specific types of ceremonies.
- **PACE**—The length of a full step in quick time, 30".
- **PARADE**—A parade is a ceremony that involves the movement of marching units.
- **PARADE SLING**—A sling that has all excess slack removed and is taught. The keeper is adjusted and locked in a position next to the sling tip. The sling lies on the left side of the rifle.
- **PIECE**—An individual firearm such as a rifle.
- **POINT OF REST**—The point toward which all elements of a unit establish their dress or alignment.
- **QUICK TIME**—Cadence of 120 steps per minute.
- **RANK**—A line of Marines or vehicles side by side. (See Figure 21-2.)

- **REVIEW**—A review is a type of ceremony that omits certain elements found in a parade, but includes an inspection (trooping the line) not found in a parade.
- **RIGGED**—This term refers to the condition when uniforms and equipment are properly fitted out in the manner for which they were intended for use. Swords are considered rigged when attached to the frog (noncommissioned officers) or sword sling (commissioned officer). A Marine is rigged when wearing the prescribed uniform or equipment.
- **SLOW TIME**—Cadence at 60 steps per minute; used for funerals only.
- **SNAP**—In commands or signals, the quality that inspires immediate response. In drill, the immediate and smart execution of movement.
- **STEP**—The distance from heel to heel between the feet of a marching individual. The half step and back step are 15". The right and left steps are 12". The steps in quick and double time are 30 and 36", respectively
- **STRONG GRIP**—The strong grip is when the thumb is wrapped around the front of the staff with the fingers wrapped to the rear.
- **UNIT LEADER**—Is the individual who is drilling the unit. This can be any individual who is conducting drill or can be those assigned a specific billet such as squad leader, platoon sergeant, platoon commander, etc.
- **"V" GRIP**—The "V" grip is with the staff placed in the "V" formed by the thumbs and forefinger with the fingers extended and joined

be delivered in a loud, clear voice. All officers and Marines in the unit must be ready to take heed of the first word of a command.

There are four types of commands: preparatory commands, commands of execution, combined commands, and supplementary commands.

- **Preparatory command**—Indicates a movement is to be made and may also indicate the direction of the movement. In this *Guidebook*, preparatory commands are shown beginning with a capital letter followed by lower case letters. The comma indicates a pause between the preparatory command and the command of execution. Examples would be "Forward," "Left," "Platoon," "About," etc.
- **Command of execution**—Causes the desired movement to be executed, such as "MARCH," "HALT," "FACE," etc. Commands of execution are given in a sharp, clear manner with force and enthusiasm.
- **Combined commands**—The preparatory command and the command of execution are combined. In this *Guidebook*, commands are shown in CAPITAL LETTERS. Examples would be "AT EASE," "REST," "FALL IN," etc.
- **Supplementary commands**—These commands that cause the component units to act individually. An example would be the commands squad leaders would give to their individual squads following the platoon commander's preparatory command, "Column of Files From the Right," and before the command of execution "MARCH." In this *Guidebook* supplementary commands may be shown as preparatory commands, commands of execution or combined commands, depending on the movement.

Commands

A drill command is the direction of the commander given orally and in standard wording. In drill for foot troops, the commander is at attention when giving commands. Commands must

Positions

The correct positions to be taken upon receiving various commands are given in detail here.

Attention

- The left heel is brought to the right heel, so the heels are on line and touching. (See Figure 21-3(a).)
- The feet are turned out equally, forming an angle of 45 degrees. Keep the heels on the same line and touching.
- The legs should be straight but not stiff at the knees.
- Keep the hips and shoulders level and your chest lifted.
- The arms should be straight but not stiff at the elbows; thumbs along the trouser seams, palms facing inward toward your legs, and fingers joined in their natural curl
- Keep the head and body erect. Look straight ahead. Keep your mouth closed and your chin pulled in slightly.
- Stand still and do not talk.

Rests

All rests are executed from the halt. The commands are: "FALL OUT," "REST," "AT EASE," and "Parade REST." All are executed from the position of attention.

- At the command "FALL OUT," Marines leave the ranks but are required to remain in the immediate vicinity. They resume their former places at attention when given the command "FALL IN."
- At the command "REST," the right foot is kept in place. Talking is permitted.
- At the command "AT EASE," the right foot is kept in place. Silence is required. Movement to the extent possible with the right foot kept in place is allowed.
- At the command of execution "REST" of "Parade, REST," the left foot is moved smartly 12" to the left of the right foot, and the legs are kept straight so that the weight of the body rests equally on both feet. At

Figure 21-3(a). Attention, as "RIGHT FACE" is given.

Figure 21-3(b). At command "FACE," face to the right.

Figure 21-3(c). Bring left foot up beside the right foot.

the same time, the hands are clasped behind the back, palms to the rear, thumb and fingers of the right hand holding the left thumb without constraint. Fingers are extended and joined. Head and eyes are kept to the front as in the position of attention. Silence is required, and no further movement is permitted. The command is executed from the position of attention only.

The only command that may be given from "AT EASE," "REST," or "Parade REST" is "ATTENTION." If "AT EASE" or "REST," on the preparatory command of Squad/Platoon, assume the position of "Parade REST." On the command of execution, "ATTENTION," assume the position of attention.

Eyes Right or Left

The commands are: "Eyes, RIGHT (LEFT)," "Ready, FRONT." At the command "RIGHT (LEFT)," the head and eyes are turned smartly to the right (left). On the command "FRONT," turn your head and eyes back smartly to the front. During reviews at which the reviewing officer troops the line, "Ready, FRONT" will not be given after eyes right. At such ceremonies, turn your head and eyes smartly toward the reviewing officer upon the command "RIGHT." As the reviewing officer passes to the left, follow the officer with your head and eyes until you are looking directly to the front.

When marching in review the Marines in the right (left) file do not turn their head and eyes on the command of "Eyes RIGHT (LEFT)."

Facing

All facings are executed from the halt and in the cadence of quick time.

To the Flank. The command is: "Right (Left), FACE." At the command "FACE," the left heel and the right toe are slightly raised; face to the right is made turning on the right heel, assisted by a slight pressure on the ball of the left foot. The left leg is held straight without stiffness. The left foot is then placed smartly beside the right. (See Figures 21-3(a-c) on previous page.) "Left, FACE" is executed by turning on the left heel and the ball of the right foot in a corresponding manner.

To the Rear. The command is: "About, FACE." At the command "FACE," the toe of the right foot is carried to a position touching the ground a half-foot length to the rear and slightly to the left of the left heel without changing the position of the left foot; the weight of the body is mainly on the heel of the left foot; the right leg is straight without stiffness. Then face to the rear is executed by turning to the right on the left heel and on the ball of the right foot. (See Figures 21-4 (a-d) on next page.)

Hand Salute. The command is: "Hand, SALUTE." At the command "SALUTE," the right hand is raised smartly until the tip of the forefinger touches the lower part of the headdress or forehead above and slightly to the right of the right eye, thumb and fingers extended and joined, palm down, upper arm horizontal, forearm inclined at 45-degrees, hand and wrist straight. The hand is then returned smartly in one motion to its normal position by the side, at the same time the head and eyes are turned to the front unless facing that direction.

Saluting distance is the distance at which recognition is easy. Usually, it does not exceed 30 paces. The salute is rendered when the person to be saluted is six paces distant, or at the nearest point of approach if it is apparent that the individual is not going to approach within six paces. The first position of the salute is held until the person saluted has passed or the salute is returned. The second movement of the salute is then executed.

Steps and Marching

As a general rule, all steps and marching beginning from a halt start with the left foot. The instructor indicates the proper rhythm by counting cadence and will do so only when necessary. To change direction on the march, the command of execution is given as the foot on the side of the desired direction of the movement strikes the deck

Quick Time

If at a halt, the command to march forward at

Figure 21-4(a). From left to right, movements of "ABOUT FACE" are shown. First stand at attention as command is given.

Figure 21-4(b). Second, at command "FACE," carry the toe of the right foot to a position touching the ground a half foot length to the rear and slightly to the left of the left heel.

Figure 21-4(c). Third, face to the rear, turning to the right on the left heel and on the ball of the right foot.

Figure 21-4(d). Fourth, place the right heel beside the left.

quick time is: "Forward, MARCH.

• At the command "Forward," the weight of the body is shifted to the right leg without noticeable movement.

• At the command "MARCH," the individual steps off smartly, left foot first, and marches straight ahead marching at 112-120 steps per minute taking 30" steps. Arms are swung easily in natural arcs, 6" straight to the front and 3" to the rear. Movements are not exaggerated or made in a stiff way.

Double Time

The command is: "Double Time, MARCH." It can be executed as either foot strikes the deck.

• If at a halt, at the command "Double Time," the weight of the body is shifted to the right leg without noticeable movement. At the command "MARCH," the forearms are raised, fingers closed, knuckles out, to a horizontal position along the waistline and an easy run is started with the step and cadence of double time. The arms are moved in a natural swinging motion across the front of the body. The cadence and step at double time are 180 36" steps per minute.

• If marching in quick time, at the command "MARCH," one more step in quick time is taken before stepping off in double time.

• To resume quick time from double time,

the command is: "Quick Time, MARCH." At the command "MARCH," given as either foot strikes the ground, the other foot is advanced and lowered in double time; quick time is resumed; the hands are dropped by the sides.

Mark Time

The command is: "Mark Time, MARCH."

• Being in march, at the command "MARCH," given as either foot strikes the ground, the other foot is advanced and lowered; the foot in the rear is brought up so that both heels are on line, and the cadence is continued by alternately raising and planting each foot. When feet are raised, the balls of the feet are 2" from the ground.

• Being at a halt, at the command "MARCH," the left foot is raised and lowered, then the right as described above.

• Mark time may be executed in either quick time or double time.

• The halt is executed from mark time as from quick time or double time by taking 2" vertical steps in place of 30" horizontal steps. Forward march, halt and mark time may be executed one from the other in quick or double time.

Half Step

The command is: "Half Step, MARCH."

• At the command "MARCH," steps of 15" are taken in quick time. The half step is executed in quick time only. The half step may be executed from the halt or marching.

• To resume the full step from half step or mark time, the command is: "Forward, MARCH."

Side Step

The command is: "Right (Left) Step, MARCH." At the command "MARCH," the right foot is moved 12" to the right; then the left foot is placed beside the right, the left knee straight. The cadence is continued in quick time. The side step is executed in quick time from a halt for short distances only. The arms do not swing during the side step.

Back Step

The command is: "Backward, MARCH." At the command "MARCH," steps of 15" are taken straight to the rear. The back step is executed in quick time from a halt for short distances only. The arms swing naturally during the back step.

To Face in Marching

This is an important part of the movements in Column Right (Left), Close, Take Interval and Extend. For instructional purposes, at the halt, the command is: "By the Right (Left) Flank, MARCH." At the command "MARCH," a 90-degree pivot to the right (left) is made on the ball of the right foot and a 30" step is taken in the new direction with the left foot.

To March by the Flank

Being in march, the command is: "By the Right (Left) Flank, MARCH." At the command "MARCH," given as the right (left) foot strikes the ground, the left (right) foot is advanced and planted, a pivot to the right (left) is made, and a 30" step is taken with the right (left) foot in the new direction. This command is not given from the halt.

To March to the Rear

Being at march, the command is: "To the Rear, MARCH." It is given when the right foot strikes the deck. At the command "MARCH," the left foot is advanced a normal 30" step, a pivot to the right is made on the balls of both feet, and immediately another 30" step is taken with the left foot in the new direction. Being at the halt, on the command of execution, "MARCH," take one step forward with the left foot; a pivot to the right is made on the balls of both feet and take a 30" step in the new direction with the left foot.

To March Other Than at Attention

Being in march, the commands are: "Route Step, MARCH" or "At Ease, MARCH."

• "Route Step, MARCH." At the command "MARCH," Marines are not required to maintain silence or to march in cadence at attention.

Figure 21-5. M16A4 prepared for drill.

- "At Ease, MARCH." At the command "MARCH," Marines are not required to march in cadence at attention but are required to maintain silence.
- To resume marching at attention the command is: "Squad, ATTENTION." Members of the squad immediately pick up the step and cadence.

To Change Step

The command is: "Change Step, MARCH." It may be given while marching or marking, quick or double time. The command of execution is given as the right foot strikes the deck.

- While marching at quick or double time, at the command "MARCH," one more step is taken. As the right foot comes forward to the next step, place the toe near the left heel and step out again with the left foot. This changes the cadence count but not the rhythm.
- While marking time, at the command "MARCH," the left foot is raised and lowered twice in succession. The second time it touches the deck, raise the right foot and continue marking time.
- While marking time at double time, at the command "MARCH," a hop is repeated on the left foot before continuing marking double time.

Manual of Arms with the M16A4

The following information describes each individual movement for the manual of arms with the M16A4 rifle.

Sling Position

Prior to commencement of the manual of arms for honors and ceremonies, the magazine is removed and the sling is prepared.

The sling is positioned on the left side of the rifle. It is drawn tight with the keeper lying flat in a position next to the sling tip. This configuration facilitates execution of the manual of arms. (See Figure 21-5.)

Order Arms

Order arms is the position of the Marine at attention with the rifle. The rifle butt is placed on the ground alongside the right shoe, toe of the weapon on the line with the toe of the shoe. The junction of the rifle's front sight assembly and barrel rests in a "V" formed by the thumb and forefinger. All fingers are straight and together; the right hand and arm are behind the rifle. This position may cause a slight bend in the elbow. The tips of the thumb and forefinger are kept in line with the barrel. The right thumb is along the trouser seam. (See Figure 21-6.)

Trail Arms From Order Arms

Trail arms is assumed without command

Figure 21-6. Figure 21-7. Figure 21-8. Figure 21-9.

when executing a command that causes the unit to move a short distance, face a new direction, dress right, etc. At the completion of the movement, the weapon is returned to the order without command.

For training purposes, the command "Trail ARMS" may be given. The movement is executed in one count.

On "ARMS," close fingers and thumb of the right hand around the barrel between the flash compensator and the front-sight assembly. At the same time, raise the rifle butt 3" straight up. This will cause a bend in the elbow. In the proper position, the rifle will be in line with the right leg along the trouser seam. (See Figures 21-7 and 21-8.)

Order Arms From Trail Arms

On "ARMS," lower the rifle to the position of order. As the butt touches the deck, move the right hand so that the junction of the rifle's front-sight assembly and barrel rests in a "V" formed by the thumb and forefinger. All fingers are straight and together. The right hand and arm are behind the rifle. The tips of the thumb and forefinger are kept on line with the barrel. The right thumb is along the trouser seam. (See Figure 21-9.)

Port Arms From Order Arms

The command "Port, ARMS" is executed in two counts.

1. On "ARMS," slide the right hand to the barrel (fingers joined and wrapped around) and without loss of motion, raise and carry the rifle diagonally across the front of your body until the right hand is in front of and slightly to the left of your face. The right forearm is held down without strain. At the same time, smartly grasp the hand guard (including the sling) with your left hand, fingers joined and wrapped around the hand guard, little finger just above the slip ring. The thumb of the left hand is centered on the chest, and the rifle is 4" from the body. The left wrist and forearm are straight, and the left elbow is held in against the body.

2. Release the grasp of the right hand from the barrel and grasp the small of the stock with the right hand with the right thumb wrapped around the inboard portion. The right wrist and forearm are straight and parallel to the ground. The right elbow is held in against the body.

Order Arms From Port Arms

The command "Order, ARMS" is executed in three counts.

1. On "ARMS" move the right hand smartly from the stock to the barrel. The rifle does not move on the first count.

2. Release the hand guard with the left hand and lower the rifle to a position with the butt 3" off the deck, slightly to the right of the right toe and with the muzzle pointing straight up. The rifle has been rotated one-quarter turn clockwise to a straight fore and aft position. While lowering the rifle, move the left hand, thumb and fingers straight and joined, to a point near the flash suppressor. Keep the palm facing to the rear so it will not resemble a rifle salute. The forearm and wrist are straight.

3. Lower the butt gently to the deck and at the same time move the left hand smartly back to the left side.

Present Arms From Order Arms

The command "Present, ARMS" is executed in two counts.

1. Slide the right hand to the barrel, fingers joined and wrapped around, raising the rifle to a vertical position centered on your body, magazine well to the front. Right wrist and forearm are straight, elbow down without strain. At the same time, smartly grasp rifle at the hand guard with the left hand just above the slip ring, 4" from the body. Left wrist and forearm are straight and parallel to the ground, with the elbow held in to the side and the upper arm in line with the back.

2. Release grasp of the right hand from the barrel and grasp the small of the stock, fingers extended and joined with charging handle resting in the "V" formed by the thumb and fingers, elbow held against the body.

Present Arms From Port, Left or Right Shoulder Arms

When a member of a color guard or when posted as a sentry, "Present ARMS" may be executed from Port, Left or Right Shoulder Arms. The movement may be executed on the command of "Present, ARMS" or in the case of a sentry, without command.

If at port arms, "Present Arms" is executed in one count. The rifle is rotated clockwise with the right hand, the muzzle moves to the right, and the rifle is regrasped above the slip ring with the left hand so that the position of present arms is assumed. To return to port arms, the rifle is rotated counterclockwise to the position of port arms.

If at left or right shoulder arms, present arms is executed in three counts. For the first two counts, the rifle is first brought to port arms as described elsewhere in this chapter. For the third count, the rifle is moved to present arms as described above. To return to the left or right shoulder, the rifle is brought to port arms then to left or right shoulder arms as described elsewhere in this chapter.

Order Arms From Present Arms

The command "Order, ARMS" is executed in three counts.

1. On "ARMS," release the grip with the right hand and regrasp the rifle at the juncture of the front sight assembly and barrel.

2. Release the hand guard with the left hand and lower the rifle to a point where the butt is 3" from the ground, slightly to the right of the right toe, and the muzzle is pointing straight up. While lowering the rifle, move the left hand, thumb and fingers straight and joined, to a point near the flash compensator. Keep the palm facing to the rear so it will not resemble a rifle salute. The forearm and wrist are straight.

3. Lower the butt gently to the deck and move the left hand smartly back to the left side.

Right Shoulder Arms From Order Arms

The command is "Right Shoulder, ARMS." This is a four-count movement.

1. At the command "ARMS," the right hand should grasp the barrel just above the front sight assembly. The rifle is raised diagonally across the body; the left hand grasps the hand guard just above the slip ring.

2. The rifle is regrasped at the butt with the right hand, the heel of the butt between the first two fingers, and the thumb and fingers closed around the butt.

3. Place the rifle into the shoulder with the pistol grip in the armpit. At the same time the left hand is allowed to slide to the junction of the stock and receiver just below the charging handle where it is used to guide the rifle into the shoulder. The thumb and fingers of the left hand are extended and joined with the first joint of the forefinger touching the charging handle and the palm turned toward the body. The left wrist and forearm are straight and held against the body. The weapon is tilted at an angle of 60 degrees to the deck, toe of the weapon pointed to the front. The right wrist and forearm are straight and parallel to the ground with the elbow held against the body.

4. On the fourth count, the left hand is cut smartly back to the left side. The right forearm is horizontal with the right elbow against the side.

Order Arms From Right Shoulder Arms

The return to order arms is a four-count movement. The command is: "Order, ARMS."

1. On the command "ARMS," the rifle butt is pulled quickly toward the body with the right hand. As the rifle clears the shoulder, the right hand twists the stock 90 degrees in a clockwise direction, causing the rifle to fall diagonally across the body. At the same time, the left hand is raised smartly to catch the rifle at the hand guard.

2. The right hand is moved to grasp the front sight assembly.

3. Release the rifle with the left hand and with the right hand, lower it directly to the side, 3" from the deck and with the muzzle pointing straight up. While lowering

the rifle, the left hand is moved, with fingers extended and joined, to a point near the flash suppressor. The wrist is kept straight with the palm to the rear.

4. On the fourth count, the butt is gently lowered to the deck, and the left hand is moved smartly to the side.

Port Arms From Right Shoulder Arms

The command "Port, Arms" is executed in two counts.

1. On "Arms," jerk the butt down so the rifle will spring from the shoulder. As it leaves the the shoulder twist the butt clockwise one-quarter turn so the rifle will fall in front of the chest, barrel up. Keep a tight grip on the butt. Raise the left hand smartly to catch the hand guard 4" in front of the center of the chest.

2. Move the right hand to the junction of the stock and receiver just below the charging handle.

Right Shoulder Arms From Port Arms

The command "Right Shoulder, ARMS" is executed in three counts.

1. On "ARMS," release the stock and grip the heel of the butt between the first two fingers of the right hand. Close the thumb and fingers around the stock. The thumb and forefinger touch.

2. Place the rifle into the shoulder with the pistol grip in the armpit. At the same time, the left hand is allowed to slide to the junction of the stock and receiver just below the charging handle where it is used to guide the rifle into the shoulder. The thumb and fingers of the left hand are extended and joined with the first joint of the forefinger touching the charging handle and the palm turned toward the body. The left wrist and forearm are straight and held against the body. The weapon is tilted at an angle of 60 degrees to the deck, toe of the weapon pointed to the front. The right wrist and forearm are straight and parallel to the

ground with the elbow held against the body.

3. On the third count, move the left hand smartly back to the left side.

Left Shoulder Arms From Order Arms

The command "Left Shoulder, ARMS" is executed in four counts.

1. On the command of "ARMS," and for the first two counts the rifle is brought to port arms.

2. For the third count, place the rifle into the shoulder with the pistol grip in the armpit. The fingers of the right hand remain wrapped around the small of the stock, and the right arm is held against the body. At the same time, release the hand guard with the left hand and regrasp the butt of the rifle. The heel of the butt is between the first two fingers of the left hand, the remaining fingers closed around the butt of the rifle. The thumb and forefinger touch. The weapon is tilted at an angle of 60 degrees to the deck, toe of the weapon pointed to the front. The left wrist and forearm are straight and parallel to the ground with the elbow held against the body.

3. For the fourth count, release the right hand and move it smartly back to the side.

Port Arms From Left Shoulder Arms

The command "Port, ARMS" is executed in two counts.

1. On "ARMS," grip the stock with the right hand.

2. Release the butt with the left hand. At the same time, move the rifle across the body with the right hand and grip the hand guard just above the slip ring with the left hand. The right forearm is parallel to the ground. The front-sight assembly is at the same level as the eyes. Both elbows are at the sides.

Order Arms From Left Shoulder Arms

The command "Order, ARMS" is executed in five counts.

1. On "ARMS," grip the stock with the right hand with the right thumb along the receiver in line with the barrel.

2. Release the butt with the left hand. At the same time, move the rifle across the body with the right hand and grip the hand guard with the left hand.

3. Move the right hand smartly from the stock to the barrel with the left hand on the hand guard.

4. Release the hand guard with the left hand and lower the rifle to a point where the butt is 3" off the ground, slightly to the right of the right toe, and the muzzle pointing straight up. The rifle has been rotated one-quarter turn clockwise to a straight fore and aft position. While lowering the rifle, move the left hand (thumb and fingers straight and joined) to a point near the flash suppressor. Keep the left palm facing to the rear so it will not resemble a rifle salute. The forearm and wrist are straight.

5. Lower the butt gently to the ground and move the left hand smartly back to the left side.

Left Shoulder Arms From Port Arms

The command "Left Shoulder, ARMS" is executed in two counts.

1. On "ARMS," release the hand guard with the left hand and place the rifle on the left shoulder with the right hand. At the same time, take the heel of the butt between the first two fingers of the left hand. Close the left thumb and fingers around the stock. The thumb and forefinger touch. The rifle is at an angle of 60 degrees to the ground and held so it points directly fore and aft. The pistol grip fits snugly into the armpit. The left elbow is against the side, and the left forearm is parallel to the ground.

2. Move the right hand smartly back to the side.

Parade Rest From Order Arms

The command "Parade, REST" is executed in one count.

On "REST," move the left foot smartly 12"

to the left. Keep legs straight so the weight rests equally on both feet. Keep the butt of the rifle on the ground on line with the front of the right shoe. Slide the right hand upward grasping the barrel just below the flash suppressor, fingers joined and curled around, touching the thumb. Straighten the right arm directly to the front so that the muzzle points forward and up. Place the left hand behind the back, just on the belt. Fingers should be straight and joined, the palm flat and facing rear.

Rifle Salute at Right or Left Shoulder Arms

This is a one-count movement executed on each of two set of commands—"Rifle, SALUTE" and "Ready, TWO."

On "SALUTE," move the left (right) hand smartly to the receiver just below the charging handle. Keep the forearm level with the ground, palm down, thumb and fingers joined and straight. The first joint of the forefinger touches the charging handle. When not in ranks, turn head and eyes toward the person or colors saluted.

On "TWO," move left (right) hand smartly back to the side.

Rifle Salute at Order or Trail Arms

These are one-count movements executed on each of two sets of commands—"Rifle, SALUTE," and "Ready, TWO."

On "SALUTE," move the left hand smartly to the right side, palm down, thumb and fingers straight and joined. The first joint of the forefinger touches the flash compensator. When not in ranks, turn head and eyes toward the person or colors saluted.

On "TWO," move left hand smartly back to the left side.

Facings

All facing movements will be made on their respective command in three counts. When armed with the rifle, all facing movements are executed while at order arms only.

1. On "FACE," tighten the grasp, without moving fingers of the right hand, around the barrel between the flash compensator and front sight assembly, raising the rifle butt 3" straight up. At the same time, execute the first count of the facing movement.

2. Execute the second count of the facing movement.

3. Lower the butt gently to the ground and move the right hand back to the order arms position.

Note: Should the manual of arms be done at fix bayonet, all movements would be the same except that the hand grip would include the bayonet and barrel whenever a grip on the barrel is part of the execution as described in this *Guidebook*.

Inspection Arms From Order Arms

Inspection arms from order arms with the M16A4 rifle is a seven-count movement. The command is: "Inspection, ARMS."

1 and 2. On the command "ARMS," execute port arms in two counts. (See Figure 21-10(a) on next page.)

3. On count three, release the hand guard with the left hand and grasp the pistol grip with the left hand, thumb over the lower portion of the bolt catch. (See Figure 21-10(b) on next page.)

4. Release the grasp of the right hand, unlock the charging handle with the thumb and forefinger and sharply pull it to the rear with the thumb and forefinger. At the same time, apply pressure on the bolt catch, locking the bolt to the rear. (See Figure 21-10(c) on next page.)

5. Push the charging handle until it is locked in its foremost position (see Figure 21-10(d) on next page) and regrasp the small of the stock with the right hand.

6. On count six, with both hands, (see Figure 21-10(e) on next page) elevate the rifle up and to the left at the same time rotating it so that the chamber is visible, inspecting the chamber to see that it is clear.

7. Resume the position of port arms. (See Figure 21-10(f).)

Note: "Port Arms" is the only command given from inspection arms. On the command,

Figure 21-10(a).

Figure 21-10(b).

Figure 21-10(c).

"PORT," move the left hand and regrasp the weapon with the thumb and fingers forming a "V" at the magazine well and trigger guard. Press the bolt catch, allowing the bolt to go forward. With the fingertips, push upward and close the dust cover. Slide the left hand toward the pistol grip and place the thumb on the trigger. On the command "ARMS," pull the trigger and resume port arms.

Sling Arms From Order Arms

This is not a precision movement; therefore, there are no counts. From the order arms position (with a parade sling) the command for sling arms is, "Sling, ARMS."

1. On the command of "ARMS," slide the right hand up and grasp the barrel near the flash compensator. Without loss of motion, raise the rifle to a vertical position where the butt is in front of the right hip with the muzzle pointing up and the pistol grip to the left. At the same time, grasp the rifle at the hand guard just above the slip ring with the left hand. The sling is included in the grasp. The fingers are joined. Place the butt on the right hip. If the rifle belt is worn, the

Figure 21-10(d).

Figure 21-10(e).

Figure 21-10(f).

butt will rest just above the belt. Release the grasp of the right hand, and with the left hand, move the rifle so that it will rest on the inside of the right elbow and cradle it there. The muzzle points slightly to the right. Release the grasp of the left hand from the hand guard and with both hands loosen the sling. After the sling has been loosened, grasp the sling with your left hand and sling the rifle on the right shoulder in the most direct manner. Regrasp the sling with the right hand. With the exception of the right arm, return to the position of attention. The palm of the right hand is toward the sling. The fingers are joined. The fingers and thumb are wrapped around the sling with the knuckles forward. The wrist and forearm are straight and parallel to the deck. The elbow is holding the rifle in a vertical position and against the body.

Sling Arms From Unsling Arms

This movement is to sling the rifle on the right shoulder when the sling has already been loosened. This is not a precision movement; therefore, there are no counts. From the unsling arms position (order arms with loosened sling), the command for sling arms is: "Sling, ARMS."

1. On the command "ARMS," slide the right hand up and grasp the barrel near the flash compensator. The fingers are joined and wrapped around the barrel with the thumb wrapped around the inboard portion. Without loss of motion, raise the rifle and grasp the sling with the left hand near the upper-sling swivel. Release the grasp of the right hand and, with the left hand, sling the rifle over the right shoulder in the most convenient manner. Regrasp the sling with the right hand. With the exception of the right arm, return to the position of attention. The palm of the right hand is toward the sling. The fingers are joined. The fingers and thumb of the right hand are wrapped around the sling with the knuckles forward. The wrist and forearm are straight and parallel to the deck. The elbow is holding the rifle in a vertical position and against the body.

Unsling Arms From Sling Arms

This is not a precision movement; therefore, there are no counts. It is executed when halted at sling arms. The command is "Unsling, ARMS."

1. On the command "ARMS," grasp the sling with the left hand in front of the armpit and unsling the rifle from the right shoulder in the most convenient manner. Grasp the rifle at the junction of the barrel and the front sight assembly. Release the grasp of the left hand from the sling and, with the right hand, carry the weapon to the right side until the butt is 3" from the deck. The barrel is in a vertical position. At the same time, guide the weapon with the left hand until the right thumb is on the trouser seam. The fingers of the left hand are extended and joined and touching the rifle near the flash compensator. The palm of the left hand is toward the rear. The left wrist and forearm are straight, and the left elbow is in against the body. Quietly lower the rifle to the deck with the right hand and at the same time return the left hand to the left side at the position of attention.

To Adjust Sling

This is not a precision movement; therefore, there are no counts. The command is: "Adjust, SLINGS."

1. From unsling arms (order arms), on the command of execution, the rifle is brought to a cradle position inside the right elbow as in the movement from order arms to sling arms. While in this position, the sling is tightened to parade sling. The rifle is then returned to order arms.

2. From sling arms, on the command of execution, grasp the sling with the left hand in front of the armpit and unsling the rifle from the right shoulder in the most convenient manner. Then place the butt on the right hip and cradle the rifle inside the right elbow. Tighten the sling to the parade sling position and automatically assume the position of order arms.

Saluting at Sling Arms

This is a two-count movement and is executed when halted at sling arms. The command is: "Present, ARMS;" however, the movement may be executed without command.

1. On the command of execution and for the count of one, reach across the body with the left hand and grasp the sling just above the right hand. On the second count, release the right hand and execute the hand salute.

2. To resume order arms, the command is: "Order, ARMS." On the command of execution, "ARMS," lower the right hand smartly to the right side and regrasp the sling at the original position. After grasping the sling with the right hand, release the sling with the left hand and return it smartly to the position of attention.

Manual of Arms With the M203

This section contains the procedures for executing manual of arms movements with the M203 Grenade Launcher. When it is necessary to conduct a drill or ceremony involving troops armed with the M203, they will carry the weapon at sling arms. The M203 will always be rigged with a loosened sling. Troops armed with the M203 will fall in at sling arms and execute all individual drill movements from that position. The only manual of arms movements they will execute are present arms (hand salute) and inspection arms. If stack arms is to be given, troops armed with the M203 will be positioned in ranks so that their weapons are treated as extras on the stacks. When armed with the M203, present arms will be executed in the same manner as the salute while at sling arms with the M16. Sling arms will be resumed when order arms is given.

Inspection Arms With the M203

This is not a precision movement; therefore, there are no counts. It is executed when halted at sling arms. The command is: "Inspection, ARMS."

1. On the command "ARMS," the initial movements bring the weapon from sling arms to port arms, then execute counts 3 through 6 of inspection arms as with the M16.

2. When at the inspection arms position as with the M16, continue with the M203 by pressing the barrel latch and sliding the barrel up to the barrel stop. Elevate the M203 again, turning the head and eyes, visually inspect the chamber of the barrel. Return to a modified port arms position with the left hand holding the barrel at its full-forward position.

Returning to Sling Arms From Inspection Arms With the M203

The command to return to the sling arms position from inspection arms is: "Port, ARMS."

1. On the preparatory command "Port," slide the barrel down to its closed and latched position. Then continue to close the bolt and dust cover of the rifle, and slide the left hand down to grasp the pistol grip and place the thumb on the rifle trigger as with the M16.

2. On the command of execution "ARMS," pull the rifle trigger with the thumb of the left hand and then move it to the trigger of the grenade launcher and pull that trigger. Return to sling arms.

Manual of the Pistol

When in ranks and armed with the pistol, facings, rests, open and close ranks, and alignments are executed as if unarmed. The pistol manual of arms is not executed in cadence. It is a simple, quick, and safe method of handling the pistol. The pistol manual of arms with the 9mm Service Pistol may be executed with the weapon holstered on either the right or left side. When in formation, remain at attention during all rifle manual movements except those listed below.

Present Arms From Attention (Pistol in Holster)

When the command of "Present ARMS" is given to the formation, those Marines armed with the pistol execute a hand salute. On the command of "Order Arms," the hand salute is terminated.

Inspection Arms from Attention (Pistol in Holster)

1. The command is: "Inspection, ARMS." It involves several movements that are executed rapidly and smartly without count. It may be executed only when halted at attention with pistol in holster. Inspection arms is not executed with the pistol as part of the rifle manual except when the unit is formed and dismissed. If the pistol is holstered on the left side, the opposite hands are used from those described below.

2. On "ARMS," with the right thumb, unfasten the holster flap, grasp the grip and pull the pistol from the holster. Raise the right hand to a position level with and 6" in front of the right shoulder. The grip should be held between the thumb and last three fingers, forefinger extended and outside the trigger guard. The muzzle points forward and up at an angle of 30 degrees.

3. Without lowering the muzzle or the right hand, turn the pistol handle to the left, look at the pistol, press the magazine catch with the right thumb, and remove the magazine with the left hand. Turn the handle back to the right so that the bottom of the magazine well is to the front. Place the magazine between the pistol belt and outer garment.

4. Without lowering the muzzle or the right hand, grasp the slide with the thumb and fingers of the left hand, thumb on the left side of the slide, and pointing downward. Keep the left forearm parallel with the deck. Push the slide all the way to the rear and engage the slide stop in its notch with the right thumb. Look into the chamber; if it is not empty, empty it. Take the magazine from under the belt with the left hand. Raise the left hand to the height of the belt, forearm parallel to the deck, elbow at the side, palm up, fingers extended, and joined. Hold the magazine in the open hand, follower toward the left wrist.

Attention (Pistol in Holster) From Inspection Arms

1. The command is: "Port, ARMS." It is the only command that may be executed from inspection arms. If the pistol is holstered on the left side, the opposite hands are used from those described below.

2. On "ARMS," return the magazine to a position between the belt and outer garment. With the thumb of the left hand, release the slide stop. Keep the muzzle up and squeeze the trigger. Remove the magazine from the belt with the left hand and insert it into the pistol. Return the pistol to the holster and fasten the flap with the right thumb.

Squad Drill

A squad is a group of individuals formed for the purpose of instruction, discipline, control, and order.

Members of the squad take positions, move, and execute the manual of arms as stated in this *Guidebook*. All individuals execute the movements at the same time. Squads may drill as squads or as part of a platoon or larger formation.

Squads are kept intact when practicable. The normal formation for a squad is a single rank (squad in line) or single file (squad in column). (See Figure 21-11.) This permits variation in the number of individuals composing the squad. The first formation is always in line. Column formation may be taken from line formation. A squad, not at drill, may be marched in column of twos by forming in two ranks.

The Squad Marches in Line For Minor Changes of Position Only

Members of the squad normally form as indicated in Figure 21-11. (e.g., maintain fire team/section integrity). However, for parades and ceremonies where appearance is more important, the squads should be sized. To size the squad the tallest member takes position 2 in Figure 21-12 with the shortest squad member in position 13. The squad leader, regardless of height, always forms as the squad leader, in position one of Figure 21-12.

When the Squad is Armed with Rifles

The command "Right (Left) Shoulder, ARMS;" "Port, ARMS;" or "Sling, ARMS" is given before commanding the squad to move, except for short distances. When moving short distances the command "Trail, ARMS" may be given or it may be executed automatically.

At the command "Squad, HALT" remain at the position of right shoulder (left shoulder, port or sling) arms until "Order, ARMS" or some other manual command is given.

If the unit leader is the squad leader, then the number two Marine (see Figure 21-12) executes the movements of the squad leader. The unit leader must maintain proper distance (three paces) from the squad and remain centered on the squad during all drill movements.

If the squad executes a right step, the unit leader, who is facing the squad, would execute a left step in cadence with the squad to maintain proper position. For a right step, the unit leader would execute a left step. If the squad executes a back step, the unit leader would execute a half step, in cadence with the squad to maintain proper position.

To Form the Squad

The squad forms at normal or, when directed to do so, at close interval. The command is: "FALL IN."

The squad forms in line and to the left of the squad leader. Each Marine in the squad, except the individual on the extreme left flank, raises the left arm shoulder high in line with the body and

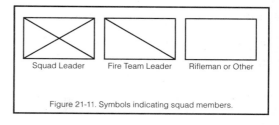

Figure 21-11. Symbols indicating squad members.

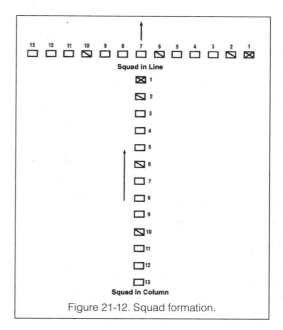

Figure 21-12. Squad formation.

with fingers extended and joined, palm down. All except the squad leader turn their heads and eyes to the right and place themselves on line with the squad leader so that each Marine's shoulder touches the fingertips of the person on the right. (See Figure 21-13 on next page.) As soon as each Marine is in line with the person on the right, and the person on the left has obtained the proper interval, the individual returns smartly and quickly to the position of attention.

To form at close interval, the command is "At Close Interval, FALL IN."

The squad forms as described above except that each Marine (except the extreme left flank person) places the left hand on the hip, elbow in line with the body, fingers of the left hand extended and joined, heel of the palm resting on the hip. (See Figure 21-14 on next page.)

When the squad is armed, it falls in at the

position of order arms. Weapons are inspected immediately after the squad is formed.

To Dismiss the Squad

The squad is dismissed only from line formation and when at the position of attention.

When armed, the squad is always given commands required to inspect weapons prior to being dismissed. These commands are: "Inspection, ARMS," "Port, ARMS," "DISMISSED."

Unarmed squads are dismissed with the command "DISMISSED."

To Count Off

In line, the command is "Count, OFF." At the command "OFF," everyone except the squad leader, turn their heads 90 degrees over the shoulder and look to the right. The squad leaders shout ONE. The person in the file to the left of the squad leaders turns his head smartly back to the front and at the same time shouts TWO. After the person to their right has shouted their number, each subsequent person to the left turns his head back to the front and at the same time shouts the next higher number. Numbers are counted off in quick time cadence.

In column, on the command "From Front to Rear, Count, OFF," the squad leader smartly turns his head to the right 90 degrees over the shoulder and shouts ONE as the head is turned back to the front. Each subsequent rank, having seen the person's head in front of them return to the front, turns his head to the right and shouts the next higher number as the head is turned smartly back to the front. This is carried on in sequence at quick time cadence.

To Align the Squad

The purpose of these movements is to dress the alignment of the squad. They may be executed when the squad is halted at attention in line. The commands are "Dress Right (Left), DRESS" or "At Close Interval, Dress Right (Left), DRESS." These commands are given only when the squad is at approximately the same interval as the interval at which the dress is commanded.

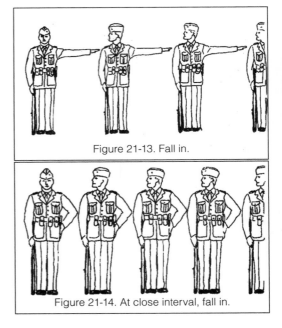

Figure 21-13. Fall in.

Figure 21-14. At close interval, fall in.

On the command "Dress Right, DRESS," everyone except the squad leader, smartly turn their heads to the right, 90 degrees over the shoulder look, and align themselves. At the same time, everyone except the individual on the left flank, provide interval by smartly raising their left arm to shoulder height and in line with their body. Fingers are extended and joined, thumb along the forefinger, palm down.

As the base of the movement, the squad leader keeps his head and eyes to the front. All other members of the squad position themselves by short steps until their right shoulders lightly touch the fingertips of the person on their right.

The unit leader, on his own command of execution "DRESS," faces half left, as in marching, and proceeds by the most direct route to a position on line with and one pace to the right of the individual on the right flank. At this position, the unit leader executes a halt in the oblique facing the rear of the formation, and then executes a right face, facing down the line of the squad. The unit leader aligns the squad by commanding those individuals in advance or rear of the line to move forward or backward until in line. These individuals are designated by name or number. For example: "Jones, FORWARD;" or "Number

Three, BACKWARD." Those individuals will move until receiving the command "STEADY." The unit leader may execute a series of short side steps to the right or left in order to identify an individual. However, prior to commanding the identified individual to move, the unit leader will be on line with the rank. After verifying the alignment of the squad, the unit leader faces to the right in marching, marches straight to a point 3 paces beyond the squad, halts, faces to the left, and commands "Ready, FRONT." Immediately after commanding "FRONT," the unit leader marches by the most direct route back to a post three paces front and centered on the squad.

On the command "Ready, FRONT," all members of the squad who raised their left arm and turned their head to the right, will smartly but quietly lower their arm to their side, and at the same time turn their head back to the front, assuming the position of attention.

When aligning a squad of well-drilled troops or when there is insufficient time to verify alignment, the unit leader may command "Ready, FRONT" from his normal position (three paces front and centered), without having verified alignment.

To Obtain Close Interval From Normal Interval in Line

The purpose of this movement is to close the interval between individuals of a squad in line to 4". It may be executed when the squad is halted at attention and in line at normal interval. The command is "Close, MARCH."

The squad leader is the base of this movement. On the command of execution "MARCH," the squad leader stands fast and places his left hand on his hip, as if dressing at close interval, to provide interval for the individuals to the left. At the same time, all other members of the squad face to the right as in marching, march toward the right flank until approximately 4" from the person in front of them, halt, and face to the left. They then execute at close interval dress right dress. After aligning and without command, they will smartly lower their left hands and turn their heads to the front as soon

as the individual to their left has touched their elbow with his right arm and stopped moving.

On his command of execution, the unit leader steps to the left in marching. He marches parallel to the squad maintaining a distance of three paces from the squad. When approximately on the center of the squad at close interval, the unit leader halts and faces the squad. He then adjusts to the center of the squad by taking small steps left, right, forward, or back.

To Obtain Normal Interval From Close Interval in Line

The purpose of this movement is to extend the interval between individuals of a squad in line to one arm length. It may be executed when the squad is halted at attention and in line at close interval. The command is "Extend, MARCH."

The squad leader is the base of this movement. On the command of execution "MARCH," the squad leader stands fast and raises his left arm to shoulder height to provide interval for the person on the left. At the same time, all other members of the squad face to the left as in marching, march toward the left flank until they have opened approximately a 30" distance from the person behind them, halt, and face to the right. They then execute dress right dress. After aligning and without command, they will smartly, and quietly, lower their left arms and turn their heads to the front as soon as the individual to their left has touched their finger tips with his right shoulder and has stopped moving.

On his command of execution, the unit leader steps to the right in marching. He marches parallel to the squad maintaining a distance of three paces from the squad. When approximately on the center of the squad at normal interval the unit leader halts and faces the squad. He then adjusts to the center of the squad by taking small steps left, right, forward, or back.

To March to the Oblique

The purpose of this movement is to shift the line of march to the right or left and then resume marching in the original direction. It may be executed from any formation that is marching at quick time cadence. The command is "Right (Left) Oblique, MARCH." The word oblique is pronounced to rhyme with strike. The command of execution is given as the foot in the direction of the turn strikes the deck. The command to resume the original direction of march is "Forward, MARCH." The command of execution is given as the foot toward the original front strikes the deck. (See Figure 21-15(a) and Figure 21-15(b).)

To teach the squad to march to the oblique, the unit leader aligns the unit and has members face half right (left). The unit leader then explains that these positions are maintained when marching to the oblique. This is achieved by individuals keeping their shoulders parallel to the persons in front and/or adjacent to them. The squad leader is the base of the movement and must maintain a steady line of march keeping his shoulders blocked perpendicular to the direction of march.

At the command "Right Oblique, MARCH," the command of execution is given as the right foot strikes the deck. Everyone then takes one more 30" step to the front with the left foot and pivots 45 degrees to the right on the ball of the left foot. Stepping out of the pivot with a 30" step, the entire squad marches to the right oblique until given another command. For the squad to resume marching in the original direction, the command is "Forward, MARCH" in this case the command of execution will be given as the left foot strikes the deck. Everyone then takes one more step in the oblique direction; pivots back to the original front and continue to march. To march to the left oblique, substitute left for right and right for left in the above sequence.

To halt the squad facing in the original direction of march, the command is "Squad, HALT." The command of execution "HALT" is given on the left foot when marching to the right oblique and on the right foot when marching to the left oblique. At the command "HALT," everyone takes one more step in the oblique direction, pivots to the original front on the toe of the right (left) foot, and places the left (right) foot beside the other at the position of attention.

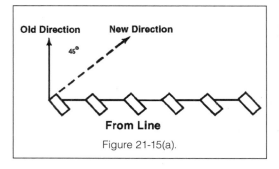

From Line

Figure 21-15(a).

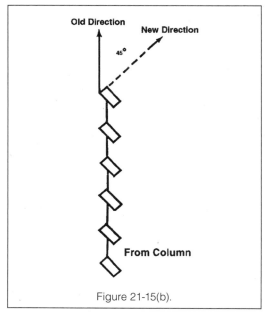

From Column

Figure 21-15(b).

To temporarily halt the squad in the oblique direction, in order to correct errors, the command is "In Place, HALT." The command of execution "HALT" may be given as either foot strikes the deck. At the command of execution "HALT," the squad halts in two counts as in quick time and remains facing in the oblique direction. The only command that can be given after halting in place is "Resume, MARCH." At that command, the movement continues marching in the oblique direction. (See Figure 21-16 on next page.)

When given half step or mark time while marching in the oblique, the only commands that may be given are "Resume, MARCH" to continue marching with a 30" step in the oblique or "In Place, HALT" to halt in the oblique in order to correct errors.

To March to the Rear

The purpose of this movement is to march the squad to the rear for a short distance. It may be executed when halted or marching forward at quick time or double time. The command is "To the Rear, MARCH." The command of execution will be given as the right foot strikes the deck.

When halted, on the command of execution "MARCH," everyone takes one 15" step to the front with the left foot and then pivots 180 degrees toward the right on the balls of both feet. Stepping out of the pivot with a 30" step, the entire squad marches to the rear. For the squad to resume marching in the original direction, the command "To the Rear, MARCH" is given again. No other command may be given when marching to the rear until the unit has resumed marching to the original front.

When marching at quick time, on the command of execution "MARCH," everyone takes one more 15" step to the front with the left foot and then pivots 180 degrees toward the right on the balls of both feet. Stepping out of the pivot with a 30" step, the entire squad marches to the rear. For the squad to resume marching in the original direction, the command "To the Rear, MARCH" is given again. No other command may be given when marching to the rear until the unit has resumed marching to the original front.

When marching at double time, on the command of execution "MARCH," everyone takes two more 36" steps to the front and then four, 6" vertical steps in place at double time cadence. On the first and third steps in place, everyone pivots 180 degrees to the right. After the fourth step in place, and for the fifth step, they step off with a 36" step in the new direction. For the squad to resume marching in the original direction, the command "To the Rear, MARCH" is given again. No other command may be given when marching to the rear until the unit has resumed marching to the original front.

To March to the Flank

The purpose of this movement is to march the squad to the right or left flank for a short distance. It may be executed from any formation

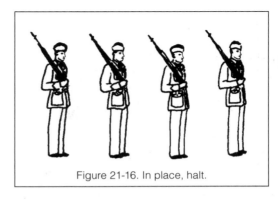

Figure 21-16. In place, halt.

that is marching at quick time or double time cadence. The command is "By the Right (Left) Flank, MARCH." The command of execution is given as the foot in the direction of the turn strikes the deck.

To march to the right flank, when marching at quick time, the command is "By the Right Flank, MARCH." On the command of execution "MARCH," everyone takes one more 30" step to the front with the left foot and then pivots 90 degrees to the right on the ball of the left foot. Stepping out of the pivot with a 30" step, the entire squad marches in line to the right flank. The unit leader executes the flanking movement with the squad maintaining his distance from the squad. For the squad to resume marching in the original direction, the command is "By the Left Flank, MARCH." To march to the left flank, substitute left for right and right for left in the above sequence. No other command may be given when marching to the flank until the unit has resumed marching to the original front.

When marching at double time, on the command of execution "MARCH," everyone takes two more 36" steps to the front and then two, 6" vertical steps in place at double time cadence. While stepping in place, everyone turns 90 degrees toward the direction commanded and then steps off with a 36" step in the new direction. No other command may be given when marching to the flank until the unit has resumed marching to the original front.

To Change the Direction of a Column

The purpose of this movement is to change the direction of march of a column. It may be executed when the squad is halted or marching in column. The command is "Column Right (Column Left, Column Half Right, or Column Half Left), MARCH." The squad leader establishes the pivot for the movement.

When marching, the commands of execution are given on the foot in the direction of the turn. On the command of execution "MARCH," the squad leader takes one more 30" step to the front and then pivots 90 degrees to the right (left) on the ball of the left (right) foot. He then takes a 30" step in the new direction. The remaining members of the squad continue to march to the point where the squad leader pivoted. They would then pivot 90 degrees in the new direction of march.

When halted, at the command of execution "MARCH," the squad leader faces to the right (left) as in marching and takes one 30" step in the new direction with the right (left) foot. The remaining members of the squad step off to the front as in forward march. The remainder of the movement is executed the same as in marching.

Column half right (left) is executed as described above except that the pivot is 45 degrees to the right (left).

During column movements, the unit leader executes the movement with the squad, maintaining proper distance from the squad.

For slight changes of direction, the command is "INCLINE TO THE RIGHT (LEFT)." At that command, the squad leader changes direction slightly as commanded. This is not a precision movement and is executed only while marching.

Platoon Drill

In platoon drill, the squad is merged with other squads into a platoon.

A platoon consists of a platoon headquarters and two or more squads or sections. Platoon headquarters consists at a minimum of a platoon commander, a platoon sergeant, and a platoon guide. One or more assistants may be designated.

A section normally forms and drills as part of a platoon. In this *Guidebook*, the instructions given for the squad or platoon also apply to a section. A section, not subdivided into squads, forms and drills as a squad. A section that is divided into two or more squads forms and drills as a platoon.

Squads in a platoon are numbered from front to rear in column (when facing the front of the column) and from right to left in line. (See Figure 21-17 on next page.)

The platoon forms in two or more ranks with a 40" distance between ranks. Movements in this Section are described for columns of threes or fours and may be executed by either formation.

The platoon changes interval while in line and counts off in the same manner as the squad. Squad leaders are the base for these movements. The guide moves to the right when interval is taken to the left and does not count off.

In platoon drill, if all members of the platoon are to execute a movement simultaneously, the movement is executed on the command of the platoon commander. In this case, squad leaders do not repeat or give any commands. When squads of the platoon are to execute a movement in successive order, such as forming column of twos (files) and reforming into column (of threes, etc.), squad leaders give appropriate supplemental commands for the movement of their squads. (See Figure 21-18 on next page.)

Unless specified for the platoon to be at close interval, all changes in formation should be executed with normal interval and distance between files and ranks.

The unit leader will march to the left and parallel to the platoon, from a position where he can best control the unit.

All commands given by the unit leader while the platoon is halted will be six paces in front of the unit and centered on the element.

Formations

Column and line are the two formations for a platoon. (See Figures 21-17 and Figure 21-18.)

The platoon normally forms in line with the squad leaders on the right of their squads and the guide on the right of the first squad leader. The platoon marches in line for short distances only.

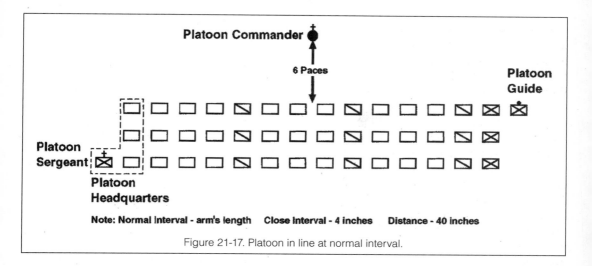

Figure 21-17. Platoon in line at normal interval.

The platoon is normally marched in column with the squad leaders in front of their squads and the guide in front of the third (right) squad leader.

Posts of Individuals

In line, the platoon commander's post is six paces in front of the center of the front rank of the platoon. In column, the platoon commander marches at the head of the left file of the platoon, unless drilling the platoon, in which case he would maintain a position six paces from the platoon.

When the platoon commander is present, the platoon sergeant takes post to the left of the left member of the rear rank when the platoon is in line. When in column, the platoon sergeant follows the last member of the right file (squad). When the platoon commander is not present, the platoon sergeant takes the platoon commander's post and drills the platoon in the manner prescribed for the platoon commander.

Extra members may fall in on the left when the platoon is in line and in the rear when in column. If the squads are evenly filled, the first extra member falls in with the first squad, the second with the third (fourth) squad, and then remaining squads. The platoon sergeant will reposition when necessary so as to remain the last person in the last rank.

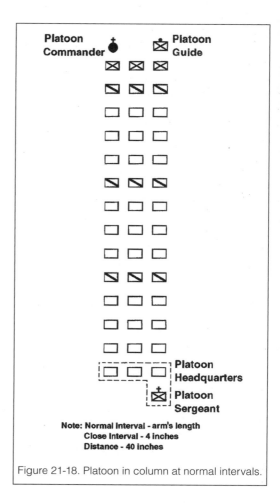

Figure 21-18. Platoon in column at normal intervals.

Rules for the Guide

Unless otherwise directed, guide is right, and the platoon guide takes post on the right. In line, the guide is posted to the right of the squad leader of the first squad. In column, the guide is posted in front of the squad leader of the third or right squad.

In column, when it is desired to guide left or center, the command "GUIDE LEFT" is given. At this command, the guide and the platoon commander exchange positions. The guide crosses between the platoon commander and the platoon. To return the guide to normal position, "GUIDE RIGHT" is commanded. The guide and platoon commander return to their normal positions with the guide again passing between the platoon commander and the platoon. This movement may be made at a halt or while marching. The base squad or file is the one behind the guide.

The guide does not change position at the command "Dress Left, DRESS."

When a platoon in line is given the command "Right, FACE," the platoon guide executes right face with the platoon. The guide then faces to the right in marching, moves to a position in front of the right squad leader, halts, and executes left face. If a platoon in line is given "Left, FACE," the guide executes left face with the platoon but does not change position within the platoon.

When a platoon in column is given the command "Column of Files from the Left," the guide takes position in front of the left squad leader so as to remain at the head of the column.

When a platoon in column is given the command "Column of Twos from the Left," the guide takes position in front of the second squad so as to remain at the head of the right file of the column. These movements are executed by facing left as in marching, moving to the appropriate position, halting, and facing right.

When reforming in a column of threes or fours from a column of files or twos, the guide takes post at his normal position when the movement is completed.

The guide sets the direction and cadence of the march. The leading member of each file is responsible for interval.

When a platoon is marching in column and the command "By the Right (Left) Flank, MARCH" or "To the Rear, MARCH" is given, the guide executes the movement with the platoon but does not change relative position except during specific movements of company drill.

The guide does not count off.

To Form the Platoon

When appropriate, the platoon may be formed by the platoon commander rather than the platoon sergeant. The procedures are the same except that the platoon commander takes post six paces in front of the point where the center of the platoon will be, faces that point, draws sword, and commands "FALL IN" or "At Close Interval, FALL IN."

The platoon forms on the platoon commander, the platoon sergeant falling in on the left of the rear rank with sword drawn, if so armed. The platoon commander then receives the report from the squad leaders and causes the platoon to execute inspection arms if the troops are armed.

To Dismiss the Platoon

The platoon is dismissed only from in line while at attention.

Armed troops are dismissed with the commands "Inspection, ARMS;" "Port, ARMS;" and "DISMISSED."

Unarmed troops are dismissed with the command "DISMISSED."

The platoon sergeant usually dismisses the platoon.

To Align the Platoon

The purpose of these movements is to dress the alignment of the platoon. They may be executed when the platoon is halted at attention in line or column. When in line, the commands are "Dress Right (Left), DRESS" or "At Close Interval, Dress Right (Left), DRESS." These commands are given only when the platoon is at approximately the same interval as the interval at which the dress is commanded. When in column, halted or marching, the command to dress alignment is "COVER."

On the command "Dress Right, DRESS," everyone except those individuals on the right flank, smartly turn their heads to the right, look, and align themselves. At the same time, everyone except those individuals on the left flank, provide interval by smartly raising their extended left arm to shoulder height and in line with their body. Fingers are extended and joined, thumb along the forefinger, palm down.

As the base of the movement, the guide stands fast and remains looking to the front. The first squad leader looks to the right and aligns on the guide. The other squad leaders cover the first squad leader and look to the front, ensuring they have a 40" distance. All other members position themselves by short steps until their right shoulders touch the fingertips of the person on their right.

The platoon commander, on his own command of execution "DRESS," faces half left, as in marching, and proceeds by the most direct route to a position on line with the front rank and one pace to the guide's right (or first squad leader if there is no guide). At this position, the platoon commander executes a halt while facing rear, and then executes a right face, facing down the line of the first rank. The platoon commander aligns the front rank by commanding those individuals in advance or rear of the line to move forward or backward until in line. These individuals are designated by name or number. For example: "Jones, FORWARD;" or "Number Three, BACKWARDS." Those commanded to move will move the designated number of steps or will continue to move (taking small steps) until receiving the command "STEADY." The commander may execute a series of short side steps to the right or left in order to identify an individual. However, prior to commanding the identified individual to move, the commander will be on line with the rank. After verifying the alignment of the first rank, the platoon commander faces to the left as in marching, and moves to a position on line with the next rank. The one pace interval from the guide is maintained (this results in a two pace interval from the second and subsequent squad leaders). The commander halts on line with each succeeding

rank, executes right face, and aligns the rank. After verifying the alignment of the last rank, the platoon commander faces to the right in marching, marches straight to a point three paces beyond the front rank, maintaining the one pace interval to the guide's right, halts, faces to the left, and commands "Ready, FRONT" and "COVER." Immediately after commanding, "COVER," the platoon commander marches by the most direct route back to a post six paces front and centered on the platoon, halts facing down line or to the front.

On the command "Ready, FRONT," all members of the platoon who raised their left arm and turned their head to the right, will smartly but quietly lower their arm to their side and at the same time turn their head back to the front, assuming the position of attention. On the command "COVER," all members of the second and subsequent ranks will cover on the individual in front of them.

When aligning a platoon of well-drilled troops or when there is insufficient time to verify alignment, the platoon commander may command "Ready, FRONT" and "COVER" from his normal position (six paces front and centered), without having verified alignment.

To Open Ranks

The purpose of this movement is to increase the distance between ranks to 70" in order to accommodate the movements of an inspection party or to stack arms. It may be executed when halted in line at attention, and at normal or close interval. If armed, rifles will be at order arms. The commands are "At Close Interval, Open Rank;" "MARCH;" "Ready, FRONT;" and "COVER."

When at normal interval, on the command of execution "MARCH," the front rank takes two 30" steps forward, halts, and executes dress right dress. The second rank takes one 30" step forward, halts, and executes dress right dress. The third rank stands fast and executes dress right. If there is a fourth rank, it takes two 15" back steps, halts, and executes dress right. When at close interval, all ranks will execute at close interval, dress right dress in place of dress right dress.

The platoon commander verifies alignment as for dress right dress, except that he will verify the 70" distance between ranks by taking two 30" steps and one 10" step when moving from one rank to the next. After verifying the alignment of the rear rank, he faces to the right in marching, marches three paces beyond the front rank, and one pace to the guide's right, halts, faces to the left, and commands "Ready, FRONT" and "COVER." The platoon responds to these commands in the same manner as when they are given following dress right dress.

If the platoon is about to be inspected the platoon commander, after the command "COVER" will take one step to the front so that he is three paces directly in front of the guide, and then execute a right face. From this position, the platoon commander reports the platoon to the inspecting officer.

To Close Ranks

The purpose of this movement is to decrease the distance between opened ranks to a normal distance (40"). It may only be given when the platoon is at attention at open ranks. The command is "Close Ranks, MARCH." It should be given immediately after the reason for opening ranks is accomplished, and before the platoon is given further drill movements or dismissed.

On the command of execution "MARCH," the front rank stands fast while the second rank takes one 30" step to the front and halts. At the same time, the third rank takes two 30" steps to the front and if there is a fourth squad, it takes three steps and halts. Each individual maintains cover and alignment while moving. No dressing movements are executed.

The platoon commander may give the command to close ranks when:

After the platoon is inspected, the platoon commander returns to a position three paces in front of the guide and halts facing to the front. It is from this position that the inspecting officer would critique the inspection. The platoon commander would exchange salutes with the inspection officer and after that officer has departed, the platoon commander would face to the left and then command "Close Ranks, MARCH."

The platoon commander, on the command "MARCH," then moves to his position six paces and centered on the platoon. After the platoon has taken arms, the platoon commander would command, "Close Ranks, MARCH" from his position six paces and centered in front of the platoon.

To Form For Physical Drill

The purpose of the movement is to form the platoon for physical exercise. It may be executed when the platoon is halted at attention and in a column of threes or fours at normal interval. If armed with rifles, they will be at order arms. The sequence of commands are: "From Front to Rear, Count, OFF;" "Take Interval to the Left, MARCH;" "Arms, DOWN;" and "Even Numbers, To the Right, MOVE." To reform to a column the commands are "Assemble, MARCH" and "COVER."

The command "From Front to Rear, Count, OFF" is given by the platoon commander in order to designate odd and even ranks. It is executed as prescribed for counting off in column.

The next command is "Take Interval to the Left, MARCH." Which is executed when the platoon is in line formation. With the platoon in column, the extended interval is set by designating the number of steps the members of each squad take to the left.

On the command of execution "MARCH," all members of the squad on the right flank (third squad if it is a three squad platoon, fourth squad if it is a four squad platoon) and the guide, will cover in file, stand fast, and each member extends both arms sideways at shoulder height, palms down with fingers extended and joined. If armed with rifles, each member will grasp the barrel of the rifle with the right hand and raise it to shoulder height with the pistol grip and magazine well facing the front. This squad forms the base of the movement. At the same time, the members of each squad to the left of the base squad will face to the left as in marching and take two, four, or six (if it is a four squad platoon) 30" steps respectively. Upon completing their designated number of steps, they will halt, execute a right face, will cover in file, stand fast, and extend their arms to the side at shoulder height in the same manner as the right file. If armed with rifles, the rifles are carried at trail arms during movement and then raised in the same manner as the right file. At the command "Arms, DOWN," the arms are lowered smartly to the side and if armed with rifles the position of order arms is assumed. On the command "Even Numbers to the Right, MOVE," all even numbered individuals and the guide will move to their right to the middle of the interval between files. This will be done by swinging the right leg to the right and springing off the left foot. The movement should be completed in one hop. If armed with rifles, the weapon is brought to trail arms and held against the right leg during movement. Once in position, even numbered members cover and assume the position of attention. Odd numbered members do not move. From this position, physical drill may be executed without the danger of collisions between individuals.

Upon the completion of physical drill, the command "Assemble, MARCH" is given. On the command of execution, the odd numbered members of the base squad stand fast. Even numbered members of the base squad step left in marching and double time to their positions covered on the odd numbered members of the base squad, and the guide will return to a position in front of the base squad leader. At the same time, all other members will face right as in marching and, at a double time cadence, reassemble in column at normal interval and stand fast. The platoon commander would then give the command of "COVER" in order for the platoon to quickly pick up its alignment and cover.

The platoon commander, once the platoon is in column, gives all commands from a position six paces in front of, centered on and facing the column. He makes those movements necessary to maintain this position during the execution of the movement(s).

To Obtain Close Interval in Column

The purpose of this movement is to close the interval between files in a column to 4". It may be executed when halted or marching at normal interval in column. The command is "Close, MARCH."

When halted and the guide is right, on the command "MARCH," members of the base (right) squad will stand fast. Members of the squad next to the base squad will execute two right steps. The next squad to the left will execute four right steps. If there are four squads in the platoon, the first (left) squad will execute six right steps. While side stepping, cover and alignment will be maintained. Steps may be adjusted slightly so that a 4" interval is obtained. Upon completion of the designated number of steps, members of the squad will halt and resume the position of attention.

When marching and the guide is right, the command of execution "MARCH" is given as the right foot strikes the deck. At this command:

The base (right) squad takes one more 30" step with the left foot and then begins to half step. The squad to the left of the base squad takes one more 30" step to the front with the left foot; execute right oblique toward the base squad for one step and then steps 30" back to the original front. The squad then begins to half step. The next squad to the left takes one more 30" step to the front and then executes right oblique toward the base squad for three steps and steps 30" back to the original front. The squad then begins to half step. If there are four squads in the platoon, the first (left) squad would execute the same movements as above except the members would take five steps in the oblique. Steps in the oblique may be adjusted slightly so that a 4" interval is obtained. At the command "Forward, MARCH" all squads resume taking 30" steps.

If the guide has been shifted to the left or center, the base squad will become the squad behind the guide. The commands of execution will be given as the left foot strikes the deck, if guide is left, or on either foot, if guide is center. Side steps or oblique movements will be made toward the base squad as appropriate.

The platoon commander, on his command "MARCH," oblique the number of steps necessary to remain parallel to the platoon and picks up the half step. The platoon commander picks up a full 30" step on his command of "Forward, MARCH."

To Extend to Normal Interval

The purpose of this movement is to extend the interval between files in a column from close to normal interval. It may be executed when halted or marching in column at close interval. The command is "Extend, MARCH."

When halted and the guide is right, on the command of execution "MARCH," members of the base (right) squad stand fast. Members of the squad next to the base squad will execute two left steps. The next squad to the left will execute four left steps. If there are four squads in the platoon, the first (left) squad will execute six left steps. While side stepping, cover and alignment will be maintained. Steps may be adjusted slightly so that one arms interval is obtained between squad leaders. Upon completion of the designated number of steps, members of the squad will halt and resume the position of attention.

When marching and the guide is right, the command of execution "MARCH" is given as the left foot strikes the deck. At this command:

The base (right) squad takes one more 30" step with the right foot and then begins to half step. The squad next to the base squad takes one more 30" step to the front with the right foot, executes left oblique away from the base squad for one step and steps 30" back to the original front. The squad then begins to half step. The next squad to the left takes one more 30" step to the front and then executes left oblique away from the base squad for three steps and steps 30" back to the original front. The squad then begins to half step. If there are four squads in the platoon, the first (left) squad would execute the same movements as above except the members would take five steps in the oblique. Steps in the oblique may be adjusted slightly so that a one-arm interval is obtained between squad leaders. At the command "Forward, MARCH," all squads resume taking 30" steps.

If the guide has been shifted to the left or center, the base squad will become the squad behind the guide. Side steps or oblique movements will then be made away from the base squad as appropriate.

The platoon commander, on his command "MARCH," oblique the number of steps necessary to remain six paces from the platoon and picks up the half step. The platoon commander picks up a full 30" step on his command of "Forward, MARCH.

To Change the Direction of March

The purpose of this movement is to change the direction of march of a column. It may be executed when the platoon is halted or marching in column at normal or close interval. The command is "Column Right (Column Left, Column Half Right or Column Half Left), MARCH." The base element during the turn is the squad on the flank in the direction of the turn. The leading member of the base squad, excluding the platoon commander and guide, establishes the pivot for the movement.

When marching, the commands of execution are given on the foot in the direction of the turn. On the command of execution "MARCH," the leading member of the base squad takes one more 30" step to the front and then pivots 90 degrees to the right (left) on the ball of the left (right) foot. He then takes one 30" step in the new direction before beginning to half step. At the same time, other members of the leading rank execute a right (left) oblique. They step in this direction until they are on line with the new line of march (normally two, four, and six steps respectively) and then execute a second right (left) oblique. The original interval is maintained while in the oblique. Stepping out of the second oblique with a 30" step, they begin to half step as soon as they are aligned on the base squad leader. When all members of the same rank have come abreast, everyone in that rank resumes a full step. Ranks in rear of the leading rank execute the pivot movements on the same points and in the same way as the leading rank.

When halted, at the command of execution "MARCH," the leading member of the base squad faces to the right (left) as in marching and takes one 30" step in the new direction with the right (left) foot. At the same time, other members of the leading rank step off in the right (left) oblique. Members behind the lead rank step off to the front as in forward march. The remainder of the movement is executed the same as in marching.

During column movements, the platoon commander and guide execute either an oblique or a 90-degree pivot (depending on the direction of the movement) on the command of execution. After completing their turn, they adjust their line of march so that they are in front of the appropriate squad.

For slight changes of direction, the command is "INCLINE TO THE RIGHT (LEFT)." At that command, the guide changes direction as commanded. This is not a precision movement and is executed only while marching.

To March To The Flank

The purpose of this movement is to march the platoon to the right or left flank for a short distance. It may be executed from any formation that is marching at quick time or double time cadence. The command is "By the Right (Left) Flank, MARCH." The command of execution is given as the foot in the direction of the turn strikes the deck.

To execute a right flank when marching at quick time, the command is "By the Right Flank, MARCH." On the command of execution "MARCH," everyone takes one more 30" step to the front with the left foot and then pivots 90 degrees to the right on the ball of the left foot. Stepping out of the pivot with a 30" step, the entire platoon marches in line to the right flank. The platoon commander and guide execute the flanking movement with the platoon but do not change their position within the platoon. For the platoon to resume marching in the original direction, the command is "By the Left Flank, MARCH." To march to the left flank, substitute left for right and right for left in the above sequence. No other command may be given when marching to the flank until the unit has resumed marching to the original front.

When this movement is executed from a column at close interval, squad(s) to the rear of the squad that becomes the leading squad takes up the half step. They resume a full step as soon as a 40" distance has opened between squads. After such a movement, the platoon maintains normal interval until close march is commanded.

When marching at double time, on the command of execution "MARCH," everyone takes two more 36" steps to the front and then two 6" vertical steps in place at double time cadence. While stepping in place, everyone turns 90 degrees toward the direction commanded and then steps off with a 36" step in the new direction.

When the platoon executes flank movements from a column at close interval, squad(s) to the rear of the squad that becomes the leading squad, will take up a half step. They resume a full step as soon as a 40" distance has opened between squads. After such a movement, the platoon maintains normal interval until close march is commanded.

To March In The Oblique

The purpose of this movement is to shift the line of march to the right or left for a short distance and then resume marching in the original direction. It may be executed from any formation that is marching at quick time cadence. The command is "Right (Left) Oblique, MARCH." The word oblique is pronounced to rhyme with strike. The command of execution is given as the foot in the direction of the turn strikes the deck. The command to resume the original direction of march is "Forward, MARCH." The command of execution is given as the foot toward the original front strikes the deck.

To teach the platoon to march to the oblique, the instructor aligns the unit and has members face half right (left). The instructor then explains that these positions are maintained when marching to the oblique. This is achieved by individuals keeping their shoulders parallel to the persons in front and/or adjacent to them. The individual at the corner of the platoon towards the direction of the oblique is the base of the movement and must maintain a steady line of march keeping his other shoulders blocked perpendicular to the direction of march.

To march the platoon in the right oblique, the command is "Right Oblique, MARCH." On the command "MARCH," everyone then takes one more 30" step to the front with the left foot and pivots 45 degrees to the right on the ball of the left foot. Stepping out of the pivot with a 30" step, the entire platoon marches to the right oblique until given another command. For the platoon to resume marching in the original direction, the command is "Forward, MARCH," in this case the command of execution will be given as the left foot strikes the deck. Everyone then takes one more step in the oblique direction with the right foot; pivots back to the original front and continue to march. To march to the left oblique, substitute left for right and right for left in the above sequence.

To halt the squad facing in the original direction of march the command is "Platoon, HALT." The command of execution "HALT" is given on the left foot when marching to the right oblique and on the right foot when marching to the left oblique. At the command "HALT," everyone takes one more step in the oblique direction, pivots to the original front on the toe of the right (left) foot, and places the left (right) foot beside the other at the position of attention.

To temporarily halt the squad in the oblique direction, in order to correct errors, the command is "In Place, HALT." The command of execution "HALT" may be given as either foot strikes the deck. At the command of execution "HALT," the squad halts in two counts as in quick time and remains facing in the oblique direction. The only command that can be given after halting in place is "Resume, MARCH." At that command, the movement continues marching in the oblique direction.

When given half step or mark time while marching in the oblique, the only commands that may be given are, "Resume, MARCH," to continue marching with a 30" step in the oblique, or "In Place, HALT," to halt in the oblique in order to correct errors.

To March to The Rear

The purpose of this movement is to march the platoon to the rear for a short distance. It may be executed when halted or marching forward at quick time or double time. The command is "To the Rear, MARCH" it will be given as the right foot strikes the deck.

When halted, on the command of execution "MARCH," everyone takes one 15" step to the front with the left foot and then pivots 180 degrees toward the right on the balls of both feet. Stepping out of the pivot with a 30" step, the entire platoon marches to the rear. For the platoon to resume marching in the original direction, the command "To the Rear, MARCH" is given again. No other command may be given when marching to the rear until the unit has resumed marching to the original front.

When marching at quick time, on the command of execution "MARCH," everyone takes one more 15" step to the front with the left foot and then pivots 180 degrees toward the right on the balls of both feet. Stepping out of the pivot with a 30" step, the entire platoon marches to the rear. For the platoon to resume marching in the original direction, the command "To the Rear, MARCH" is given again. No other command may be given when marching to the rear until the unit has resumed marching to the original front.

When marching at double time, on the command of execution "MARCH," everyone takes two more 36" steps to the front and then four 6" vertical steps in place at double time cadence. On the first and third steps in place, everyone pivots 180 degrees to the right. After the fourth step in place, and for the fifth step, they step off with a 36" step in the new direction. For the platoon to resume marching in the original direction, the command "To the Rear, MARCH" is given again. No other command may be given when marching to the rear until the unit has resumed marching to the original front.

Commandants of the Marine Corps

Major Samuel Nicholas, 1775–1781
Lieutenant Colonel William Ward Burrows, 1798–1804
Lieutenant Colonel Franklin Wharton, 1804–1818
Lieutenant Colonel Anthony Gale, 1819–1820
Brigadier General Archibald Henderson, 1820–1859
Colonel John Harris, 1859–1864
Brigadier General Jacob Zeilin, 1864–1876
Colonel Charles G. McCawley, 1876–1891
Major General Charles Heywood, 1891–1903
Major General George F. Elliott, 1903–1910
Major General William P. Biddle, 1911–1914
Major General George Barnett, 1914–1920
Major General John A. Lejeune, 1920–1929
Major General Wendell C. Neville, 1929–1930
Major General Ben H. Fuller, 1930–1934
Major General John H. Russell, Jr., 1934–1936
Lieutenant General Thomas Holcomb, 1936–1943
General Alexander A. Vandegrift, 1944–1947
General Clifton B. Cates, 1948–1951
General Lemuel C. Shepherd, Jr., 1952–1955

General Randolph McC. Pate, 1956–1959
General David M. Shoup, 1960–1963
General Wallace M. Greene, Jr., 1964–1967
General Leonard E. Chapman, Jr., 1968–1971
General Robert E. Cushman, 1972–1975
General Louis H. Wilson, Jr., 1975–1979
General Robert H. Barrow, 1979–1983
General Paul X. Kelley, 1983–1987
General Alfred M. Gray, 1987–1991
General Carl E. Mundy, Jr., 1991–1995
General Charles C. Krulak, 1995–1999
General James L. Jones, 1999–2003
General Michael W. Hagee, 2003–2006
General James T. Conway, 2006–2010
General James F. Amos, 2010–2014
General Joseph Dunford, 2014–2015
General Robert B. Neller, 2015–2019
General David H. Berger, 2019–present

Sergeants Major of the Marine Corps

Wilbur Bestwick, 1957–1959
Francis D. Rauber, 1959–1962
Thomas J. McHugh, 1962–1965
Herbert J. Sweet, 1965–1969
Joseph W. Dailey, 1969–1973
Clinton A. Puckett, 1973–1975
Henry H. Black, 1975–1977
John R. Massaro, 1977–1979
Leland D. Crawford, 1979–1983
Robert E. Cleary, 1983–1987

David W. Sommers, 1987–1991
Harold G. Overstreet, 1991–1995
Lewis G. Lee, 1995–1999
Alford L. McMichael, 1999–2003
John L. Estrada, 2003–2007
Carlton W. Kent, 2007–2011
Micheal P. Barrett, 2011–2015
Ronald L. Green, 2015–2019
Troy E. Black, 2019–present

Insignia of Grade

One of the first things you will need to know upon entering the service is how to recognize the grades and ratings of the Marines and Navy personnel with whom you serve. To help you do this, the charts on the following pages outline Marine enlisted and officer grades and give corresponding Navy, Army, and Air Force ratings. But if you are to fully understand these grades and ratings, you must do more than simply distinguish among the various insignia that are worn or the grade by which the various individuals are addressed. You must recognize at the same time everything that is represented by these grades and insignia.

Specifically, you must understand that in the Marine Corps, only those who have demonstrated ability and a willingness to accept responsibility wear insignia of grade. If these individuals are to discharge the responsibilities with which they are charged, it is necessary that they be equipped with a degree of authority as well. Remember that grade, insignia, ability, responsibility, and authority all go together.

Enlisted Grades and Ratings

Marine enlisted persons wear insignia of grade on both sleeves.

Grade chevrons of the Marine Corps are forest green on the service uniform, with a background of red. On shirts, the background is khaki. For the dress blue uniform, chevrons are gold on scarlet. Marines wear one slanting service stripe, "hash mark," near the cuff of the sleeve on the service or dress blue uniform for each four years' enlistment completed.

All rating badges of Navy enlisted personnel are worn on the left sleeve between the shoulder and elbow. Metal or embroidered breast insignia are worn on the left breast to indicate a special qualification or designation, e.g., Submarine, Surface Warfare, Fleet Marine Force, Aircrew, etc.

All specialty marks (gunner's mate, hospital corpsman, etc.) are worn on the right sleeve between the shoulder and elbow.

The pay grade and rating group of nonrated persons are indicated by diagonal stripes worn on the upper part of the left sleeve in the same position prescribed for rating badges.

	MARINES	NAVY / COAST GUARD	ARMY	AIR FORCE
E1	Private	Seaman Recruit (SR)	Private	Airman Basic TOP
E2	Private First Class (PFC) 	Seaman Apprentice (SA) 	Private E-1 (PV2) 	Airman (Amn) 
E3	Lance Corporal (LCpl) 	Seaman (SN) 	Private First Class (PFC) 	Airman First Class (A1C) 
E4	Corporal (Cpl) 	Petty Officer Third Class (PO3)** 	Corporal (Cpl)  Specialist (SPC) 	Senior Airman (SrA) 
E5	Sergeant (Sgt) 	Petty Officer Second Class (PO2)** 	Sergeant (Sgt) 	Staff Sergeant (SSgt) 

Figure A-1. Enlisted grades and ratings.

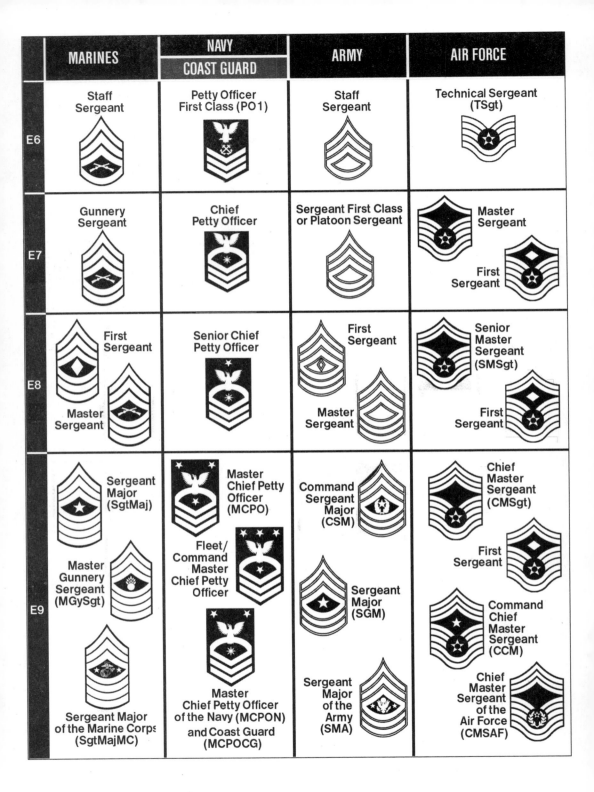

	MARINES	NAVY / COAST GUARD	ARMY	AIR FORCE
E6	Staff Sergeant	Petty Officer First Class (PO1)	Staff Sergeant	Technical Sergeant (TSgt)
E7	Gunnery Sergeant	Chief Petty Officer	Sergeant First Class or Platoon Sergeant	Master Sergeant / First Sergeant
E8	First Sergeant / Master Sergeant	Senior Chief Petty Officer	First Sergeant / Master Sergeant	Senior Master Sergeant (SMSgt) / First Sergeant
E9	Sergeant Major (SgtMaj) / Master Gunnery Sergeant (MGySgt) / Sergeant Major of the Marine Corps (SgtMajMC)	Master Chief Petty Officer (MCPO) / Fleet/ Command Master Chief Petty Officer / Master Chief Petty Officer of the Navy (MCPON) and Coast Guard (MCPOCG)	Command Sergeant Major (CSM) / Sergeant Major (SGM) / Sergeant Major of the Army (SMA)	Chief Master Sergeant (CMSgt) / First Sergeant / Command Chief Master Sergeant (CCM) / Chief Master Sergeant of the Air Force (CMSAF)

Officer Grades

Marine Corps officers wear gold or silver insignia of grade on the shoulder straps of their coats or overcoats. They also wear small replicas of this insignia on their shirt collars. Navy officers' ranks can be determined by gold stripes on shoulder boards (epaulettes) of their white coats.

The stripes are either 1/2 or 1/4" wide, depending upon the grade indicated. On blue uniforms, the rank of the officer is shown by gold stripes around the bottom part of both coat sleeves. In addition to the stripes which designate rank, Navy officers may also wear on their shirt collars insignia like that of the corresponding Marine Corps ranks—bars, leaves, eagles, and stars.

Marine Corps officers, in addition to their insignia of rank, can be identified by the quatrefoil (twisted braid) on top of their service caps.

Army and Air Force ranks are like those of Marine officers. Coast Guard ranks are like those of the Navy.

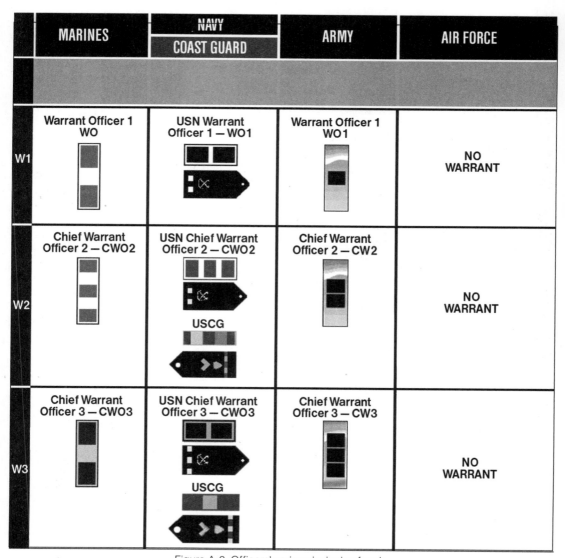

Figure A-2. Officers' various insignia of rank.

	MARINES	NAVY COAST GUARD	ARMY	AIR FORCE
W4	Chief Warrant Officer 4 — CWO4	USN Chief Warrant Officer 4 — CWO4 USCG	Chief Warrant Officer 4 — CW4	NO WARRANT
W5	Chief Warrant Officer 5 — CWO5	USN Chief Warrant Officer — CWO5	Chief Warrant Officer — CW5	NO WARRANT
O1	Second Lieutenant 2nd Lt.	Ensign ENS	Second Lieutenant LT	Second Lieutenant 2nd Lt.
O2	First Lieutenant 1st Lt.	Lieutenant Junior Grade — LTJG	First Lieutenant 1LT	First Lieutenant 1st Lt.

	MARINES	NAVY / COAST GUARD	ARMY	AIR FORCE
03	Captain Capt.	Lieutenant LT	Captain CPT	Captain Capt.
04	Major Maj.	Lieutenant Commander — LCDR	Major MAJ	Major Maj.
05	Lieutenant Colonel Lt. Col.	Commander CDR	Lieutenant Colonel LTC	Lieutenant Colonel Lt. Col.

MARINES	NAVY / COAST GUARD	ARMY	AIR FORCE
06 Colonel Col.	Captain CAPT	Colonel COL.	Colonel Col.
07 Brigadier General Brig. Gen.	Rear Admiral Lower Half — RDML	Brigadier General BG	Brigadier General Brig. Gen.
08 Major General Maj. Gen.	Rear Admiral Upper Half — RADM	Major General MG	Major General Maj. Gen.
09 Lieutenant General Lt. Gen.	Vice Admiral VADM	Lieutenant General LTG	Lieutenant General Lt. Gen.

MARINES	NAVY / COAST GUARD	ARMY	AIR FORCE
General Gen. Commandant of the Marine Corps	Admiral ADM Chief of Naval Operations and Commandant of the Coast Guard	General GEN Army Chief of Staff	General Gen. Air Force Chief of Staff
	Fleet Admiral (Reserved for wartime only)	General of the Army (Reserved for wartime only)	General of the Air Force (Reserved for wartime only)

O-10

APPENDIX C

Common Military Terms

ASSIGN

1. The placement of units or personnel in an organization where such placement is relatively permanent and/or such organization controls and administers the units or personnel for the primary function, or greater portion of the functions, of the unit or personnel.

2. The detailing of individuals to specific duties or functions where such duties or functions are primary and/or relatively permanent.

ATTACH

1. The placement of units or personnel in an organization where such placement is relatively temporary. Subject to the limitations of the attachment order, the commander of the formation, unit, or organization receiving the attachment will exercise the same degree of command and control as the commander does over units and persons belonging to the command. However, the parent formation, unit, or organization will normally retain the responsibility for transfer and promotion of personnel.

2. The detailing of individuals to specific functions where such functions are secondary or relatively temporary.

AXIS OF ADVANCE

A line of advance assigned for the purposes of control, often a road or a group of roads, or a designated series of locations, extending in the direction of the enemy.

BARRAGE

A prearranged barrier of fire designed to protect friendly troops and installations by impeding enemy movements across defensive lines or areas.

BATTALION LANDING TEAM (BLT)

In an amphibious operation, an infantry battalion normally reinforced by the necessary combat service and combat service support elements; the basic unit for planning an assault landing.

BATTERY

1. Tactical and administrative artillery unit or subunit corresponding to a company or similar unit.

2. All guns, torpedo tubes, searchlights, or missile launchers of the same size or caliber or used for the same purpose, either installed on one ship or otherwise operating as an entity.

BEACHHEAD

A designated area on a hostile shore that, when seized and held, ensures the continuous landing of troops and material, and provides maneuver space requisite for subsequent projected operations ashore. It is the physical objective of an amphibious operation.

BEATEN ZONE

The space on the ground or target on which the shots forming the cone of dispersion strike.

BILLET

1. Shelter for troops.

2. To quarter troops.

3. A personnel position or assignment which may be filled by one person.

BOOBY TRAP
An explosive charge that is exploded when an unsuspecting person disturbs an apparently harmless object or performs a presumably safe act.

BOUND
1. Single movement, usually from cover-to-cover, made by troops often under enemy artillery fire or small arms fire.
2. Distance covered in one movement by a unit that is advancing by bounds.

CHAIN OF COMMAND
The succession of commanding officers from a superior to a subordinate through which command is exercised. Also called command channel.

CHALLENGE
Any process carried out by one unit or person with the object of determining the friendly or hostile character or identity of another.

CLEAR
1. To approve or authorize, or to obtain approval or authorization for:
   a. a person or persons with regard to their actions, movements, duties, etc.
   b. an object or group of objects, such as equipment or supplies, with regard to quality, quantity, purpose, movement, disposition, etc.
   c. a request with regard to correctness of form, validity, etc.
2. Specifically, to give one or more aircraft a clearance.
3. To give a person a security clearance.
4. To fly over an obstacle without touching it.
5. To pass a designated point, line, or object. The end of a column must pass the designated feature before the latter is cleared.
6. To operate a weapon so as to unload it or make certain no ammunition remains or to free it of a stoppage.

CLOSE AIR SUPPORT (CAS)
Air action against hostile targets that are in close proximity to friendly forces and that require detailed integration of each air mission with the fire and movement of those forces.

COLLECTING POINT
A point designated for the assembly of personnel casualties, prisoners of war, stragglers, disabled materiel, or salvage for further movement to collecting stations or rear installations.

COMBAT INTELLIGENCE
That knowledge of the enemy, weather, and geographical features required by a commander in the planning and conduct of tactical operations.

COMMAND
1. The authority a commander in the military service lawfully exercises over subordinates by virtue of rank or assignment. Command includes the authority and responsibility for effectively using available resources and for planning the employment of, organizing, directing, coordinating, and controlling military forces for the accomplishment of assigned missions. It also includes responsibility for health, welfare, morale, and discipline of assigned personnel.
2. An order given by a commander—that is, the will of the commander expressed for the purpose of bringing about a particular action.
3. A unit or units, an organization or an area under the command of one individual.
4. To dominate by a field of fire or by observation from a superior position.

COMMAND POST
A unit's or subunit's headquarters where the commander and the staff perform their activities.

CONCEALMENT
The protection from observation only.

CONE OF DISPERSION

A conical-shaped pattern formed by the trajectories of a group of shots fired from the same weapon with the same sight setting.

CONTAIN

To stop, hold, or surround the forces of the enemy or to cause the enemy to center their activity on a given front and to prevent the withdrawing of any part of the forces for use elsewhere.

CONTOUR INTERVAL

The difference in elevation between two adjacent contour lines.

CONTOUR LINE

A line on a map or chart connecting points of equal elevation.

COUNTERATTACK

Attack by a part or all of a defending force against an enemy attacking force for such specific purposes as regaining ground lost or cutting off or destroying enemy advance units, and with the general objective of denying to the enemy the attainment of the purpose in attacking.

COUNTERGUERRILLA WARFARE

Operations and activities conducted by armed forces, paramilitary forces, or non-military agencies of a government against guerrillas.

COVER

1. The action of land, air, or sea forces to protect by offense, defense, or threat of either or both.
2. Shelter or protection, either natural or artificial.

COUNTERINSURGENCY

Those military, paramilitary, political, economic, psychological, and civic actions taken by a government to defeat subversive insurgency.

CRITICAL POINT

1. A key geographical point or position important to the success of an operation.
2. In point of time, a crisis or a turning point in an operation.

3. A selected point along a line of march used for reference in giving instructions.
4. A point where there is a change of direction or change in slope in a ridge or stream.
5. Any point along a route of march where interference with a troop movement may occur.

D-DAY

1. The unnamed day on which a particular operation commences or is to commence.
2. Time in plans will be indicated by a letter that shows the unit of time employed, and figures, with a minus or plus sign to indicate the amount of time before or after the reference event, e.g., "D" is for a particular day, "H" for an hour. Similarly, D+7 means seven days after D-day, H+2 means two hours after H-hour. If the figure becomes unduly large, for example, D-day plus 90, the designation of D+3 months may be employed.

DEADLINE

To remove a vehicle or piece of equipment from operation or use for one of the following reasons:

a. is inoperative due to damage, malfunctioning, or necessary repairs. The term does not include items temporarily removed from use by reason of routine maintenance and repairs that do not affect the combat capability of the item.

b. is unsafe; and

c. would be damaged by further use.

DEAD SPACE

The area within the maximum range of a weapon that cannot be covered by fire from a particular position because of the intervening obstacles or because of the nature of the ground.

DEFILADE

1. Protection from hostile ground observation and fire provided by an obstacle, such as a hill, ridge, or bank.
2. A vertical distance by which a position is concealed from enemy observation.
3. To shield from enemy fire or observation by using natural or artificial obstacles.

DEMILITARIZED ZONE (DMZ)

A defined area in which the stationing or concentrating of military forces, or the retention or establishment of military installations of any description, is prohibited.

DEMOLITION

The destruction of structures, facilities, or material by use of fire, water, explosives, mechanical, or other means.

DEPLOY

1. In a strategic sense, to relocate forces to desired areas of operations.
2. To extend or widen the front of a military unit, extending from close order to a battle formation.
3. To change from a cruising approach or contact disposition to a disposition for a naval battle.

DIRECT FIRE

Fire in which the gunner aims the weapon by means of a sight directly at the target.

DISPERSION

1. A scattered pattern of hits by bombs dropped under identical conditions or by projectiles fired from the same gun or group of guns with the same firing data.
2. The spreading or separating of troops, material, establishments, or activities that are usually concentrated in limited areas to reduce vulnerability to enemy action.

DISPLACEMENT

The movement of supporting weapons from one firing position to another.

DISTANCE

The space between adjacent personnel, vehicles, or units in a formation measured from front to rear.

DUMP

A temporary storage area, usually in the open, for bombs, ammunition, equipment, or supplies.

ECHELON

1. A subdivision of a headquarters, e.g., forward echelon, rear echelon.
2. Separate level of command. As compared to a regiment, a division is a higher echelon; a battalion is a lower echelon.
3. A fraction of a command in the direction of depth, to which a principal combat mission is assigned, e.g., attack echelon, reserve echelon.
4. A formation in which the subdivisions are placed one behind the other, extending backward either left or right at an angle from the lead element.

ELEVATION

The vertical distance of ground forms, usually measured in feet or meters, above mean sea level (plus elevation) or below mean sea level (minus elevation).

EMPLACEMENT

1. A prepared position for one or more weapons or pieces of equipment for protection against hostile fire or bombardment and from which they can execute their tasks.
2. The act of fixing a gun in a prepared position from which it may be fired.

ENFILADE FIRE

Fire delivered on a target so that the beaten zone of the fire coincides with the long axis of the target (fire in the direction of the length of a line or column).

ENVELOPMENT

An attack made on one or both of the enemy's flanks or rear, usually accompanied by an attack in the front.

ESCALATION OF FORCE

An authorized procedure used when security personnel determine an immediate threat or danger in effect.

FIELD OF FIRE

The area which a weapon or group of weapons may cover effectively with fire from a given position.

FINAL PROTECTIVE LINE

A predetermined line along which, in order to stop enemy assaults, interlocking fire is placed from all available flat-trajectory weapons, fixed as to direction and elevation and capable of delivery under any conditions of visibility. Barrages fired by mortars and artillery fill in gaps in these interlocking bands of fire.

FIRE DISCIPLINE

A state of order, coolness, efficiency, and obedience existing among troops engaged in a firefight.

FIRE MISSION

1. Specific assignment given to a fire unit as part of a definite plan.
2. Order used to alert the weapon battery and indicate that the message following is a call for fire.

FIXED FIRE

Fire from a weapon or weapons directed at a single point or a small area.

FLANKING FIRE

Fire directed against a target from an area on its flank. Flanking fire may be enfilade or oblique fire.

FLAT TRAJECTORY

A trajectory having little or no curvature.

FLEET MARINE FORCE (FMF)

A balanced force of combined arms comprising land, air, and service elements of the USMC. A Fleet Marine Force is an integral part of a U.S. Fleet and has the status of a type command.

FORWARD AIR CONTROLLER (FAC)

An officer (aviator) member of the tactical air control party/team who, from a forward position, controls aircraft engaged in close air support of ground troops.

FORWARD EDGE OF THE BATTLE AREA (FEBA)

A line at the forward edge of the battle area, designated for the purpose of coordinating the fire of all units and supporting weapons, including air and naval gunfire. It defines the forward limits of a series of mutually supporting defensive areas but does not include the areas occupied or used by covering or screening forces.

FORWARD OBSERVER (FO)

An observer operating with front line troops and trained to adjust ground or naval gunfire and air bombardment and pass battlefield information to the rear.

FORWARD OPERATIONSBASE (FOB)

In special operations, a base usually located in friendly territory or afloat that is established to extend command and control or communications or to provide support for training and tactical operations. Facilities may be established for temporary or longer duration operations and may include an airfield or an unimproved airstrip, an anchorage, or a pier.

FRONT

1. The lateral space occupied by an element, measured from the extremity of one flank to the extremity of the other flank.
2. The direction of the enemy.
3. The line of contact of two opposing forces.

GENERAL ORDERS

1. Permanent instructions issued in order form that apply to all members of a command, as compared with special orders which affect only individuals or small groups. General orders are usually concerned with matters of policy or administration.
2. A series of permanent guard orders that govern the duties of a sentry on post.

GRAZING FIRE

Fire that is approximately parallel to the ground and does not rise above the height of a person standing.

GUERRILLA WARFARE

Military and paramilitary operations conducted in enemy-held or hostile territory by irregular, predominantly indigenous forces.

HARASSING FIRE

Fire designed to disturb the rest of the enemy troops, to curtail movement and, by threat of losses, to lower morale.

HELICOPTER ASSAULT FORCE

A task organization combining helicopters, supporting units and helicopter-borne troop units for use in helicopter-borne assault operations.

HELICOPTER LANDING ZONES

A specified ground area for landing assault helicopters to embark or disembark troops and/or cargo. A landing zone may contain one or more landing sites.

HELICOPTER TEAM

The combat-equipped troops lifted in one helicopter at one time.

H-HOUR

The specified hour on D-Day at which a particular operation commences.

INDIRECT FIRE

Fire delivered at a target that cannot be seen from the gun position.

INFILTRATION

The movement through or into an area or territory occupied by either friendly or enemy troops or organizations. The movement is made by either small groups or by individuals at extended or irregular intervals. When used in connection with the enemy, it implies that contact is avoided.

IN SUPPORT OF

Assisting or protecting another formation, unit, or organization while remaining under original control.

INSURGENCY

A condition resulting from a revolt or insurrection against a constituted government that falls short of a civil war.

INTERDICT

To prevent or hinder, by any means, enemy use of an area or route.

KEY POINT

A concentrated site or installation, the destruction or capture of which would seriously affect the war effort or the success of operations.

LINE OF DEPARTURE (LOD)

1. A line designated to coordinate the departure of attack or scouting elements; a jump-off line.

2. A suitably marked offshore coordinating line to assist assault craft to land on designated beaches at scheduled times.

LOCAL SECURITY

A security element independent of any outpost established by a leader to protect the unit against surprise and assure its readiness for action.

LINES OF COMMUNICATION (LOC)

All of the routes, land, water, and air, that connect an operating military force with a base of operations and along which supplies and reinforcements move.

LOGISTICS

The science of planning and carrying out the movement and maintenance of forces. In its most comprehensive sense, those aspects of military operations that deal with:

a. design and development, acquisition, storage, movement, distribution, maintenance, evacuation, and disposition of material;

b. movement, evacuation, and hospitalization of personnel;

c. acquisition or construction, maintenance, operation, and disposition of facilities; and

d. acquisition or furnishing of services.

MAIN ATTACK

The principal attack or effort into which the commander throws the full weight of the offensive power at his disposal. An attack directed against the chief objective of the campaign or battle.

MANEUVER

The operation of a ship, aircraft, vehicle, or unit to cause it to perform desired movements.

MARINE AIR-GROUND TASK FORCE (MAGTF)

A Marine Corps air-ground team consisting of one ground combat unit, one air combat unit, one combat support unit, and one command unit. Examples of MAGTF are MEU, MEF, and SPMAGTF.

MARINE EXPEDITIONARY FORCE (MEF)

A Marine air-ground task force built around a Marine division and a Marine aircraft wing. The Marine expeditionary force normally employs the full combat resources of one Marine division/wing team and Marine Logistics Group.

MARINE EXPEDITIONARY UNIT (MEU)

A Marine air-ground task force built around a battalion landing team and a composite squadron (includes two or more types of helicopters and may include VSTOL attack aircraft). The Marine expeditionary unit normally employs about one-ninth of the combat resources of one Marine division/wing team and a logistical support unit.

MASK

Any natural or artificial obstruction that affords shelter or interferes with observation or fire.

MASS

1. The concentration of combat power.
2. To concentrate or bring together, as to mass the fire of all batteries.
3. The military formation in which units are spaced at less than normal distances and intervals.

MILITARY CIVIC ACTION

The use of preponderantly indigenous military forces on projects useful to the local population at all levels in such areas as education, training, public works, agriculture, transportation, and others contributing to economic and social development, which would also serve to improve the standing of the military forces with the population. (U.S. Forces may at times advise or engage in military civic actions in overseas areas.)

MISSION

1. The objective; the task together with the purpose, which clearly indicate the action to be taken and the reason therefore.
2. In common usage, especially when applied to lower military units, a duty assigned to an individual or unit; a task.
3. The dispatching of one or more aircraft to accomplish one particular task.

MUZZLE VELOCITY

The velocity of a projectile at the instant the projectile leaves the muzzle of a weapon.

OBJECTIVE

The physical object of the action taken, e.g., a definite tactical feature, the seizure and/or holding of which is essential to the commander's plan.

OBLIQUE FIRE

Fire placed on a target from a direction that is diagonal to the long dimension of the target or on an enemy from a direction that is between the enemy's front and flank.

OBSERVATION POST (OP)

A position from which military observations are made or fire directed and adjusted, and which possesses appropriate communications: it may be airborne.

OBSERVED FIRE

Fire for which the points of impact or burst can be seen by an observer. The fire can be controlled and adjusted on the basis of observation.

OCCUPY

To take possession of or to remain in a place or area.

OPERATION ORDER

A directive, usually formal, issued by a commander to subordinate commanders for the purpose of effecting the coordinated execution of an operation.

ORDER

A communication, written, oral, or by signal, that conveys instructions from a superior to a subordinate. In a broad sense, the terms "order" and "command" are synonymous. However, an order implies discretion as to the details of execution whereas a command does not.

ORGANIZE

To prepare a position or terrain for defense.

OUTPOST

A stationary body of troops placed at some distance from the main body, while at the halt or in a defensive position, to protect the main body from surprise, observation, and annoyance from enemy ground troops.

PASSAGE OF LINES

A rearrangement of units in which the rear unit moves forward through the already established line while the replaced unit remains in position or moves to the rear.

PATROL

A detachment of ground, sea, or air forces sent by a larger unit for the purpose of gathering information or carrying out a destructive, harassing, mopping-up, or security mission.

PENETRATION

A form of offensive maneuver that seeks to break through the enemy's defensive positions, widen the gap created, and destroy the continuity of their positions.

PERIMETER DEFENSE

A defense without an exposed flank consisting of forces deployed along the perimeter of the defended area.

PHASE LINE

The line utilized for control and coordination of military operations, usually a terrain feature extending across the zone of action.

POSITION

The area or locality occupied by combat elements, especially for defense.

PREPARATION FIRE

Fire delivered on a target preparatory to an assault.

PRIMARY FIRING POSITION

The best available position from which the primary fire mission of a weapon, individual, unit, or units is executed.

RAID

An operation, usually small scale, involving a swift penetration of hostile territory to secure information, confuse the enemy, or destroy installations. It ends with a planned withdrawal upon completion of the assigned mission.

RANGE

1. The distance between any given point and an object or target.
2. Extent or distance limiting the operation or action of something, such as the range of an airplane, vehicle, or weapon.
3. Area equipped for practice in shooting at targets.

RATE OF FIRE

The number of rounds fired from a weapon in a minute.

REAR GUARD

Security detachment that protects the rear of a column from hostile forces. During a withdrawal, it delays the enemy by armed resistance, destroying bridges, and blocking roads.

RECONNAISSANCE

A mission undertaken to obtain, by visual observation or other detection methods, information about the activities and resources of an enemy or potential enemy or to secure data concerning the meteorological, hydrographic, or geographic characteristics of a particular area.

RECONNAISSANCE BY FIRE

A method of reconnaissance in which fire is placed on a suspected enemy position to cause the enemy to disclose a presence by movement or return of fire.

REGISTRATION FIRE

Fire delivered to obtain accurate data for subsequent effective engagement of targets.

REINFORCE

To strengthen by the addition of personnel or military equipment.

RESERVE

A fraction of a unit held initially under the control of a unit leader as a maneuvering element to influence future action.

RULES OF ENGAGEMENT (ROE)

Directives issued by competent military authority that delineate the circumstances and limitations under which U.S. forces will initiate and/or continue combat engagement with other forces encountered.

SEARCHING FIRE

Fire distributed in depth by successive changes in the elevation of the weapon.

SECTOR OF FIRE

An area, limited by boundaries, assigned to a unit or to a weapon to cover by fire.

SECURE

To gain possession of a position or terrain feature with or without force, and to make such disposition as will prevent, as far as possible, its destruction or loss by enemy action.

SECURITY

All measures taken by a unit to protect itself from observation, annoyance, or surprise attack by the enemy.

SENSOR

A technical means to extend man's natural senses; equipment that detects and indicates terrain configuration, the presence of military targets, and other natural and man-made objects and activities by means of energy emitted or reflected by such targets or objects.

SITE

The position of anything. For example, the position of a gun emplacement.

SMALL ARMS

All arms including automatic weapons, up to and including caliber .60 and shotguns.

SPECIAL PURPOSE MAGTF

A SPMAGTF is organized to accomplish missions for which the MEF and MEU are not appropriate or are too large to employ. It can be deployed by amphibious or commercial ships, tactical or strategic airlift, or organic Marine Corps aviation.

a. The command element (CE) is structured to conduct command and control of operational functions and is tailored to the mission and task organization of the SPMAGTF.

b. The ground combat element (GCE) is composed of at least a platoon-sized element.

c. The aviation combat element (ACE) is a task-organized detachment of aircraft.

d. The combat service support element (CSSE) is task-organized to meet the specific service support requirements of the SPMAGTF and is centered on the unit designated to provide most of the service support.

SUPPLEMENTARY FIRING POSITION

A position assigned to a unit or weapon to accomplish fire missions other than those to be accomplished from the primary or alternate positions.

SUPPORT

1. The action of a force that aids, protects, complements, or sustains another force in accordance with a directive requiring such action.

2. A unit that helps another unit in battle.

3. A part of any unit held back at the beginning of an attack as a reserve.

4. An element of a command that assists, protects, or supplies other forces in combat.

SUPPORTING FIRE

Fire delivered by supporting units to assist or protect a unit in combat.

TACTICS

1. The employment of units in combat.

2. The ordered arrangement and maneuver of units in relation to each other and/or to the enemy in order to realize the full potentialities.

TARGET OF OPPORTUNITY

A target visible to a surface or air vehicle or observer, which is within range of available weapons and against which fire has not been scheduled or requested.

TERRAIN

An area of ground considered as to its extent and natural features in relation to its use in a particular operation.

TRAJECTORY

The curved path followed by any projectile in its flight through the air.

UNIT

1. Any military element whose structure is prescribed by competent authority, such as a table of organization and equipment; specifically part of an organization.
2. A standard or basic quantity into which an item of supply is divided, issued, or used. In this meaning, also called "unit of issue."

VEHICLE CONTROL POINT

A point on a vehicle access route controlled by a barrier, or similar means, at which a vehicle is required to stop.

ZONE OF ACTION

A tactical subdivision of a larger area, the responsibility for which is assigned to a tactical unit; generally applied to offensive action.

ZONE OF FIRE

An area within which a particular unit delivers, or is prepared to deliver, fire.

"The Marines' Hymn"

From the Halls of Montezuma
To the shores of Tripoli,
We fight our country's battles
In the air, on land, and sea.
First to fight for right and freedom,
And to keep our honor clean,
We are proud to claim the title
Of United States Marine.

Our flag's unfurl'd to every breeze
From dawn to setting sun;
We have fought in every clime and place
Where we could take a gun.
In the snow of far-off northern lands
And in sunny tropic scenes,
You will find us always on the job
The United States Marines.

Here's health to you and to our Corps
Which we are proud to serve;
In many a strife we've fought for life
And never lost our nerve.
If the Army and the Navy
Ever look on Heaven's scenes,
They will find the streets are guarded
By United States Marines.